Real Math™

Dear Student:

We hope that this Real Math book will help you learn about mathematics in an interesting way.

You'll find stories about important people in the history of mathematics. Discussions and examples will show you how mathematics can help you solve problems and save you work. Seminars will show you ways that you can use mathematics to explore things and ideas in the world around you.

Games will give you practice with many of the skills that you will be learning and will help you understand what probability is about. Activities will introduce you to puzzles and other ways that you can enjoy mathematics in your free time.

You'll be discussing the ideas behind all this mathematics in class with your classmates and your teacher. We put most of this information in the book too so that you can go back over it and can take the book home to discuss these ideas with your family and friends. Mathematics is not something to do alone. To do a good job of learning and doing mathematics, you need other people.

You can see that Real Math is not all fun and games. You will need to think, to calculate, to estimate, and to measure, but doing these well can be very satisfying.

We hope that you enjoy this book and that you learn about many new things. But most of all we hope that you become very good at thinking and problem solving.

The Authors of Real Math

Real Math™

Stephen S. Willoughby
Carl Bereiter
Peter Hilton
Joseph H. Rubinstein

Real Math™ is a product of the
Open Court Mathematics and Science
Curriculum Development Center.

Catherine Anderson, Director

 Open Court   **La Salle, Illinois**

President and Publisher
M. Blouke Carus

Executive Vice President
Paul Carus

Education Director
Carl Bereiter

Operations Manager
Ruth A. Berke

Editorial Director
Dale E. Howard

Coordinator of Editorial Services
Juanita A. Raman

Production Manager
LeRoy Ceresa

Art Director
Todd Sanders

Design
James Buddenbaum/Design

Acknowledgments
Bruce Coleman, Inc.: 69 (left); Leonard Lee Rue III, 69 right; James H. Carmichael.   Marilyn Gartman Agency: 2 (top); Lee Balterman, 172 (top, left); Michael Philip Manheim, 172 (top, right); Lee Balterman, 172 (bottom); Michael Philip Manheim, 173 (bottom); Lee Balterman, 269; Michael Philip Manheim.   The Granger Collection: 96, 97, 211, 279, 308, 309.   NASA: 73 (left), 295.   Stock, Boston, Inc.: 73 (middle); Jean-Claude Lejeune, 120; Richard Pasley, 175; Cary Wolinsky, 176; Steve Hansen, 200; John Running, 201; Michael Collier.   West Light: 2 (bottom); Bill Ross, 45; Bill Ross, 73 (right); William James Warren, 172 (top, middle); Craig Aurness, 173 (top); Chuck O'Rear, 339; Bill Ross.

CONTENTS

CHAPTER 3

PROBLEM SOLVING

CHAPTER 4

PERMUTATIONS

CHAPTER 5

GEOMETRY

CHAPTER 6

MATHEMATICS IN EVERYDAY LIFE

CHAPTER 7

**FUNCTIONS
AND GRAPHING
ALGEBRA**

CHAPTER 8

GEOMETRY

CHAPTER 9

ALGEBRA

CHAPTER 10

RATIONAL AND IRRATIONAL NUMBERS
UNCERTAINTY IN MEASUREMENT
EXPONENTS AND SCIENTIFIC NOTATION

Real Math™

CHAPTER 1
PROBABILITY REVIEW

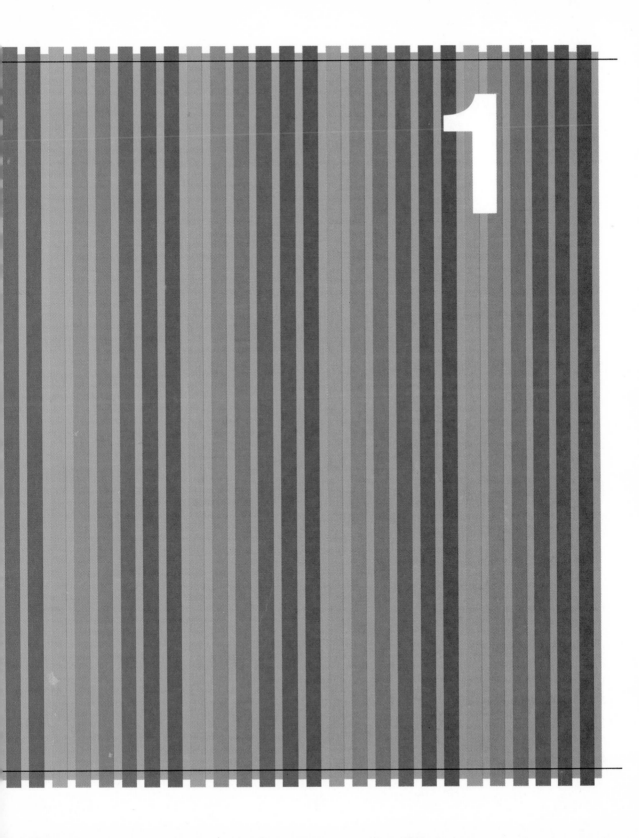

"What is the probability that I'll get an A in social studies this year?" "There is a 60:40 chance that it will snow today." "The United States is favored 3 to 1 to win the 10-kilometer race."

In each of these cases, the speaker is attempting to predict a future event. In each case, the speaker seems not to know for sure what will happen but wants to indicate how likely a certain event seems. These statements are statements of probability or of odds.

The word *probability* is used both as the likelihood that a certain event will occur and as the name of the branch of mathematics that is concerned with such likelihoods. Sometimes that branch of mathematics is called *probability theory*. The likelihood that a certain event will occur can be described either as a probability or as odds. *Odds* is the ratio of favorable to unfavorable outcomes for a given event.

Probability was first used by gamblers who wanted to increase their chances of winning in certain games of chance. In spite of this less than noble beginning, probability has grown to be one of the most respected and useful branches of mathematics. It is the basis for determining insurance rates and is important in modern physical and social science.

Girolamo Cardano (1501–1576) wrote the first known book on probability, *Liber de Ludo Aleae* ("Handbook of the Game of Dice"). Apparently the book was used by gamblers at that time. The book was not printed, however, until long after Cardano's death—in 1663, when his complete works were published. Cardano's work did not have much effect on the study of probability.

In 1654 a French nobleman interested 2 famous mathematicians, Blaise Pascal and Pierre de Fermat, in the problem of how 2 gamblers should divide the stakes of an interrupted game, depending on what each score was at the interruption. Pascal and Fermat wrote many letters to each other about this problem. These letters greatly influenced the development of probability theory and introduced the notations that came to be used in it.

Often we assume, with good reason, that certain outcomes are equally likely. The probability of a given event is easy to determine if there are several equally likely outcomes.

For example, think about rolling a 0–5 number cube (a cube with the numbers 0, 1, 2, 3, 4, and 5 on the 6 faces). We can assume that 1 number is as likely to land up as another. The probability of getting an even number (0, 2, or 4) is $\frac{3}{6}$, or $\frac{1}{2}$, because there are 3 ways to get an even number (the given event) and 6 equally likely outcomes.

We would write:

$$P \text{ (even number)} = \frac{3}{6}$$

To read this, we say, "The probability of an even number equals three-sixths."

In general, the probability of an event equals the number of favorable outcomes divided by the total number of outcomes, if we assume that all outcomes are equally likely.

$$P \text{ (event)} = \frac{\text{number of favorable outcomes}}{\text{total number of equally likely outcomes}}$$

Think again about rolling a 0–5 cube.

$$P \text{ (6)} = \frac{0}{6} = 0 \text{ (There is no number 6 on the cube.)}$$

$$P \text{ (0, 1, 2, 3, 4, or 5)} = \frac{6}{6} = 1.$$

The smallest possible probability is 0. The greatest possible probability is 1.

1. What is the probability that a normal coin will come up heads when tossed?

2. What is the probability that a 2-headed coin will come up tails when tossed?

3. What is the probability that a normal coin will come up tails when tossed?

4. What is the probability that a 2-headed coin will come up heads when tossed?

5. If you roll a 0–5 cube, what is the probability of getting a 5?

6. What is the probability of rolling an odd number with a 0–5 cube?

7. What is the probability of rolling a number divisible by 3 with a 0–5 cube?

8. What is the probability of rolling a number that is not 5 with a 0–5 cube?

9. There are 7 gold coins, 2 silver coins, and 1 iron coin in a bag. You draw one coin out of the bag without looking.

   a. What is the probability of drawing a gold coin?
   b. What is the probability of drawing a silver coin?
   c. What is the probability of drawing an iron coin?
   d. What is the sum of the answers to parts a, b, and c?
   e. What is the probability of drawing a gold or a silver coin?

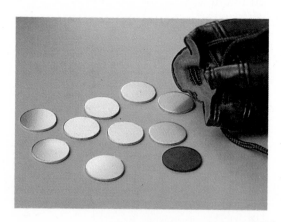

Odds

Another way to describe probability is in terms of *odds*. If you roll a 0–5 cube, the odds are 5 to 1 that you will roll a 1, 2, 3, 4, or 5, and the odds are 1 to 5 that you will roll a 0.

You say that the odds in favor of something happening are *r* to *s* if there are *r* favorable outcomes and *s* unfavorable outcomes out of *r* + *s* equally likely outcomes.

Event	Favorable Outcomes	Unfavorable Outcomes	Odds
Getting heads when tossing a normal coin	1	1	1 to 1
Getting 7 when rolling a 5–10 cube	1	5	1 to 5
Getting an even number when rolling a 5–10 cube	3	3	3 to 3, or 1 to 1

You may wonder why the odds are 3 to 3 *or* 1 to 1 for getting an even number while rolling a 5–10 cube. Odds are a ratio, and you can reduce odds just as you would reduce any other ratio.

In general, if outcomes are assumed to be equally likely, the odds for an event are *r* to *s* if there are *r* favorable outcomes and *s* unfavorable outcomes.

If the odds for an event are *r* to *s*, the probability is $\frac{r}{r+s}$.

If the probability is $\frac{r}{r+s}$, the odds are *r* to *s*.

1. If you toss a normal coin, what are the odds for getting tails?

2. If you toss a 2-headed coin, what are the odds for getting heads?

3. If you toss a 2-headed coin, what are the odds for getting tails?

4. If you roll a 0–5 cube, what are the odds for getting an odd number?

5. Suppose you draw 1 coin from a bag containing 7 gold coins, 2 silver coins, and 1 iron coin. What are the odds in favor of getting

   a. a gold coin?
   b. a silver coin?
   c. an iron coin?
   d. a silver or a gold coin?

Suppose you roll a 0–5 cube and a 5–10 cube.

[1] What is the probability that the sum of the numbers rolled is 5?

[2] What is the probability that the sum of the numbers rolled is 10?

[3] What is the probability that the sum of the numbers rolled is 15?

Think about these 3 questions. Discuss them with your friends. Decide what you think the answers are.

Try the following experiment. Roll a 0–5 cube and a 5–10 cube 66 times. Use tally marks to record how many times the sum of the numbers rolled was 5, 10, or 15. For each of those sums, also write down the 2 numbers rolled. Ignore other outcomes (other sums).

Amanda decided that her answers to the 3 discussion questions on this page were the same. She said that the probabilities would each be $\frac{1}{11}$, because there are 11 possible sums: 5, 6, 7, 8, 9, 10, 11, 12, 13, 14, and 15. Then she did the experiment. Here is the record of her experiment.

5	‖	`0` `5` , `0` `5`
10	卌 ‖‖	`1` `9` , `3` `7` , `2` `8` , `0` `10` , `5` `5` `3` `7` , `5` `5` , `4` `6` , `3` `7`
15	∣	`5` `10`

She looked at her results and said, "I rolled the cubes 66 times altogether. If the probability were $\frac{1}{11}$ for each sum, I'd expect about 6 of each. But in my experiment it looks as though 10 occurs more often than either 5 or 15.

Compare your results with Amanda's. Compare your results with those of other members of your class.

[4] Is it almost always true that there are more 10s than 5s or 15s?

[5] How many different pairs of numbers (on a 0–5 and a 5–10 cube) produce a sum of 5? Of 15? Of 10?

The 0–5 cube can land 6 ways.

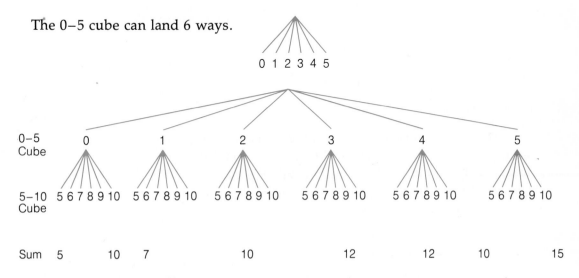

With *each* of those 6 ways, the 5–10 cube can land 6 ways. For example, with 0 on the 0–5 cube, there are 6 ways for the 5–10 cube to land. With 1, there are 6 ways also, and so on. So there are 6 × 6, or 36, ways that the 2 cubes can land. We can list them this way:

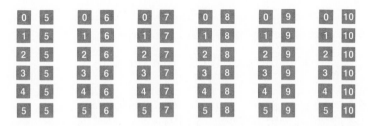

[6] Copy and complete the column showing all the sums for the 2 cubes.

[7] Now what are your answers to the first 3 discussion questions (on page 6)?

1. There are 36 ways that the 0–5 and 5–10 cubes can land when they are rolled together.

   a. How many give a sum of 5?
   b. What is the probability that the sum is 5?
   c. What is the probability that the sum is 15?
   d. What is the probability that the sum is 10?

2. If you roll a 0–5 cube and a 5–10 cube, what is the probability that the sum of the numbers rolled is

a. 5?	c. 7?	e. 9?	g. 11?	i. 13?	k. 15?
b. 6?	d. 8?	f. 10?	h. 12?	j. 14?	l. 16?

3. What is the sum of your answers for parts a–k in problem 2?

4. If you roll two 0–5 cubes, there are also 36 ways that they can land. (A cube cannot tell whether it has the numerals 0, 1, 2, 3, 4, and 5 or the numerals 5, 6, 7, 8, 9, and 10 painted on it.) List the 36 different ways that two 0–5 cubes can land. (Notice that 3, 2 and 2, 3 are 2 different ways.)

5. If you roll two 0–5 cubes, what is the probability that

   a. the sum will be 0?
   b. the sum will be 10?
   c. the sum will be 5?

6. If you roll two 0–5 cubes, what is the probability that the sum will be

a. 0?	c. 2?	e. 4?	g. 6?	i. 8?	k. 10?
b. 1?	d. 3?	f. 5?	h. 7?	j. 9?	l. 11?

7. What is the sum of your answers for parts a–k in problem 6?

8. If you roll two 5–10 cubes, what is the probability that the sum will be

a. 10?	c. 12?	e. 14?	g. 16?	i. 18?	k. 20?
b. 11?	d. 13?	f. 15?	h. 17?	j. 19?	

BLOCK AND RACE GAME

Players: 2
Materials: Two 0–5 cubes, 2 markers, 2 blockers (to cover 3 squares each)
Object: To get around the race track to or past 0

Rules

1. A blocker may be placed only on a group of 3 empty squares.

2. To start, place each blocker on a group of 3 empty squares and put both markers on 0.

3. On each turn, move your blocker wherever you like. Roll the 2 cubes and add the numbers rolled. Try to move your marker ahead that many spaces.

4. A marker may land only on an empty square.

5. The winner is the first person to get around the track.

Sample Game

Start: Ken blocked 7, 8, 9. Jan blocked 4, 5, 6.

Round 1: Ken rolled **3** and moved to 3. Jan blocked 10, 11, 12 and rolled **7** but couldn't move.

Round 2: Ken blocked 4, 5, 6, rolled **4**, and moved to 7. Jan blocked 11, 12, 13, rolled **2**, and moved to 2.

Round 3: Ken blocked 8, 9, 10 and rolled **3** but couldn't move. Jan rolled **4** and moved to 6.

Round 4: Ken rolled **7** and moved to 14. Jan blocked 19, 20, 21, rolled **7**, and moved to 13.

Round 5: Ken blocked 15, 16, 17 and rolled **5** but couldn't move. Jan rolled **9** and moved to 22.

Round 6: Ken blocked 28, 29, 30, rolled **4**, and moved to 18. Jan blocked 32, 33, 34, rolled **5**, and moved to 27.

0	1	2	3	4	5	6	7	8	9	10
39										11
38										12
37										13
36										14
35										15
34										16
33										17
32										18
31										19
30	29	28	27	26	25	24	23	22	21	20

If you toss a penny, it can land 2 ways—heads or tails.

Penny

H

T

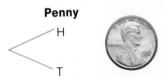

If you toss a penny and a nickel, the nickel can land heads or tails with each of the 2 ways the penny can land.

Penny	Nickel	Ways to Land
H	H	HH
	T	HT
T	H	TH
	T	TT

So there are 4 ways that 2 coins can land when tossed: *HH, HT, TH,* and *TT.*

[1] If you toss 2 coins, what is the probability of getting 2 heads?

[2] If you tossed 2 coins 100 times, about how many of those times would you expect to get 2 heads? 2 tails? 1 head and 1 tail?

If you toss a penny, a nickel, and a dime, the dime can land heads or tails with each of the 4 ways the other 2 coins can land.

Penny	Nickel	Dime	Ways to Land
H	H	H	HHH
		T	HHT
	T	H	HTH
		T	HTT
T	H	H	THH
		T	THT
	T	H	TTH
		T	TTT

So there are 8 ways that 3 coins can land when tossed: *HHH, HHT, HTH, HTT, THH, THT, TTH,* and *TTT.*

[3] If you toss 3 coins, what is the probability of getting 3 heads?

[4] If you toss 3 coins, what is the probability of getting 2 heads and 1 tail?

1. What is the probability of getting a head if you toss 1 coin?

2. If you toss a coin 100 times, about how many heads would you expect? Do you think you would get *exactly* that number of heads?

3. If you toss 2 coins, what is the probability of getting

   a. 2 heads? **b.** 1 head and 1 tail? **c.** 2 tails?

4. What is the sum of your answers for problem 3?

5. If you toss 2 coins 200 times, about how many times would you expect to get

   a. 2 heads? **b.** 1 head and 1 tail? **c.** 2 tails?

6. If you toss 3 coins, what is the probability of getting

   a. 3 heads? **c.** 1 head and 2 tails?
   b. 2 heads and 1 tail? **d.** 3 tails?

7. What is the sum of your answers for problem 6?

8. If you toss 3 coins 200 times, about how many times would you expect to get

   a. 3 heads? **c.** 1 head and 2 tails?
   b. 2 heads and 1 tail? **d.** 3 tails?

[5] Would you expect to get exactly these numbers?

9. Try the experiment described in problem 8. Compare your results with your predictions.

10. If you toss 4 coins, what is the probability of getting

    a. 4 heads? **c.** 2 heads and 2 tails? **e.** 4 tails?
    b. 3 heads and 1 tail? **d.** 1 head and 3 tails?

11. What is the sum of your answers to problem 9?

Play the Block and Race Game.

1. If you roll a 0–5 cube, what is the probability that you'll roll a 3?

2. If you roll a 0–5 cube, what are the odds that you'll roll a 3?

3. If you roll two 0–5 cubes, what is the probability that the sum of the numbers rolled will be 5?

4. If you roll two 0–5 cubes, what are the odds that the sum will be 5?

5. Copy and complete this chart.

If you roll two 0–5 cubes, to get this sum:	The probability is:	The odds are:
4		
6		
3		
7		
3 or 4 or 5 or 6 or 7		
0 or 1 or 2 or 8 or 9 or 10		

6. If you toss a coin, what is the probability that you'll get a head?

7. If you toss a coin, what are the odds that you'll get a head?

8. If you toss 2 coins, what is the probability that you'll get 1 head and 1 tail?

9. If you toss 2 coins, what are the odds that you'll get 1 head and 1 tail?

10. If you toss 3 coins, what is the probability that you'll get 2 heads and 1 tail?

11. If you toss 3 coins, what is the probability that you'll get 1 head and 2 tails?

12. If you toss 3 coins, what is the probability that you'll get 2 heads and 1 tail or 1 head and 2 tails?

13. If you toss 3 coins, what is the probability that you'll either get no tails or get no heads?

14. If you toss 3 coins, what are the odds that all 3 will not be the same (that you'll get neither 3 heads nor 3 tails)?

15. If you toss 3 coins, what are the odds that all 3 will be the same?

16. If you toss 4 coins, what is the probability of getting

    a. 4 heads? **c.** 2 heads? **e.** 0 heads?
    b. 3 heads (and 1 tail)? **d.** 1 head?

17. If you toss 4 coins, what is the probability of getting 4 heads or 4 tails?

Play the Block and Race Game.

A. Multiplying 2 fractions is like taking a fraction of a fraction.

1. Multiply the numerators to get the numerator of the product.
2. Multiply the denominators to get the denominator of the product.

$$\frac{a}{b} \text{ of } \frac{c}{d} = \frac{a}{b} \times \frac{c}{d} = \frac{a \times c}{b \times d}$$

Examples: $\frac{3}{5} \times \frac{10}{9} = \frac{30}{45}^{2}_{3} = \frac{2}{3}$, or $\frac{3}{5} \times \frac{10}{9} = \frac{2}{3}$

$\frac{4}{7} \times 21 = \frac{84}{7} = 12$, or $\frac{4}{7} \times 21 = 12$, or $\frac{4}{7} \times \frac{21}{1} = 12$

B. To add (or subtract) 2 fractions:

1. Change to equivalent fractions with a common denominator.
2. Add the numerators to get the numerator of the sum.
3. The common denominator is the denominator of the sum.

$$\frac{a}{c} + \frac{b}{c} = \frac{a + b}{c}$$

Examples: Addition Subtraction

$\frac{1}{6} + \frac{2}{3} = \frac{1}{6} + \frac{4}{6} = \frac{5}{6}$ $\frac{2}{3} - \frac{1}{6} = \frac{4}{6} - \frac{1}{6} = \frac{3}{6} = \frac{1}{2}$

$\frac{3}{7} + \frac{4}{5} = \frac{15}{35} + \frac{28}{35} = \frac{43}{35}$ $\frac{4}{5} - \frac{3}{7} = \frac{28}{35} - \frac{15}{35} = \frac{13}{35}$

If you have trouble finding a common denominator, remember that you can always multiply both denominators to find a common denominator and then cross-multiply to find the new numerators.

$\frac{a}{b} \times \frac{c}{d}$ bd is the common denominator $\frac{a}{b} + \frac{c}{d} = \frac{ad + bc}{bd}$
        ad and bc are the numerators

C. To divide a fraction by a fraction:

1. Invert the divisor (the second fraction).
2. Multiply.

$$\frac{a}{b} \div \frac{c}{d} = \frac{a}{b} \times \frac{d}{c} = \frac{ad}{bc}$$

Examples: $\frac{1}{3} \div 4 = \frac{1}{3} \div \frac{4}{1} = \frac{1}{3} \times \frac{1}{4} = \frac{1}{12}$

$4 \div \frac{1}{3} = 4 \times 3 = 12$

Solve for n. For practice, change improper fractions to mixed numbers and reduce all fractions completely.

1. $\frac{1}{3}$ of $30 = n$

2. $\frac{2}{3} \times 45 = n$

3. $\frac{3}{4} \times \frac{1}{3} = n$

4. $\frac{4}{7} \times \frac{14}{3} = n$

5. $\frac{1}{5}$ of $\frac{1}{20} = n$

6. $\frac{1}{5} + \frac{3}{5} = n$

7. $\frac{1}{6} + \frac{1}{3} = n$

8. $\frac{2}{3} - \frac{1}{6} = n$

9. $\frac{5}{36} + \frac{7}{36} = n$

10. $\frac{3}{8} - \frac{1}{4} = n$

11. $1 - \frac{1}{2} = n$

12. $1 - \frac{1}{6} = n$

13. $1 - \frac{5}{36} = n$

14. $\frac{1}{3} + \frac{1}{4} = n$

15. $\frac{1}{3} - \frac{1}{4} = n$

16. $\frac{5}{7} + \frac{2}{3} = n$

17. $\frac{9}{10} \div \frac{3}{10} = n$

18. $\frac{12}{17} \div \frac{3}{17} = n$

19. $\frac{1}{3} \div \frac{1}{6} = n$

20. $\frac{3}{7} \div \frac{5}{4} = n$

21. $\frac{5}{6}$ of $36 = n$

22. $\frac{3}{4}$ of $36 = n$

23. $\frac{2}{5} \times \frac{10}{21} = n$

24. $\frac{8}{3} \times \frac{9}{16} = n$

25. $\frac{2}{3}$ of $\frac{1}{12} = n$

26. $\frac{1}{36} + \frac{5}{36} = n$

27. $\frac{3}{8} + \frac{3}{8} = n$

28. $1 - \frac{1}{8} = n$

29. $1 - \frac{3}{8} = n$

30. $\frac{3}{7} - \frac{1}{3} = n$

31. $\frac{4}{9} - \frac{3}{7} = n$

32. $\frac{1}{2} + \frac{1}{3} = n$

33. $\frac{1}{6} + \frac{5}{6} = n$

34. $\frac{1}{4} - \frac{1}{8} = n$

35. $\frac{3}{8} + \frac{4}{7} = n$

36. $\frac{5}{6} \div \frac{1}{6} = n$

37. $\frac{3}{7} \div \frac{2}{5} = n$

38. $\frac{2}{5} \div \frac{3}{7} = n$

39. $\frac{2}{3} \div 2 = n$

40. $2 \div \frac{2}{3} = n$

41. $\frac{1}{5} + \frac{3}{5} = n$

42. $\frac{3}{7} - \frac{2}{7} = n$

43. $\frac{3}{4} \times \frac{1}{4} = n$

44. $\frac{1}{8} \div \frac{3}{64} = n$

45. $\frac{5}{7} \times \frac{3}{5} = n$

46. $\frac{3}{16} + \frac{1}{4} = n$

47. $\frac{3}{16} - \frac{1}{8} = n$

48. $\frac{6}{17} \div \frac{3}{17} = n$

49. $\frac{6}{17} + \frac{3}{17} = n$

50. $\frac{6}{17} - \frac{3}{17} = n$

51. $\frac{1}{3} \times 6 = n$

52. $6 \times \frac{1}{3} = n$

53. $6 \div \frac{1}{3} = n$

54. $\frac{1}{3} \div 6 = n$

55. $\frac{1}{7} + \frac{1}{8} = n$

56. $\frac{1}{7} - \frac{1}{8} = n$

57. $\frac{5}{9} - \frac{2}{9} = n$

58. $\frac{1}{8} + \frac{3}{8} = n$

59. $\frac{1}{3}$ of $\frac{3}{10} = n$

60. $\frac{3}{10}$ of $\frac{1}{3} = n$

Arithmetic with fractions greater than 1 is very similar to arithmetic with fractions less than 1.

For multiplication and division, convert mixed numbers to improper fractions and proceed in the usual way.

Example 1: $1\frac{2}{3} \times 3\frac{5}{7} = \frac{5}{3} \times \frac{26}{7} = \frac{130}{21} = 6\frac{4}{21}$

Example 2: $1\frac{2}{3} \div 3\frac{5}{7} = \frac{5}{3} \div \frac{26}{7} = \frac{5}{3} \times \frac{7}{26} = \frac{35}{78}$

Remember

To convert a mixed number to an improper fraction, multiply the denominator by the whole number and add the numerator. This sum is the numerator, and the original denominator is the denominator.

$$W\frac{n}{d} = \frac{dw + n}{d} \qquad 3\frac{5}{7} = \frac{(7 \times 3) + 5}{7} = \frac{26}{7}$$

To convert an improper fraction to a mixed number, do the indicated division and use the remainder as the numerator of the fractional part of the answer.

$$\frac{73}{5} = 14\frac{3}{5} \qquad \frac{17}{15} = 1\frac{2}{15}$$

For addition and subtraction, you can add or subtract after you convert to improper fractions. Or you can add or subtract the whole-number parts and fractional parts separately (except for "borrowing" and "carrying," or regrouping).

Example 3: $1\frac{2}{3} + 3\frac{5}{7}$

$$\frac{2}{3} + \frac{5}{7} = \frac{14}{21} + \frac{15}{21} = \frac{29}{21} = 1\frac{8}{21}$$
$$\text{so } 1\frac{2}{3} + 3\frac{5}{7} = 1 + 3 + 1\frac{8}{21} = 5\frac{8}{21}$$

Example 4: $10\frac{2}{3} - 3\frac{5}{7}$

$$\frac{2}{3} - \frac{5}{7} = \frac{14}{21} - \frac{15}{21} \left(\text{Can't do this, so take 1 from the 10} \right.$$
$$\left. \text{to make } \frac{21}{21}, \text{ and add it to the } \frac{14}{21}. \right) \frac{35}{21} - \frac{15}{21} = \frac{20}{21}$$
$$9 - 3 = 6$$

Answer is $6\frac{20}{21}$.

Convert each mixed number to an improper fraction.

1. $5\frac{2}{3}$ 4. $6\frac{1}{7}$ 7. $2\frac{7}{8}$ 10. $4\frac{4}{9}$ 13. $5\frac{3}{4}$

2. $1\frac{1}{2}$ 5. $1\frac{2}{3}$ 8. $5\frac{1}{6}$ 11. $8\frac{1}{4}$ 14. $4\frac{3}{5}$

3. $3\frac{3}{4}$ 6. $5\frac{1}{2}$ 9. $4\frac{3}{5}$ 12. $5\frac{3}{8}$ 15. $3\frac{4}{5}$

Convert each improper fraction to a mixed number or whole number.

16. $\frac{19}{5}$ 19. $\frac{19}{4}$ 22. $\frac{7}{2}$ 25. $\frac{11}{7}$ 28. $\frac{10}{10}$

17. $\frac{23}{5}$ 20. $\frac{23}{3}$ 23. $\frac{11}{6}$ 26. $\frac{10}{9}$ 29. $\frac{32}{5}$

18. $\frac{23}{4}$ 21. $\frac{19}{3}$ 24. $\frac{9}{8}$ 27. $\frac{9}{9}$ 30. $\frac{32}{8}$

Solve for n. Leave answers as mixed or whole numbers with all fractions reduced completely.

31. $\frac{1}{3}$ of $30 = n$ 41. $2\frac{1}{7} \times 4\frac{1}{5} = n$ 51. $4 - 2\frac{1}{3} = n$

32. $\frac{2}{3}$ of $30 = n$ 42. $6\frac{3}{4} \div 1\frac{1}{8} = n$ 52. $4 \times 2\frac{1}{3} = n$

33. $\frac{3}{3}$ of $30 = n$ 43. $5\frac{1}{3} \div 2\frac{2}{3} = n$ 53. $4 \div 2\frac{1}{3} = n$

34. $\frac{4}{3}$ of $30 = n$ 44. $10\frac{2}{3} \div 5\frac{1}{3} = n$ 54. $6\frac{1}{8} \div 1\frac{3}{4} = n$

35. $1\frac{2}{3}$ of $30 = n$ 45. $2\frac{2}{3} \div 1\frac{1}{3} = n$ 55. $6\frac{1}{8} \div 3\frac{1}{2} = n$

36. $1\frac{3}{4} + 2\frac{1}{3} = n$ 46. $1\frac{1}{3} \div \frac{2}{3} = n$ 56. $6\frac{1}{8} \div \frac{7}{8} = n$

37. $3\frac{1}{6} - 2\frac{2}{3} = n$ 47. $1\frac{1}{3} + \frac{2}{3} = n$ 57. $1\frac{3}{5} \div \frac{2}{5} = n$

38. $3\frac{1}{6} - 1\frac{2}{3} = n$ 48. $1\frac{1}{3} - \frac{2}{3} = n$ 58. $1\frac{3}{5} + \frac{2}{5} = n$

39. $5\frac{1}{6} - 3\frac{2}{3} = n$ 49. $3\frac{1}{2} \times \frac{4}{7} = n$ 59. $1\frac{3}{5} - \frac{2}{5} = n$

40. $4\frac{3}{4} + 5\frac{1}{3} = n$ 50. $4 + 2\frac{1}{3} = n$ 60. $1\frac{3}{5} \times \frac{2}{5} = n$

A decimal is a number written with a decimal point. In a decimal, the digit just to the left of the point represents the units. As with whole numbers, digits farther to the left represent larger powers of 10, and digits to the right represent smaller powers of 10.

A. To add or subtract decimals:

1. Line up the decimal points and proceed as with whole numbers.
2. Place the point in the answer below the points in the problem. Remember that you may put a decimal point and zeros to the right of a whole number. You may also add zeros at the extreme right of a decimal number. Adding zeros is done only to help you keep digits in line.

Examples

2.3 + 4.1	3.27 + 104.8	48 − 3.75	43.8 − 35.73

$$
\begin{array}{r} 2.3 \\ + \ 4.1 \\ \hline 6.4 \end{array}
\qquad
\begin{array}{r} 3.27 \\ + \ 104.8 \\ \hline 108.07 \end{array}
\qquad
\begin{array}{r} 48.00 \\ - \ \ 3.75 \\ \hline 44.25 \end{array}
\qquad
\begin{array}{r} 43.80 \\ - \ 35.73 \\ \hline 8.07 \end{array}
$$

B. To multiply 2 decimals:

1. Multiply as with whole numbers.
2. Place the point in the answer so that the number of places to the right of the point equals the sum of the numbers of places to the right of the point in the 2 factors.

Examples

$$34.721 \times 5.36 = 186.10456 \qquad (3 \quad 2 \quad 3+2=5)$$

$$47 \times 8.341 = 392.027 \qquad (3 \quad 3)$$

$$2.15 \times 34.6 = 74.390 = 74.39 \qquad (2 \quad 1 \quad 3)$$

C. To divide 2 decimals:

1. Move the decimal point in the divisor so that the divisor becomes a whole number.
2. Move the decimal point in the dividend the same number of places in the same direction. Write in zeros if you need to.
3. Divide as with whole numbers.
4. Place the point in the quotient directly over the new point in the dividend.

Examples

$$
4.921 \div 7.03 \qquad 7.03 \overline{)\,4.92.1}^{\,0.7}
$$

$$
39.6 \div .085 \qquad .085 \overline{)\,39.600.}^{\,465.9}
$$

You can also use estimation to decide where the decimal point goes. By moving the decimal points in the dividend and the divisor the same number of places in the same direction, you can make the divisor a number from 1 through 10. The examples will show you how this method works.

Examples

0.07681434 ÷ 940.2 = ? Move both points to the *left* 2 places: .00.07681434 ÷ 9.40.2. Divide 0.000768 . . . by 9, getting 0.00008. . . . The actual division produces nonzero digits 817, so the answer is 0.0000817.

$$
2765 \div .0073 \qquad .007.3 \overline{)\,2765.000.}
$$

Estimate: 2,800,000 ÷ 7 = 400,000. The actual division produces nonzero digits 37876712, so the answer is 378,767.

Do these calculations. In division problems, carry the answer out
to 3-digit accuracy.

1. 4.12 + 31.57	**21.** 15.1 + 8.7	**41.** 5.73 + 3.64
2. 31.57 − 4.12	**22.** 15.1 − 8.7	**42.** 5.73 − 3.64
3. 5.06 − 0.47	**23.** 15.1 × 8.7	**43.** 10.65 − 8.39
4. 5.06 + 0.47	**24.** 15.1 + 0.87	**44.** 10.65 + 8.39
5. 3.9 + 5.18	**25.** 15.1 − 0.87	**45.** 10 − 3.78
6. 5.18 − 3.9	**26.** 15.1 × 0.87	**46.** 10 + 3.78
7. 5.18 × 3.9	**27.** 87 + 1.51	**47.** 10 × 3.78
8. 5.06 × 0.47	**28.** 87 − 1.51	**48.** 1.4 × 1.4
9. 3.4 × 1.002	**29.** 87 × 1.51	**49.** 0.14 × 0.14
10. 16.2747 ÷ 5.07	**30.** 86.67 ÷ 13.5	**50.** 1.4 × 0.014
11. 16.2747 ÷ 0.0507	**31.** 86.67 ÷ 1.35	**51.** 14 × 0.0014
12. 0.0162747 ÷ 5.07	**32.** 8.667 ÷ 13.5	**52.** 13.0626 ÷ 5.31
13. 0.0162747 ÷ 50.7	**33.** 0.08667 ÷ 0.135	**53.** 1306.26 ÷ 5.31
14. 0.162747 ÷ 0.0507	**34.** 8667 ÷ 0.0135	**54.** 1.30626 ÷ 53.1
15. 54.3 + 3.21	**35.** 0.003 + 0.007	**55.** 130.626 ÷ 0.0531
16. 54.3 − 3.21	**36.** 0.01 − 0.007	**56.** 130.626 ÷ 531
17. 54.3 × 3.21	**37.** 0.003 × 0.007	**57.** 5.31 + 2.46
18. 0.543 + 0.0321	**38.** 0.3 − 0.07	**58.** 53.1 + 0.246
19. 0.543 − 0.0321	**39.** 0.3 + 0.07	**59.** 5.31 − 2.46
20. 0.543 × 0.0321	**40.** 0.3 × 0.07	**60.** 53.1 − 0.246

HARDER ROLL A DECIMAL GAME

Players: 2
Materials: One 0–5 cube, one 5–10 cube
Object: To get the greater total score

Rules

1. Roll the 0–5 cube. If a `0` is rolled, roll again.

2. Write a decimal point followed by as many blanks as the number rolled. If you roll a `3`, you would write this: .＿＿ ＿＿ ＿＿

3. Roll the 5–10 cube as many times as there are blanks in your decimal. If you roll a `10`, roll again.

4. Each time you roll the 5–10 cube, write that number in one of your blanks.

5. After both players have made decimals, subtract the smaller decimal from the greater decimal. Award the difference to the person who made the greater decimal.

6. After an agreed-upon number of rounds, add up your score.

7. The player with the greater total is the winner.

Sample Game

Round	Umberto's Roll	Celia's Roll	Umberto's Score	Celia's Score
1	.76	.966		.206
2	.957	.676	.281	
3	.97775	.9665	.01125	
4	.8	.9576		.1576
5	.99	.866	.124	
6	.86855	.8875		.01895
7	.7	.5	.2	
8	.775	.97755		.20255
Total			.61625	.58510

Umberto was the winner.

Fraction-Decimal Equivalents

As you have seen, fractions often arise in calculating probabilities. Sometimes it is convenient to convert the fractions to decimals. Decimals are usually easier than fractions to compare (unless the fractions have the same denominator) and to add and subtract. But, most important, they are more convenient to use with most calculators. You can convert a fraction to a decimal or a decimal approximation by dividing the numerator by the denominator.

Examples: $\frac{2}{9} \rightarrow 9\overline{)2.000000\ldots}$, quotient $0.222222\ldots$ — There is no exact decimal equivalent of $\frac{2}{9}$. To 4 places, the approximation is 0.2222.

$\frac{1}{7} \rightarrow 7\overline{)1.00000}$, quotient 0.142857 — To 4 places, $\frac{1}{7} = 0.1429$ (round up, since the next digit is 5 or greater).

Copy and complete this chart of equivalents and approximations. Round approximations to 3 places.

$\frac{1}{2}$	$\frac{2}{2}$	$\frac{3}{2}$	$\frac{4}{2}$	$\frac{5}{2}$	$\frac{6}{2}$	$\frac{7}{2}$	$\frac{8}{2}$	$\frac{9}{2}$	$\frac{10}{2}$
0.5									5

$\frac{1}{3}$	$\frac{2}{3}$	$\frac{3}{3}$	$\frac{4}{3}$	$\frac{5}{3}$	$\frac{6}{3}$	$\frac{7}{3}$	$\frac{8}{3}$	$\frac{9}{3}$	$\frac{10}{3}$
0.333			1.333						

$\frac{1}{4}$	$\frac{2}{4}$	$\frac{3}{4}$	$\frac{4}{4}$	$\frac{5}{4}$	$\frac{6}{4}$	$\frac{7}{4}$	$\frac{8}{4}$	$\frac{9}{4}$	$\frac{10}{4}$
0.25									

$\frac{1}{5}$	$\frac{2}{5}$	$\frac{3}{5}$	$\frac{4}{5}$	$\frac{5}{5}$	$\frac{6}{5}$	$\frac{7}{5}$	$\frac{8}{5}$	$\frac{9}{5}$	$\frac{10}{5}$

$\frac{1}{6}$	$\frac{2}{6}$	$\frac{3}{6}$	$\frac{4}{6}$	$\frac{5}{6}$	$\frac{6}{6}$	$\frac{7}{6}$	$\frac{8}{6}$	$\frac{9}{6}$	$\frac{10}{6}$

$\frac{1}{7}$	$\frac{2}{7}$	$\frac{3}{7}$	$\frac{4}{7}$	$\frac{5}{7}$	$\frac{6}{7}$	$\frac{7}{7}$	$\frac{8}{7}$	$\frac{9}{7}$	$\frac{10}{7}$
0.143									

$\frac{1}{8}$	$\frac{2}{8}$	$\frac{3}{8}$	$\frac{4}{8}$	$\frac{5}{8}$	$\frac{6}{8}$	$\frac{7}{8}$	$\frac{8}{8}$	$\frac{9}{8}$	$\frac{10}{8}$

$\frac{1}{9}$	$\frac{2}{9}$	$\frac{3}{9}$	$\frac{4}{9}$	$\frac{5}{9}$	$\frac{6}{9}$	$\frac{7}{9}$	$\frac{8}{9}$	$\frac{9}{9}$	$\frac{10}{9}$
	0.222						0.889		

$\frac{1}{10}$	$\frac{2}{10}$	$\frac{3}{10}$	$\frac{4}{10}$	$\frac{5}{10}$	$\frac{6}{10}$	$\frac{7}{10}$	$\frac{8}{10}$	$\frac{9}{10}$	$\frac{10}{10}$
								0.9	

UP TO 1 GAME

Players: 2 or more
Materials: Four 0–5 cubes
Object: To be the last player to get to 1

Rules

1. Take turns rolling all four 0–5 cubes.

2. On your turn, use any 2 of the numbers you roll to make a fraction or a decimal less than 1. (For example, if you roll `2` `3` `2` `1`, you could make $\frac{1}{3}$, $\frac{2}{3}$, $\frac{1}{2}$, or any of these decimals: .12, .21, .22, .23, .32, .13, .31.)

3. Keep a record of the amount you make on each turn. Write the amount as a decimal. If you make a fraction, write the decimal equivalent or an approximation.

4. On each turn, you must write an amount greater than the amount you made on your previous turn. But you cannot make an amount of 1 or greater.

5. On any turn, if you cannot write an amount less than 1 but greater than your previous turn, you are out.

6. The last player to go out wins.

Sample Game

Turns	Sharon's Record Numbers Rolled	Amount Made	Dewey's Record Numbers Rolled	Amount Made
1	`3` `2` `0` `3`	.00 $\left(\frac{0}{2}\right)$	`3` `2` `5` `2`	.22
2	`2` `3` `3` `4`	.23	`1` `0` `3` `5`	.30
3	`1` `2` `0` `5`	.23	`1` `3` `0` `5`	.333 $\left(\frac{1}{3}\right)$
4	`1` `2` `2` `5`	.40 $\left(\frac{2}{5}\right)$	`1` `0` `4` `5`	.41
5	`2` `2` `0` `3`	.667 $\left(\frac{2}{3}\right)$	`3` `0` `3` `5`	.50
6	`2` `2` `0` `5`	Can't go.	`5` `5` `2` `3`	.52

Dewey was the winner.

UP TO 2 GAME

Players: 2 or more
Materials: Two 0–5 cubes, two 5–10 cubes
Object: To make a bigger number on each turn, but to be the last player to go past 2

Rules

1. Take turns rolling all 4 cubes.

2. Use any 2 of the numbers you roll to make a fraction or a decimal from 0 through 2. (For example, if you roll `3` `3` `5` `10` , you could make $\frac{3}{3}, \frac{3}{5}, \frac{3}{10}, \frac{5}{3}, \frac{5}{10}, \frac{10}{5}$, or any of these decimals: .103, .105, .310, .33, .35, .510, .53, 1.03, 1.05. Notice that you may place the point between the 1 and the 0 if you roll a `10` .)

3. Keep a record of the number you make on each turn. Write the number as a decimal. If you make a fraction, write the decimal equivalent or an approximation. You may round approximations to the nearest thousandth. (For example, if you make $\frac{2}{3}$, you may write .667.) Use the chart on page 22.

4. On each turn, you must write a number greater than the number you made on your previous turn. But you cannot make a number greater than 2.

5. On any turn, if you cannot write 2 or a number less than 2 but greater than your previous turn, you are out.

6. The last player to go out wins.

Another Way to Play This Game

For rule 2, make only fractions but write the decimal equivalent next to each fraction. This will make the game faster.

MAKE 4 FRACTION GAME

Players: 2 or more
Materials: Two 0–5 cubes, two 5–10 cubes
Object: To get a total score as close to 4 as possible

Rules

1. Take turns rolling all 4 cubes.

2. On your turn, make 2 fractions. Add, subtract, multiply, or divide them, recording your answer as a fraction.

3. On your next turn, repeat step 2 but do not use an operation you used before. Stop after 4 turns. Be sure you have used all 4 operations.

4. Add the fractions from your 4 turns.

5. The player whose sum is closest to 4 wins.

6. To decide who has won, first estimate the sums. If everyone agrees who won, that settles the matter. If there's doubt, convert all answers to decimals (with a calculator if needed) and add them on a calculator.

Sample Game

Sonya's Roll	Sonya's Answer	Decimal Answer	Roger's Roll	Roger's Answer	Decimal Answer
5 5 5 8	$\frac{8}{5} - \frac{5}{5} = \frac{3}{5}$	0.6	5 5 3 9	$\frac{3}{5} \times \frac{5}{9} = \frac{1}{3}$	0.33
1 3 5 8	$\frac{1}{3} + \frac{5}{8} = \frac{23}{24}$	0.958	8 4 5 0	$\frac{0}{5} \div \frac{8}{4} = 0$	0
0 1 6 7	$\frac{6}{7} \times \frac{0}{1} = 0$	0	5 5 5 10	$\frac{10}{5} + \frac{5}{5} = 3$	3
2 5 6 7	$\frac{5}{2} \div \frac{7}{6} = \frac{30}{14} = 2\frac{1}{7}$	2.1428	5 8 7 1	$\frac{5}{7} - \frac{1}{8} = \frac{33}{56}$	0.59
		Sum 3.70			Sum 3.92

Roger was the winner.

Using Calculators

Calculators and computers can be used to take much of the drudgery out of arithmetic. You should learn how to use them efficiently. We may sometimes be tempted to use calculators or computers when we could do the job more efficiently in our heads or with pencil and paper. Often it is most efficient to do some thinking first and then use the calculator.

Examples

$70{,}000 \times 500{,}000 = ?$

You should know that the answer is 35 with 9 zeros; that is,

$$\overset{4}{\overbrace{70{,}000}} \times \overset{5}{\overbrace{500{,}000}} = \overset{4 + 5 = 9}{\overbrace{35{,}000{,}000{,}000}}.$$

If you tried to do this problem on a calculator you might get an error signal or something like 3.5   10, which tells you to move the point in 3.5 ten places to the right, or some other answer. In any case, this problem is easier to do without the calculator.

$735 \times 56{,}879 = ?$

If you want the precise answer, using a calculator will be much more efficient than trying to do this problem in your head or with pencil and paper. However, often a good approximation will do.

If so, round 735 to $\overset{2}{\overbrace{700}}$ and 56,879 to $\overset{4}{\overbrace{60{,}000}}$.

The answer should be about 42,000,000. A calculator gives 41,806,065 as the answer.

$534{,}000 \times 82{,}000 \times 641{,}000 = ?$

If you try to do this problem on a calculator it will probably "overload." On some calculators you can keep the partial product and continue calculating. However, you can also just multiply the nonzero parts of the numbers ($534 \times 82 \times 641$) on the calculator and then write 9 zeros after the product, getting the answer 28,068,108,000,000,000.

For each of the following problems, decide whether it would be more efficient to use a calculator (*c*), pencil and paper (*p*), your head (*h*), or some combination of these (*hc* or *hp* or *pc* or *hpc*). Write the appropriate symbols on your paper next to the number of the problem. Then do the problems. Round decimal answers to 4 places.

1. $10,000 \times 734$

2. $10,000 + 734$

3. $734 \div 10,000$

4. $10,000 \div 734$

5. 1000×839

6. 999×839

7. $10,000 - 8000$

8. $10,000 - 8700$

9. $10,000 - 8765$

10. $5643 \div 100$

11. $\frac{1}{2} + \frac{1}{4}$

12. $\frac{1}{2} - \frac{1}{4}$

13. $\frac{5}{9} - \frac{1}{3}$

14. $\frac{4}{7} + \frac{1}{3}$

15. $\frac{5}{13} - \frac{4}{17}$

16. $\frac{5}{13} + \frac{4}{17}$

17. $53 + 47$

18. $53,000 + 47,000$

19. $53 - 47$

20. $53,000 - 47,000$

21. $3.21 + 4.68$

22. $4.68 - 3.21$

23. 4.68×3.21

24. $\frac{4}{7} \times \frac{1}{3}$

25. $\frac{5}{13} \times \frac{4}{17}$

26. $4.68 \div 3.21$

27. $63.05 + 1.74$

28. $63.05 - 1.74$

29. 63.05×1.74

30. $63.05 \div 1.74$

Play the Up To 2 Game.

Adding or subtracting fractions with most calculators is messy if you don't know the decimal equivalent of the second fraction.

Here is an example:

$$\frac{6}{7} - \frac{8}{13}$$

To do this problem on a calculator, you might find the decimal equivalent of $\frac{8}{13}$ (0.6153846) and write it down or store it. Then you would find the decimal equivalent of $\frac{6}{7}$ (0.8571429). Finally you would enter or recall 0.6153846 and subtract to get 0.2417583. There is a way to make this procedure easier. One method is based on this identity:

$$\frac{a}{b} + \frac{c}{d} = [(a \times d \div b) + c] \div d$$

Each step may seem reasonable to you except (perhaps) multiplying a by d. If you look at what happens in the last step, you will see why we multiply a by d in the first step. After the last step, you get $\frac{ad}{bd} + \frac{c}{d}$, which equals $\frac{a}{b} + \frac{c}{d}$. If we hadn't multiplied a by d, we would get $\frac{a}{bd} + \frac{c}{d}$ in the last step. For subtraction, you simply subtract c instead of adding:

$$\frac{a}{b} - \frac{c}{d} = [(a \times d \div b) - c] \div d$$

Example 1: $\frac{3}{5} + \frac{2}{7}$.
Push `3`, `×`, `7`, `÷`, `5`, `+`, `2`, `÷`, `7`, `=` `0.8857142` .

Example 2: $\frac{3}{5} + \frac{2}{7}$. You know that $\frac{3}{5} = 0.6$.
Push `2`, `÷`, `7`, `+`, `.`, `6`, `=` `0.8857142` .

Example 3: $\frac{3}{5} - \frac{2}{7}$. Calculate $\frac{2}{7}$: `2`, `÷`, `7`, `=` `0.2857142` .
Write this number down (or put it in the calculator's memory).
Push `.`, `6`, `−`, `.`, `2`, `8`, `5`, `7`, `1`, `4`, `2`, `=` `0.3142858` .

Example 4: $\frac{3}{5} - \frac{2}{7}$.
Push `3`, `×`, `7`, `÷`, `5`, `−`, `2`, `÷`, `7`, `=` `0.3142857` .

(Answers for examples 3 and 4 differ in the last place because of rounding errors. Most calculators do not round answers.)

Remember that a calculator can only give decimal approximations, so you shouldn't use a calculator when you need precise fractional answers.

Do these problems in whatever way seems easiest. Use a calculator when it will make the arithmetic easier for you. Most answers will be fractions (you don't have to reduce them). Round decimals to 4 places.

1. $\frac{5}{9} - \frac{2}{9}$

2. $\frac{5}{9} + \frac{2}{9}$

3. $\frac{5}{9} \times \frac{2}{9}$

4. $\frac{5}{9} \div \frac{2}{9}$

5. $\frac{3}{13} \times \frac{2}{11}$

6. $\frac{3}{13} + \frac{2}{11}$

7. $\frac{3}{13} - \frac{2}{11}$

8. $\frac{3}{13} \div \frac{2}{11}$

9. $\frac{2}{11} \times \frac{3}{13}$

10. $\frac{1}{36} + \frac{1}{18} + \frac{1}{12} + \frac{1}{9}$

11. $\frac{5}{18} + \frac{5}{36}$

12. $\frac{15}{36} + \frac{1}{6}$

13. $1 - \frac{1}{36}$

14. $1 - \frac{1}{12}$

15. $1 - \frac{1}{6}$

16. $\frac{1}{8} + \frac{3}{8}$

17. $\frac{1}{8} + \frac{3}{8} + \frac{3}{8}$

18. $\frac{1}{6} \times \frac{1}{6}$

19. $\frac{5}{7} + \frac{3}{11}$

20. $\frac{5}{7} - \frac{3}{11}$

21. $\frac{7}{9} + \frac{5}{13}$

22. $\frac{7}{9} - \frac{5}{13}$

23. $\frac{7}{9} - \frac{5}{18}$

24. $\frac{7}{9} + \frac{5}{18}$

25. $\frac{5}{7} \times \frac{3}{11}$

26. $\frac{5}{7} \div \frac{3}{11}$

27. $\frac{7}{9} \times \frac{5}{13}$

28. $\frac{7}{9} \div \frac{5}{13}$

29. $\frac{7}{9} \times \frac{5}{18}$

30. $\frac{7}{9} \div \frac{5}{18}$

31. If you roll two 0–5 cubes, what is the probability of getting a total of 2 or 3 or 4?

32. If you roll two 0–5 cubes, what is the probability of getting 0, 1, 2, or 3 (that is, 3 or less)?

33. If you toss 4 coins, what is the probability of getting 0, 1, or 2 heads?

34. If you toss 5 coins, what is the probability of getting
    a. 5 heads (0 tails)? c. 3 heads (2 tails)?
    b. 4 heads (1 tail)?

35. If you toss 5 coins, what is the probability of getting 3 or more heads?

Could you have figured out the answer to problem 35 without doing the calculation? How?

You may find it interesting to begin collecting daily data about something that interests you. After you have recorded the data for a while, you can make graphs and analyze your data. Look for trends. Then you can start to make predictions about future readings. Some things for which you might like to collect data are:

- Daily temperature, including highs and lows, perhaps even for several cities
- Daily precipitation, including its form
- Daily value of one or more stocks, including highs and lows
- Daily value of the Dow-Jones or some other stock market indicator, including highs and lows
- Daily value of the price of gold or silver, including highs and lows
- Daily value of the dollar in some other currency, including highs and lows
- Daily attendance at your school

There are many other kinds of data that you can collect on a daily basis. Choose something that interests you. Keep a record like the one below.

Dan decided to collect data about daily temperature. He measured the outdoor temperature every day at 6:00 P.M. and got the highs and lows from the newspaper. Here is his chart for the first 10 days in September.

Month: September

Date	Outdoor Temperature (Measured at 6:00 P.M.)	Daily High	Daily Low
1	21°C	24°C	18°C
2	23°C	24°C	19°C
3	23°C	25°C	20°C
4	22°C	24°C	21°C
5	22°C	24°C	21°C
6	22°C	25°C	20°C
7	22°C	24°C	19°C
8	21°C	23°C	19°C
9	20°C	22°C	18°C
10	20°C	22°C	18°C

Dan made a graph to show the temperatures he measured. Since he recorded highs and lows, he used this special way to show them. Your teacher can tell you how to do this.

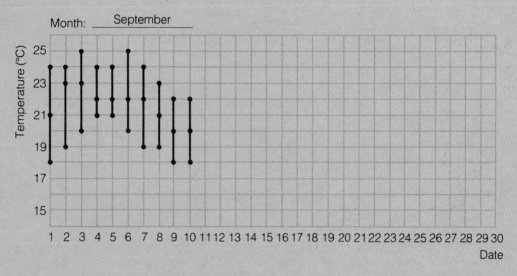

Month: _____ September _____

Dan's teacher asked him these questions:

"What will the high temperature be for September 27?"
"What will the mean high temperature be for the month of September?"

Dan tried to predict the answers for these questions. He said that it was easier to predict the mean high temperature for September than to predict the high temperature for September 27. Dan noticed that the daily temperatures seemed to get lower during September.

Make a graph of your data. What can you tell from your graph?

You may be able to find records of data from last year for your interest. Make graphs from that information. Sometimes, particularly if you are collecting weather data, last year's data will help you make predictions for this year.

Suppose you roll a 0–5 cube.

1. What is the probability that you'll get a 3?

2. What are the odds that you'll get a 3?

3. What is the probability that you'll get an odd number?

4. What are the odds that you'll get an odd number?

Suppose you roll two 0–5 cubes.

5. What is the probability that the sum of the numbers rolled will be 0?

6. What is the probability that the sum of the numbers rolled will be 5?

7. What is the probability that the sum of the numbers rolled will be 3, 4, 5, 6, or 7?

8. What is the probability that the sum of the numbers rolled will be 0, 1, 2, 8, 9, or 10?

9. What are the odds that the sum of the numbers rolled will be 6, 7, or 8?

Suppose you toss 3 coins.

10. What is the probability that you'll get 3 heads?

11. What is the probability that you'll get 2 heads and 1 tail?

12. What is the probability that you'll get at least 1 head?

13. What are the odds that you'll get more heads than tails?

Solve for n. Reduce all fractions completely. Change improper fractions to mixed numbers. Round decimal answers to 4 decimal places.

14. $\frac{3}{5} \times \frac{1}{3} = n$

15. $\frac{3}{5} + \frac{1}{3} = n$

16. $\frac{3}{5} - \frac{1}{3} = n$

17. $\frac{3}{5} \div \frac{1}{3} = n$

18. $\frac{5}{36} + \frac{1}{6} = n$

19. $\frac{11}{12} + \frac{7}{12} = n$

20. $32.68 - 14.75 = n$

21. $32.68 + 14.75 = n$

22. $3.41 \times 2.33 = n$

23. $34.1 \times 0.233 = n$

24. $101.088 \div 2.34 = n$

25. $10.1088 \div 23.4 = n$

Enrichment: Falling Cents

Sometimes, outcomes that we expect to be equally likely turn out not to be.

Try the following experiment. Balance 10 U.S. 1-cent coins on a table.

Arrange them so the heads are pointed in different directions.

Tap the table lightly from above with your hand. Hit just hard enough that some of the coins fall. Keep tapping harder and harder until all of the coins fall.

1. How many of the coins fell heads?

2. Compare your results with results other students got when they tried this experiment.

3. Make a prediction about what will happen if you repeat the experiment. (Will there be more heads, more tails, or about an equal number of heads and tails?)

4. Repeat the experiment and compare your results with your predictions.

5. What do you conclude?

Suppose you roll a 0–5 cube.

1. What is the probability that you'll get a 4?
2. What are the odds that you'll get a 4?
3. What is the probability that you'll get an even number?
4. What are the odds that you'll get an even number?

Suppose you roll two 0–5 cubes.

5. What is the probability that the sum of the numbers rolled will be 10?
6. What is the probability that the sum of the numbers rolled will be 6?
7. What is the probability that the sum of the numbers rolled will be 4, 5, or 6?
8. What is the probability that the sum of the numbers rolled will be 0, 1, 2, 3, 4, 8, 9, or 10?
9. What are the odds that the sum of the numbers rolled will be 3, 4, 5, 6, or 7?

Suppose you toss 3 coins.

10. What is the probability that you'll get 3 tails?
11. What is the probability that you'll get 1 head and 2 tails?
12. What is the probability that you'll get 2 or more heads?
13. What are the odds that you'll get more tails than heads?

Solve for n. Reduce all fractions completely. Change improper fractions to mixed numbers. Round decimal answers to 4 decimal places.

14. $\frac{5}{7} \times \frac{1}{5} = n$
15. $\frac{5}{7} + \frac{1}{5} = n$
16. $\frac{5}{7} - \frac{1}{5} = n$
17. $\frac{5}{7} \div \frac{1}{5} = n$

18. $\frac{3}{12} + \frac{1}{3} = n$
19. $\frac{9}{14} + \frac{3}{14} = n$
20. $22.14 + 7.38 = n$
21. $22.14 - 7.38 = n$

22. $2.63 \times 3.41 = n$
23. $26.3 \times 0.341 = n$
24. $898.35 \div 1.13 = n$
25. $8.9835 \div 11.3 = n$

Arrange 6 cents in a triangle. Use this triangle as the start for both puzzles below.

You may move 1 coin at a time. You cannot lift the coins or push them through spaces they do not fit through. Each time you move a coin to a new position, it must be touching 2 other coins.

1. Can you form a straight line of cents with 7 moves?

2. Can you form a hexagon of cents with 4 moves?

If you do either puzzle in fewer moves, please send us your solution.

CHAPTER 2
ALGEBRA

Norman likes to do number tricks. He told Rowena to pick any number. Then he asked her to follow these directions.

A. Multiply the number by 6.
B. Add 12.
C. Divide by 3.
D. Subtract 4.
E. Divide by 2.

"Now," he said, "you have exactly the number you started with."

[1] Try a number and see if you get back the number you started with. Can you figure out why?

Norman tried a different number trick. He told Rowena, "Pick any number. But remember what it is—you'll use it later." Then he asked her to follow these directions:

A. Multiply the number by 8.
B. Add 14.
C. Divide by 2.
D. Add 1.
E. Divide by 4.
F. Subtract the number you started with.
G. Subtract 2.

"I'll say that your answer is 0," he said.

[2] Do you think he was right?
[3] See if you can figure out how he did it.

To help understand Norman's number tricks, we'll start with n as Rowena starts with 7.

Norman's Directions	Our Calculation with n	What Rowena Does with 7
Multiply by 6.	$6 \times n = 6n$	$6 \times 7 = 42$
Add 12.	$6n + 12$	$42 + 12 = 54$
Divide by 3.	$\dfrac{6n + 12}{3} = 2n + 4$	$\dfrac{54}{3} = 18$
Subtract 4.	$2n + 4 - 4 = 2n$	$18 - 4 = 14$
Divide by 2.	$\dfrac{2n}{2} = n$	$\dfrac{14}{2} = 7$

We get n, and Rowena gets 7. So we both get back the number we started with.

Let's try Norman's second trick with n as Rowena uses 8.

Norman's Directions	Our Calculation with n	What Rowena Does with 8
Multiply by 8.	$8 \times n = 8n$	$8 \times 8 = 64$
Add 14.	$8n + 14$	$64 + 14 = 78$
Divide by 2.	$\dfrac{8n + 14}{2} = 4n + 7$	$\dfrac{78}{2} = 39$
Add 1.	$4n + 7 + 1 = 4n + 8$	$39 + 1 = 40$
Divide by 4.	$\dfrac{4n + 8}{4} = n + 2$	$\dfrac{40}{4} = 10$
Subtract the number you started with.	$n + 2 - n = 2$	$10 - 8 = 2$
Subtract 2.	$2 - 2 = 0$	$2 - 2 = 0$

We and Rowena both got 0. So Norman's trick works again.

[4] If you doubt that the tricks work, try other numbers.

[5] Make up 2 or 3 number tricks like Norman's. Check them yourself with 1 or 2 numbers to be sure they do what you think they do. Then try them on a friend.

Notation Used in Algebra

When an $\times$ is used as a times sign along with letters, the $\times$ is easy to confuse with x. Generally, a times sign is not used with letters. Sometimes a raised dot is used: $3 \cdot n = 3 \times n$. More often, no symbol at all is used: $3n = 3 \times n$. Parentheses are sometimes used to help indicate what is meant: $3(n)$ means $3 \times n$ and $3(8)$ means 3×8.

It is also conventional to perform multiplications and divisions before additions and subtractions unless parentheses are used to indicate a different order of operations. However, parentheses are usually used to prevent any possibility of misunderstanding.

Here are some examples.

A. Evaluate $27 - 3n$ when $n = 6$.

   $27 - 3 \cdot 6 = 27 - 18 = 9$

B. Evaluate $(27 - 3)n$ when $n = 6$.

   $(27 - 3) \times 6 = 24 \times 6 = 144$

C. Evaluate $(6x + 12) \div 3$ when $x = 5$.

   $(6 \cdot 5 + 12) \div 3 = (30 + 12) \div 3 = 42 \div 3 = 14$
   or $(6 \cdot 5 + 12) \div 3 = 2 \cdot 5 + 4 = 10 + 4 = 14$
   (Notice that if you divide first, you must divide both terms inside the parentheses.)

D. Evaluate $6x + 12 \div 3$ when $x = 5$.

   $6 \cdot 5 + 12 \div 3 = 30 + 4 = 34$
   We would prefer to write the problem as $6x + (12 \div 3)$.

Evaluate each of the following functions.

   1. $2x$ when $x = 5$
   2. $3x - 7$ when $x = 4$
   3. $3(x + 2)$ when $x = 5$
   4. $3x + 2$ when $x = 5$
   5. $3x + 6$ when $x = 5$
   6. $(x + y) + z$ when $x = 8$, $y = 4$, $z = 3$
   7. $x + (y + z)$ when $x = 8$, $y = 4$, $z = 3$
   8. $(x - y) - z$ when $x = 8$, $y = 4$, $z = 3$

9. $x - (y - z)$ when $x = 8$, $y = 4$, $z = 3$

10. $(xy)z$ when $x = 8$, $y = 4$, $z = 2$

11. $x(yz)$ when $x = 8$, $y = 4$, $z = 2$

12. $(x \div y) \div z$ when $x = 8$, $y = 4$, $z = 2$

13. $x \div (y \div z)$ when $x = 8$, $y = 4$, $z = 2$

14. $x(y + z)$ when $x = 7$, $y = 5$, $z = 3$

15. $xy + xz$ when $x = 7$, $y = 5$, $z = 3$

16. $x(y - z)$ when $x = 7$, $y = 5$, $z = 3$

17. $xy - xz$ when $x = 7$, $y = 5$, $z = 3$

18. $(y - z)x$ when $x = 7$, $y = 5$, $z = 3$

19. $(y + z)x$ when $x = 7$, $y = 5$, $z = 3$

20. $4n - 7$ when $n = 7$

21. Write an expression using x for a function that equals 35 when $x = 10$.

22. Write an expression using x for a different function that equals 35 when $x = 10$.

23. Write an expression using x for a third function that equals 35 when $x = 10$.

24. Write an expression using x for a fourth function that equals 35 when $x = 10$.

There are many correct answers to problems 21–24. Several such answers are $3x + 5$, $2x + 15$, $x + 25$, $45 - x$, $55 - 2x$, $65 - 3x$, $\frac{1}{2}x + 30$, and $\frac{3}{2}x + 20$.

25. In each case, write expressions using x for 4 different functions that equal

   a. 20 when $x = 4$.

   b. 30 when $x = 2$.

   c. 10 when $x = 0$.

   d. 0 when $x = 10$.

   e. 2 when $x = 7$.

Here are 5 rules. Use them to help with computations in arithmetic and algebra.

A. The commutative law for addition: The order in addition makes no difference. For all pairs of numbers x and y, $x + y = y + x$.

Example: $27 + 13 = 13 + 27$

B. The commutative law for multiplication: The order in multiplication makes no difference. For all pairs of numbers x and y, $xy = yx$.

Example: $27 \times 13 = 13 \times 27$

C. The associative law for addition: When 3 numbers are added, it makes no difference whether the first 2 are combined and then the third is added to the sum, or the second 2 are combined and then added to the first. For all triples of numbers x, y, and z, $(x + y) + z = x + (y + z)$. (A triple is a set of 3 numbers.)

Example: $(6 + 27) + 13 = 6 + (27 + 13)$

D. The associative law for multiplication: When 3 numbers are multiplied, it makes no difference whether the first 2 are multiplied and then the third is multiplied by the product, or the second 2 are multiplied and then multiplied by the first. For all triples of numbers x, y, and z, $(xy)z = x(yz)$.

Example: $(6 \times 27)13 = 6(27 \times 13)$

E. The distributive law for multiplication over addition: For any 3 numbers, the product of the first number and the sum of the other 2 equals the sum of the products of the first and second and of the first and third. For all triples of numbers x, y, and z, $x(y + z) = xy + xz$.

Example: $13(27 + 6) = 13(27) + 13(6)$

Do you believe that all 5 rules are true?

You probably don't have any problem believing the first 4 rules are true. You have used the commutative laws to help memorize the addition and the multiplication facts. If you knew that $9 + 3 = 12$, then you also knew that $3 + 9 = 12$. For multiplication, once you learned that $3 \times 9 = 27$, you knew that $9 \times 3 = 27$.

One thing that the associative laws allow us to do is to avoid parentheses. Since $7 + (8 + 2) = (7 + 8) + 2$, we can simply write $7 + 8 + 2$. For multiplication, since $(7 \times 8) \times 2 = 7 \times (8 \times 2)$, we write $7 \times 8 \times 2$.

It may be harder for you to believe that the distributive law is true. The distributive law is used in multiplication: $2 \times 24 = (2 \times 20) + (2 \times 4) = 40 + 8 = 48$. It is useful because it is a 2-way law.

$$9(81 + 19) = (9 \times 81) + (9 \times 19), \text{ so}$$
$$(9 \times 81) + (9 \times 19) = 9(100) = 900.$$

There is another distributive law, which may be called the "right-handed" distributive law.

$$(x + y)z = xz + yz$$

It is easy to see that the distributive law can be used with numbers that have more than 2 digits.

$$\text{If } 2 \times 24 = (2 \times 20) + (2 \times 4) = 40 + 8 = 48,$$
$$\text{then } 4 \times 357 = (4 \times 300) + (4 \times 50) + (4 \times 7)$$
$$= 1200 + 200 + 28 = 1428.$$

We can write a general form of the distributive law this way:

$$x(y_1 + y_2 + \ldots + y_n) = xy_1 + xy_2 + \ldots + xy_n$$

Solve for n. You may use any of the 5 laws if they help. Be careful.

1. $37 + 89 = n$
2. $89 + 37 = n$
3. $37 \times 89 = n$
4. $89 \times 37 = n$
5. $(43 + 57) + 65 = n$

6. $43 + (67 + 65) = n$
7. $(43 + 65) + 57 = n$
8. $43 + (65 + 57) = n$
9. $(16 - 8) - 4 = n$
10. $16 - (8 - 4) = n$

11. $(16 \div 8) \div 4 = n$
12. $16 \div (8 \div 4) = n$
13. $8 \times (7 + 3) = n$
14. $(8 \times 7) + (8 \times 3) = n$
15. $(7 \times 8) + (3 \times 8) = n$

16. $(7 + 3) \times 8 = n$
17. $24 \div 8 = n$
18. $8 \div 24 = n$
19. $5 \times (5 + 5) = n$
20. $(5 \times 5) + (5 \times 5) = n$

21. $(83 + 25) + 25 = n$
22. $83 + (25 + 25) = n$
23. $(16 \div 4) + (8 \div 4) = n$
24. $(16 + 8) \div 4 = n$
25. $(17 \times 18) - (17 \times 8) = n$

26. $17 \times (18 - 8) = n$
27. $14 \times (23 - 13) = n$
28. $(14 \times 23) - (14 \times 13) = n$
29. $5 - 3 = n$
30. $3 - 5 = n$

31. $4 \times (40 + 10) = n$
32. $4 \times (25 + 15 + 10) = n$
33. $(25 + 15 + 10) \times 4 = n$
34. $(4 \times 25) + (4 \times 15) + (4 \times 10) = n$
35. $(47 + 53) \times 5 = n$

36. $(5 \times 47) + (5 \times 53) = n$
37. $(47 \times 5) + (53 \times 5) = n$
38. $(27 - 17) \times 6 = n$
39. $(27 \times 6) - (17 \times 6) = n$
40. $(25 \times 25) + (25 \times 25) + (25 \times 25) + (25 \times 25) = n$

41. Do you believe the commutative law is true for subtraction? Why or why not?

42. Do you believe the associative law is true for subtraction? Why or why not?

Do these problems. If your answer to a problem is yes, give 3 examples showing that the law works. If your answer is no, give 1 example showing that the law doesn't work.

43. Do you believe that the commutative law for division is true?

44. Do you believe that the associative law for division is true?

45. Do you believe that the right-handed distributive law for division over addition is true? That is, that for all triples of numbers x, y, and z, $(x + y) \div z = (x \div z) + (y \div z)$.

46. Do you believe that the distributive law for addition over multiplication is true? That is, that for all triples of numbers x, y, and z, $x + (yz) = (x + y)(x + z)$.

Numbers less than zero are called negative numbers. 1 below zero is called negative 1 and is written −1. 2 below zero, or negative 2, is written −2, and so on.

Do you remember how to add and subtract on the number line? Remember that adding a negative number is the same as subtracting a positive number. If you start at +17 and go 10 steps to the left, you end at +7.

$$+17 - 10 = +7, \text{ or } +17 + (-10) = +7$$

If you start at +7 and go 10 steps to the left, you end at −3.

$$+7 - 10 = -3, \text{ or } +7 + (-10) = -3$$

If you start at −7 and go 3 steps to the left, you end at −10.

$$-7 - 3 = -10, \text{ or } -7 + (-3) = -10$$

If you start at −10 and go 3 steps to the right, you end at −7.

$$-10 + 3 = -7, \text{ or } -10 - (-3) = -7$$

You can think about using signed numbers as having, borrowing, and owing money.

Sam has $17.
When he pays Beatriz the $10 he owes her, he has $7 left.

$$17 - 10 = 7, \text{ or } 17 + (-10) = 7$$

Rosa has $7. Since she owes Carl $10, she is $3 in debt. You could say that she has $(−3).

$$7 - 10 = -3, \text{ or } 7 + (-10) = -3$$

Victor owes Judy $7 and he owes Ruth $3. So he is in debt for a total of $10. You could say that he has $(−10).

$$-7 - 3 = -10, \text{ or } -7 + (-3) = -10$$

Joan owes $10 to Bob. After she pays him $3, she still owes him $7. You could say that she has $(−7).

$$-10 + 3 = -7$$

Barbara owes Alan $10. When she fixes a flat tire on his bicycle, he agrees to cancel $3 of her debt. You could say that she has $(−7).

$$-10 - (-3) = -7$$

We say that adding −4 is the same as subtracting 4:

$$20 - 4 = 20 + (-4) = 16$$

In the same way, we can say that subtracting 4 times something is the same as adding (−4) times something:

$$20 - (4 \times 2) = 20 + [(-4) \times 2] = 12$$

We know that $4 \times 2 = 8$, so we find that $(-4) \times 2 = -8$. Because we know that $4 \times (-2) = -8$, we could show in the same way that $(-4) \times (-2) = 8$.

Use the number line, reasoning with money, the 5 laws, and so on to help you do these problems.

1. $8 - 6$
2. $9 - 9$
3. $7 - 9$
4. $3 - 8$
5. $5 + (-3)$
6. $8 + (-5)$
7. $5 - 3$
8. $8 - 5$
9. $(-3) + 5$
10. $(-5) + 8$

11. $4 - 9$
12. $4 + (-9)$
13. $(-2) + 2$
14. $(-2) - 2$
15. $(-2) - 7$
16. $(-2) + (-7)$
17. $(-5) + (-8)$
18. $(-4) + (-2)$
19. $8 + (-8)$
20. $-4 - 7$

21. $3 + 3 + 3 + 3$
22. 4×3
23. $(-3) + (-3) + (-3) + (-3)$
24. $4 \times (-3)$
25. $(-3) \times 4$
26. $12 \times \frac{1}{3}$
27. $12 \div 3$
28. $-12 \div 3$
29. $12 \div (-3)$
30. $12 \times \left(-\frac{1}{3}\right)$

31. Yesterday En-biao owed $7 to Lloyd and $3 to Beth.

   a. What was his total debt?
   b. Today En-biao did a favor for Beth and she canceled his debt. Now how much does he owe?

32. $-8 - (-5)$
33. $-2 - (-5)$
34. $0 - (-5)$
35. $8 - (-5)$
36. $0 - 5 - 5 - 5 - 5$
37. $(-4) \times 5$
38. $0 - 7 - 7 - 7$
39. $(-3) \times 7$
40. $0 - (-2) - (-2) - (-2)$

41. $(-3) \times (-2)$
42. $0 - (-4) - (-4) - (-4)$
43. $(-3) \times (-4)$
44. $(-7) \times (-8)$
45. $(-4) \times (-6)$
46. $(-3) \times (-9)$
47. $(-7) \times (-6)$
48. $(-8) \times (-8)$
49. $(-9) \times (-9)$

SIGNED MATHNESS

Players: 2 or more
Materials: One 0–5 cube, one 5–10 cube, pencil and paper
Object: To get an answer as close to 0 as possible

Rules

1. The first player rolls both cubes 5 times. On each roll, write the number that comes up on the 5–10 cube. Give the number a sign determined by the 0–5 cube: + for even numbers (0, 2, or 4) and − for odd numbers (1, 3, or 5).

2. Add any 2 of the numbers.

3. Subtract another of the numbers from the sum in step 2.

4. Multiply the difference in step 3 by one of the 2 unused numbers.

5. Divide the product in step 4 by the remaining number.

6. The other players repeat steps 1–5.

7. The player whose final answer is closest to 0 wins.

Sample Game

Alice rolled [2] [9], [5] [5], [1] [9], [3] [10], and [0] [5]. She wrote 9, −5, −9, −10, 5. She added 9 and −5 to get 4, then subtracted 5 to get −1, multiplied by −9 to get 9, and divided by −10 to get $-\frac{9}{10}$.

Bryan rolled [3] [5], [5] [9], [0] [6], [4] [5], and [3] [5]. He wrote −5, −9, 6, 5, −5. He added −9 and 5 to get −4, then subtracted −5 to get 1, multiplied by −5 to get −5, and divided by 6 to get $-\frac{5}{6}$.

Cora rolled [5] [6], [2] [7], [3] [6], [5] [9], and [2] [5]. She wrote −6, 7, −6, −9, 5. She added −9 and 5 to get −4, subtracted −6 to get 2, multiplied by −6 to get −12, and divided by 7 to get $-1\frac{5}{7}$.

Bryan was the winner, because $-\frac{5}{6}$ is closer to 0 than $-\frac{9}{10}$ or $-1\frac{5}{7}$.

Finding Equivalent Expressions

In algebra, letters are used in expressions to stand for numbers. You can use the commutative, associative, and distributive laws to find equivalent expressions. Equivalent expressions are different ways of showing the same function.

Suppose we had a function that we could describe with this function rule: $3x + 7 + 2x + 5 + 4x$. We could find a simpler expression for the same function this way:

$$3x + 7 + 2x + 5 + 4x$$

$$= 3x + 2x + 4x + 7 + 5 \quad \text{We used the commutative and associative laws several times.}$$

$$= (3 + 2 + 4)x + 12 \quad \text{Now we use the distributive law.}$$

$$= 9x + 12$$

You don't have to write all these steps each time, of course. They are written out here to show why we can take each step. Most people would look at the first expression and see $3x + 2x + 4x$ and say "$9x$." Then they would see $7 + 5$ and say "12." So the original expression equals $9x + 12$.

You know that $7 - 3 = 7 + (-3)$, $-2 - 5 = -2 + (-5)$, $-4 - (-6) = -4 + 6$, and so on. Therefore, if you want to use the commutative and associative laws on a problem involving subtraction, you can first turn the problem into an addition problem. Doing so may be helpful in problems involving subtraction. For example:

$$15 - [(4x - 7) - 2x]$$

$$= 15 - (4x - 2x - 7) \quad \text{commutative and associative laws}$$

$$= 15 - (2x - 7)$$

$$= 15 - 2x + 7 \quad \text{(Remember to change the sign of the 7.)}$$

$$= 22 - 2x$$

Notice that you must be very careful to make sure the signs are right when you start to remove parentheses or brackets from an expression. Sometimes square brackets [ ] and curly brackets { }, also called braces, are used when more than 1 set of parentheses are needed.

Sometimes it is helpful to find an expression that is equivalent to a given expression but has fewer terms. For example:

$$(7x - 3x + 5) - 2x + 8 - 7 = 2x + 6$$

Sometimes we use the distributive law first to make the terms easier to handle. For example:

$$7(3x + 4) + 8(2x - 5) = 21x + 28 + 16x - 40 = 37x - 12$$

Find an equivalent expression for each of the following expressions. Try to make it as simple as you can.

1. $[(8x + 4) \div 4] - 1$
2. $3x + 5x - 7 + 9$
3. $[5(x + 8) - 40] \div 5$
4. $4x - 2 + 3x - 5$
5. $x + x + x + x$

6. $4x - x + 3 - 3x$
7. $7 - 2x + 4x - 8$
8. $7 - 2y + 4y - 8$
9. $7 - 2n + 4n - 8$
10. $5y + 2y - 7$

11. $x + 2x - x - 2x$
12. $x + 2x + 3x$
13. $y + 2y + 3y$
14. $[(7n + 14) \div 7] - 2$
15. $(3x + 5) - (3x + 5)$*

16. $(4x + 7) - (4x + 6)$
17. $(x + 5) - (x + 3)$
18. $(x + 5) - (x + 1)$
19. $(x + 5) - (x - 1)$†
20. $(x + 5) - (x - 3)$

21. Try using some of these problems to do magic number tricks like Norman's (see page 38). What happens if somebody starts with 7 in your trick?

   a. Use problem 1.
   b. Use problem 3.
   c. Use problem 14.

*Think about problem 15. Are you subtracting $3x + 5$ from itself? What should the answer be? Is that the same as $3x + 5 - 3x - 5$? Notice the second 5.
†Think about this one.

Solve for n.

1. $8 + 7 = n$
2. $8 - 7 = n$
3. $-8 + 7 = n$
4. $-8 - 7 = n$
5. $-8 + (-7) = n$

6. $8 + (-7) = n$
7. $8 - (-7) = n$
8. $-8 - (-7) = n$
9. $8 \times 7 = n$
10. $-8 \times 7 = n$

11. $8 \times (-7) = n$
12. $-8 \times (-7) = n$
13. $24 \div 8 = n$
14. $-24 \div 8 = n$
15. $24 \div (-8) = n$

16. $-24 \div (-8) = n$
17. $-24 - (-8) = n$
18. $24 - (-8) = n$
19. $-24 - 8 = n$
20. $24 + (-8) = n$

21. $24 \times 8 = n$
22. $24 - 8 = n$
23. $-24 + 8 = n$
24. $-24 + (-8) = n$
25. $8 - (-24) = n$

26. $36 + 4 = n$
27. $36 \div 4 = n$
28. $36 - 4 = n$
29. $36 - (-4) = n$
30. $36 \div (-4) = n$

31. $-36 + (-4) = n$
32. $-36 \div (-4) = n$
33. $36 \times 4 = n$
34. $36 \times (-4) = n$
35. $-36 \div 4 = n$

36. $-36 \div (-4) = n$
37. $-36 \times (-4) = n$
38. $6 - 12 = n$
39. $-6 \times 12 = n$
40. $-6 \div 12 = n$

41. $-12 \div (-6) = n$
42. $-12 \times (-6) = n$
43. $-12 + 6 = n$
44. $-12 - (-6) = n$
45. $12 \div 6 = n$

46. $12 \times 6 = n$
47. $-12 + (-6) = n$
48. $-6 - (-12) = n$
49. $-6 - 12 = n$
50. $-6 \div (-12) = n$

Play Signed Mathness.

You know that parentheses can be used to tell you which operations should be done first when you are combining terms in an expression. Sometimes you'll find parentheses inside other parentheses or brackets in an expression.

When this happens, you need to remember only one thing— start working in the innermost parentheses and work your way out.

Remove the parentheses and brackets from each of the following expressions. Write each expression as simply as possible. Remember that the negative of a negative number is positive.

1. $3 - 2(x + 1)$
2. $3 - 2(x - 1)$
3. $2[3 - 2(x + 1)]$
4. $12(x + 2) - 6(x + 1)$
5. $12(x + 2) - 6(x - 1)$
6. $12[(x + 2) - 6(x - 1) + 3]$
7. $33(x + 1) + (x + 1)$
8. $33[(x + 1) + (x + 1)]$
9. $33(x - 1) + (x - 1)$
10. $33[(x - 1) + (x - 1)]$
11. $[(6x + 9) \div 3] + 3$
12. $3 - [(6x + 9) \div 3]$
13. $[3 + (36 \div 9)x] + 3x$

14. $6 - 1[3x - 3(x + 3) + 2]$
15. $3[(x + 2) + (x + 2)]$
16. $12 + \{x + [2 + (x + 2)]\}$
17. $2\{x + [x + (x + 2) + 2] + 2\}$
18. $2\{x - [x - (x - 2) - 2] - 2\}$
19. $-2\{x - [x - (x - 2) - 2] - 2\}$
20. $-2\{x - [x + (x - 2) + 2] - 2\}$
21. $(4x + 2) - (4x + 2)$
22. $(4x + 2) - (4x + 1)$
23. $(4x + 2) - (4x + 3)$
24. $(4x + 2) - 4x$
25. $(4x + 2) - (4x - 1)$
26. $(4x + 2) - (4x - 2)$

27. For each of these sets of numbers, put in parentheses and brackets wherever you wish. Try first to make as large an answer as possible, then to make as small an answer as possible. Compare your results with those of other students. Remember, for example, that -7 is less than -5.

   a. $10 - 8 - 6 - 4$
   b. $10 + 7 - 5 - 3$
   c. $5 - 5 - 5 - 5$
   d. $10 - 10 - 10 - 10$
   e. $4 - 5 - 6 - 7$
   f. $5 + 4 - 3 - 2$

Mrs. Clearwater is trying to decide how much it will cost to take some people to a movie. The cost of a ticket to the movie is $4.00. She figures that the cost of driving her van to and from the theater will be $6.00.

[1] If she goes to the movie by herself, what will be the total cost?

[2] If she takes 1 friend, what will be the total cost?

[3] If she takes 5 friends, what will be the total cost?

She decides that an appropriate formula to show the total cost is:

$$c = 4n + 6$$

where c is the cost in dollars and n is the number of people who go to the movie.

Let's check to see if the formula works.

If 1 person goes, the formula says $c = 4(1) + 6 = 10$, so the cost is $10. Was your answer to the first discussion question $10?

If 5 people go, the formula says $c = 4(5) + 6 = 26$, so the cost is $26. Does that agree with your answer to the third discussion question?

Suppose the cost of going to a movie on a certain occasion was $18. How many people went to the movie? We can answer this question by finding out what values of n will make $c = 18$ in the equation $c = 4n + 6$. That is, we find what value of n makes the equation $18 = 4n + 6$ true. We call this solving the equation, $18 = 4n + 6$, for n.

When we solve an equation, we are looking for the value of the unknown (n, or x, or some other symbol) that will make the equation true. There are many ways to solve an equation like $c = 4n + 6$. We will look at several of them.

Solve: $c = 4n + 6$ when $c = 18$

A. Guess. Guess a value for n, say 10. $4(10) + 6 = 46$. Too large. Now $4n + 6$ obviously increases as n increases. So, since $4(10) + 6$ was too large, our next guess should be smaller than 10. Let's guess 9. $4(9) + 6 = 42$. Still much too large. Let's try a much smaller number, 2. $4(2) + 6 = 14$. Too small. Try 3. $4(3) + 6 = 18$. Right. So $n = 3$ is the solution.

B. Guess and check. Guess 10: $4(10) + 6 = 46$. This is exactly 28 too large. When n is reduced or increased by 1, c is reduced or increased by 4 because n is multiplied by 4. We'd like to reduce c by 28. So, since $28 = 4 \times 7$, reduce n by 7: ($10 - 7 = 3$)

$$4(3) + 6 = 18 \qquad \text{The solution is } n = 3.$$

C. Think backward. If $4n + 6 = 18$, what must $4n$ be? Since you can add 12 to 6 to get 18, $4n$ must be 12: $4n = 12$. What can you multiply by 4 to get 12? $4 \times 3 = 12$, so the solution is $n = 3$.

D. Use arrow arithmetic. $4n + 6 = 18$ can be written using arrow arithmetic as $n \longrightarrow \boxed{\times 4} \longrightarrow x \longrightarrow \boxed{+6} \longrightarrow c$

If you put 10 in for n, you get 40 for x and 46 for c. If you put 1 in for n, you get 4 for x and 10 for c, and so on.

If you know c and want to find n, you reverse the arrows and "undo" the functions. So, if you know c is 10, reverse the arrows and use inverse operations: $x = 10 - 6 = 4$, $n = 4 \div 4 = 1$. Or, in this case, since c is 18, x is $18 - 6$, or 12, and n is $12 \div 4$, or 3.

E. Manipulate symbols on both sides of the equals symbol (=) to produce an equivalent equation that is easy to solve. We will consider this method of solving equations in the next lesson.

After each of the following problems, some equations are given. One of the equations describes the situation correctly. The others do not. For each problem, choose the correct equation and solve the problem by whatever means you like.

1. It costs $28 to hire a bus to go from camp to a movie theater. Theater tickets cost $3 apiece. If the total cost for the trip and the tickets was $154, how many people saw the movie?

$$3n + 28 = 154 \qquad 28n + 3 = 154$$

where n is the number of people

2. Thelma plans to drive 600 kilometers today. She has already driven 200 kilometers. If she drives at the rate of 80 kilometers per hour, how much longer must she drive?

$$80 + 600x = 200 \qquad\qquad 200 + 600x = 80$$
$$600 = 80x + 200 \qquad\qquad 600 = 200x + 80$$

where x is the number of hours still to drive

3. The charge for a checking account at Midville Bank is $2.00 a month plus 10¢ for every check cashed. The cost in October for one account was $8.30. How many checks were cashed in that account during October?

$$100x + 2 = 830 \qquad 10x + 200 = 830$$

where x is the number of checks cashed

4. A different kind of checking account costs $5.00 each month plus 4¢ for each check cashed. The cost in October for one of these accounts was $7.52. How many checks were cashed in this account during October?

$$5x + 4 = 752 \qquad\qquad 4x + 500 = 752$$
$$500x + 4 = 752 \qquad\qquad 4x + 5 = 752$$

where x is the number of checks cashed

Formulas for Temperature

In the metric system, temperature is measured in degrees Celsius (°C). In the traditional system, temperature is measured in degrees Fahrenheit (°F). A formula that relates these systems is $F = \frac{9}{5}C + 32$ where F stands for degrees Fahrenheit and C stands for degrees Celsius.

Use the formula to answer these questions.

1. For each of the following temperatures on a Celsius thermometer, find (to the nearest tenth of a degree) the temperature in degrees Fahrenheit.

   a. 0°C   b. 20°C   c. 100°C   d. 37°C   e. 25°C

2. For each of the following temperatures on a Fahrenheit thermometer, find (to the nearest tenth of a degree) the temperature in degrees Celsius.

   a. 32°F   b. 0°F   c. 98.6°F   d. 72°F   e. 100°F

For estimation, some people use the formula $F = 2C + 30$. This gives a rough approximation of the temperature on one scale when the temperature on the other is known. Even though the estimation formula doesn't give exactly correct answers, they are close enough for practical purposes, especially for the common temperatures that occur in everyday living.

3. Use the formula $F = 2C + 30$ to estimate the Fahrenheit temperature for each of the following Celsius temperatures.

   a. 0°C   b. 20°C   c. 100°C   d. 37°C   e. 25°C

4. Compare your estimates for problem 3 with your answers for problem 1. For what Celsius temperatures does the estimation formula seem to work well?

5. Use the formula $F = 2C + 30$ to estimate the Celsius temperature for each of the following Fahrenheit temperatures.

   a. 32°F   b. 0°F   c. 98.6°F   d. 72°F   e. 100°F

6. What is the Celsius temperature for which the estimation formula $F = 2C + 30$ gives the same Fahrenheit temperature as the accurate formula, $F = \frac{9}{5}C + 32$?

For each of these 4 discussion questions, Leann and Sue have the same number of marbles.

[1] **Leann won 5 marbles from Ben. What does Sue have to do to have the same number of marbles as Leann?**

[2] **Sue gave away $\frac{1}{2}$ of her marbles. What does Leann have to do in order for Sue and Leann to have the same number of marbles?**

[3] **Leann lost 6 marbles. What can Sue do so that she will have the same number of marbles as Leann?**

[4] **Sue bought enough marbles to triple the number of marbles she had. What can Leann do so they have the same number of marbles?**

A mathematical sentence with the equals symbol (=) in it is called an *equation*. The = symbol means that the numbers represented on both sides are the same. So, $830 = 80x + 130$ means that 830 and $80x + 130$ are the same number.

Remember that Leann and Sue both had to do the same thing to continue having the same number of marbles.

If we do something to one side of an equation, we must do the same thing to the other side to retain the equality relationship.

We can add 5 to both sides. So:

$$\text{if } 830 = 80x + 130,$$
$$\text{then } 830 + 5 = 80x + 130 + 5,$$
$$\text{or } 835 = 80x + 135.$$

[5] **Start again with $830 = 80x + 130$. Show the new equation you would get by taking $\frac{1}{2}$ of each side. Remember, $\frac{1}{2}$ of $80x + 130 = \frac{1}{2}(80x) + \frac{1}{2}(130)$.**

[6] **Start with $830 = 80x + 130$. Show the new equation you would get by subtracting 6 from each side.**

[7] **Start with $830 = 80x + 130$. Show the new equation you would have if you tripled both sides.**

The equations *a* and *b* are *equivalent* if whenever *a* is true *b* is true and whenever *b* is true *a* is true. Equivalent equations have the same solution.

If equations a and b are equivalent, and equations b and c are equivalent, then equations a and c are equivalent.

The equation $E = F$ is equivalent to the equation $F = E$. (Here E and F are different expressions for the same function.)

For any equation, you can find an equivalent equation by doing the same thing to both sides of the equation. Here are some examples:

$$830 = 80x + 130$$

We can subtract 130 to get the following equivalent equation:

$$700 = 80x$$

Now we can divide by 80 to get another equivalent equation:

$$8.75 = x$$

Find an equivalent equation for each of the following equations. Follow the instructions in parentheses.

1. $830 = 80x + 130$ (Add 20.)
2. $4x + 3 = 12$ (Add 5.)
3. $4x + 3 = 12$ (Subtract 3.)
4. $10 = 5x - 15$ (Subtract 10.)
5. $10 = 5x - 15$ (Add 10.)
6. $10 = 5x - 15$ (Add 15.)
7. $25 = 5x$ (Subtract 25.)
8. $25 = 5x$ (Subtract 5.)
9. $25 = 5x$ (Divide by 5.)
10. $8x + 7 = 25$ (Subtract 7.)
11. $8x - 7 = 25$ (Subtract 25.)
12. $8x - 7 = 25$ (Add 7.)
13. $8x = 32$ (Subtract 32.)
14. $8x = 32$ (Multiply by 3.)
15. $8x =$ (Divide by 8.)
16. $3x + 8 = 5x + 3$ (Subtract 8).
17. $3x = 5x - 5$ (Subtract $5x$.)
18. $-2x = -5$ (Divide by -2.)
19. $3x + 8 = 5x + 3$ (Subtract 3.)
20. $3x + 5 = 5x$ (Subtract $3x$.)
21. $5 = 2x$ (Divide by 2.)
22. $15 = 3x + 8$ (Multiply by 3.)
23. $7x + 4 = 18$ (Subtract 4.)
24. $7x = 14$ (Divide by 7.)
25. $7x + 14 = 21$ (Subtract 14, then multiply by 2.)
26. $7x = 7$ (Divide by 7, then multiply by 2.)
27. $7x + 14 = 21$ (Divide by 7, then add 7.)
28. $x + 2 = 3$ (Subtract 2, then multiply by 3.)
29. $\frac{1}{4}x + 5 = 7$ (Subtract 5, then multiply by 4.)
30. $\frac{1}{4}x = 2$ (Multiply by 4, then subtract 5.)

Another Way to Solve Equations

You can solve an equation by finding an equivalent equation for which the solution is obvious. Here are 3 examples:

Example 1: Solve for x: $830 = 80x + 130$

This means to find all values of x that make the equation true.

It will often make it easier to work with the equation if you first rewrite it so that the side with the unknown is on the left.

$$80x + 130 = 830$$

Subtract 130 from each side: $80x = 700$

Divide each side by 80: $x = 8.75$

Can you guess what value of x satisfies the equation $x = 8.75$? Check to see if 8.75 is a solution to $830 = 80x + 130$.

$$830 \stackrel{?}{=} 80(8.75) + 130$$
$$830 \stackrel{?}{=} 700 + 130$$
$$830 = 830$$

Since replacing x by 8.75 makes the equation true, 8.75 is a solution.

Example 2: Solve for x: $5x - 7 = 8x + 12$

$$\text{Subtract } 5x: \quad -7 = 3x + 12$$
$$\text{Subtract } 12: \quad -19 = 3x$$
$$\text{Divide by } 3: \quad -\frac{19}{3} = x$$

The answer is $-\frac{19}{3}$, or $-6\frac{1}{3}$.

Check: $\quad 5\left(-\frac{19}{3}\right) - 7 \stackrel{?}{=} 8\left(-\frac{19}{3}\right) + 12$

$$-\frac{95}{3} - 7 \stackrel{?}{=} -\frac{152}{3} + 12$$
$$-31\frac{2}{3} - 7 \stackrel{?}{=} -50\frac{2}{3} + 12$$
$$-38\frac{2}{3} = -38\frac{2}{3}$$

Most people find that it is easier to start by first finding an equivalent equation with a positive multiple of x on one side (usually the left side) and then finding another equivalent equation with *only* that positive multiple of x on that side.

Example 3: Solve for C: $98.6 = \frac{9}{5}C + 32$

$$\text{Subtract 32:} \quad 66.6 = \frac{9}{5}C$$

$$\text{Multiply by } \tfrac{5}{9}: \quad \tfrac{5}{9}(66.6) = \tfrac{5}{9}\left(\tfrac{9}{5}\right)C$$

$$37 = C$$

Check: $\frac{9}{5}(37) + 32 = \frac{333}{5} + 32 = 66.6 + 32 = 98.6$

Solve each of the following equations. Use any method you choose. Check your answers.

1. $3x + 5 = 20$

2. $3x - 5 = 20$

3. $17 = 2x - 4$

4. $3x + 4 = 2x - 1$

5. $x = 7 + 13.4$

6. $100x + 90 = 830$

7. $100x + 90 = 890$

8. $100x + 125 = 850$

9. $100x + 125 = 825$

10. $10x + 200 = 830$

11. $10x + 200 = 750$

12. $4x + 500 = 752$

13. $4x + 500 = 528$

14. $830 = 80x + 130$

15. $440 = 80x + 130$

16. $3y + 5 = 20$

17. $3n - 5 = 20$

18. $17 = 2q - 4$

19. $3z + 4 = 2z - 1$

20. $b = 7 + 13.4$

A solution is given for each of the following equations. Half the solutions are correct. Check the answers. If a solution is wrong, find the correct one.

21. $5x - 4 = 2x + 8$
$x = -4$

22. $2x + 8 = 5x - 4$
$x = 4$

23. $3x - 1 = 8x - 16$
$x = 3$

24. $x - 2 = 3x + 5$
$x = -\frac{2}{7}$

25. $50 = \frac{9}{5}C + 32$
$C = 100$

26. $68 = \frac{9}{5}C + 32$
$C = 200$

27. $77 = \frac{9}{5}C + 32$
$C = 25\frac{5}{9}$

28. $32 = \frac{9}{5}C + 32$
$C = 0$

29. $23 = \frac{9}{5}C + 32$
$C = -5$

30. $5 = \frac{9}{5}C + 32$
$C = -15$

1. **a.** Write an expression using x that equals 35 when $x = 10$.

   b. Write a different expression using x that equals 35 when $x = 10$.

   c. Write an equation by setting the expressions in part a and part b equal to each other.

   d. Solve the equation you wrote in part c.

2. Repeat the 4 parts of problem 1 with expressions that use x and equal 28 when $x = 5$.

3. Repeat the 4 parts of problem 1 with expressions that use x and equal 0 when $x = 3$.

4. Repeat the 4 parts of problem 1 with expressions that use y and equal 35 when $y = 10$.

5. Repeat the 4 parts of problem 1 with expressions that use n and equal 28 when $n = 5$.

6. If you fly on Flihi Airlines, you are allowed to take 25 kilograms of luggage free but must pay $3 for each additional kilogram of luggage. (Any fraction of a kilogram is counted as a kilogram.) Which of the following function rules could be used to show the extra charge for luggage weighing more than 25 kilograms? We'll let k be the weight of your luggage in kilograms and c the extra charge.

   a. $25k + 3 = c$ **c.** $3k + 25 = c$
   b. $3k - 25 = c$ **d.** $3(k - 25) = c$

7. Use the formula you chose for problem 6 to calculate the extra charge for luggage weighing 26 kilograms. (If this answer seems unreasonable, reconsider your answer to problem 6.)

8. If Mr. Bagshaw was charged $21 for his luggage, about how much does the luggage weigh?

9. Can you be sure of your answer to problem 8?

10. One of Flihi's employees decided that he could be more efficient if he used the formula for all passengers—no matter what their luggage weighed. What happened when Ms. Travelight came along with only 20 kilograms of luggage?

11. Was the Flihi employee really more efficient?

EQUATION GAME

Players: 2 or more
Materials: Two 0–5 cubes, two 5–10 cubes
Object: To write an equation with a solution closest to some agreed-upon number

Rules

1. The lead player picks a number.
2. Each player rolls 4 cubes and makes an equation of the form ___x + ___ = ___ or ___x − ___ = ___ by using 3 of the 4 numbers rolled to fill in the blanks.
3. The player whose equation has a solution closest to the picked number wins.

Sample Game

Round 1: Ana, the lead player, chose 7.
Ana rolled 4 5 6 8 . She made $4x − 6 = 8$. She solved for x: 3.5
Gregorio rolled 0 1 5 7 . He made $1x + 0 = 7$. He solved for x: 7
Gregorio won, since 7 is closer to 7 than 3.5 is.

Round 2: Gregorio chose 100.
Gregorio rolled 0 5 6 10 . He made $5x − 6 = 10$. He solved for x: 3.2
Ana rolled 3 5 7 8 . She made $3x − 7 = 8$. She solved for x: 5
Ana won, since 5 is closer to 100 than 3.2 is.

Round 3: Ana chose 0.
Ana rolled 0 3 5 10 . She made $10x − 5 = 0$. She solved for x: 0.5
Gregorio rolled 0 4 8 10 . He made $10x − 4 = 0$. He solved for x: 0.4
Gregorio won, since 0.4 is closer to 0 than 0.5 is.

This Year's Model Sprint

$184 down/$188.36 per month

A typical finance transaction for this vehicle: 16.39% annual percentage rate, 48 monthly payments of $188.36, $184 down payment. Taxes, title, and destination charges extra. With O.K. credit.

The New Sprint

4 cylinder, 4 speed, with steel-belted radial tires and rack and pinion steering

$5935*

*$195 down cash or trade plus tax, title, license, preparation, and transportation.

These 2 advertisements for the same car appeared on the same page in a local newspaper. We've changed the names of the dealers and the name of the car. But the pricing information is the same.

[1] **What is the total price for this car at Classy Cars? Consider title, licenses, and transportation fees totaling about $300. The sales tax rate in this state is 5%.**

[2] **What is the total price for this car at Acme Autos? Title, licenses, transportation fees, and sales tax will be the same as in the first question.**

Here is another advertisement from a local newspaper:

Shelly's Deluxe Nuts
12-ounce can

Cashews
Reg. $6.59.
Big and fresh party nuts.

Mixed Nuts
Reg. $4.99.
Less than 50% peanuts.

[3] **Why do you think the ad says that a can of mixed nuts is less than 50% peanuts?**

[4] **Make up your own questions based on this advertisement.**

[5] **Find advertisements in your newspaper. Make up questions and share them with the class.**

Chapter Review

Evaluate each of the following expressions.

1. $3x - 4$ when $x = 7$
2. $3(x + 2)$ when $x = 8$
3. $3x + 6$ when $x = 8$
4. $xy + xz$ when $x = 7; y = 2, z = 8$
5. $xy + xz$ when $x = 54, y = 73, z = 27$
6. $x + y$ when $x = 3, y = -7$
7. $x - y$ when $x = 3, y = -7$
8. $x - y$ when $x = -3, y = -7$

9. xy when $x = -3, y = -7$
10. xy when $x = 3, y = -7$
11. $x \div y$ when $x = 8, y = 2$
12. $x \div y$ when $x = -8, y = 2$
13. $x \div y$ when $x = -8, y = -2$
14. xy when $x = \left(-\frac{1}{2}\right), y = 6$
15. $x + y$ when $x = -4, y = -8$

Find an equivalent expression for each of the following expressions. Make it as simple as you can.

16. $[(12x + 6) \div 3)] - 2$
17. $5(2x + 7) - 35$
18. $(x + x + x + x) \div 4$
19. $(5x - 3 + 8x + 16) \div 13$
20. $x + 2x + 3x + 4x$

Solve each of the following equations. Check your solutions.

21. $2x + 5 = 27$
22. $2x - 5 = 27$
23. $75x + 200 = 950$
24. $3(x + 2) = 42$
25. $3(x - 2) = 42$

26. $2y + 5 = 27$
27. $75n + 200 = 950$
28. $3(w - 2) = 42$
29. $\frac{9}{5}C + 32 = 59$
30. $2C + 30 = 59$

31. The cost of natural gas in West Plainville is $25.00 per month plus 7¢ for each unit of gas used. Mr. Yamato's bill for the month of November was $45.09. How many units of gas did he use?

Here's another number trick. See if you can figure out why it works.

   Start with any whole number. Add 5. Multiply by 3. Subtract 5. Multiply by 6.

   Add together the digits of the number you now have. If your answer has more than 1 digit, add together the digits of that number. Repeat this process until you have a single-digit answer. The single-digit answer is 6.

Examples: Start with 3. Add 5 (8). Multiply by 3 (24). Subtract 5 (19). Multiply by 6 (114). Find the sum of the digits (6).

Start with 7. Add 5 (12). Multiply by 3 (36). Subtract 5 (31). Multiply by 6 (186). Find the sum of the digits (15). Find the sum again (6).

Chapter Test

Evaluate each of the following expressions.

1. $2x - 4$ when $x = 8$
2. $3(x + 3)$ when $x = 7$
3. $3x + 9$ when $x = 7$
4. $xy + xz$ when $x = 9$, $y = 2$, $z = 8$
5. $xy + xz$ when $x = 24$, $y = 73$, $z = 27$
6. $x + y$ when $x = 4$, $y = -6$
7. $x - y$ when $x = 4$, $y = -6$
8. $x - y$ when $x = -4$, $y = -6$

9. xy when $x = -4$, $y = -6$
10. xy when $x = 4$, $y = -6$
11. $x \div y$ when $x = 12$, $y = 3$
12. $x \div y$ when $x = -12$, $y = 3$
13. $x \div y$ when $x = -12$, $y = -3$
14. xy when $x = \left(-\frac{2}{3}\right)$, $y = 12$
15. $x + y$ when $x = -3$, $y = -6$

Find an equivalent expression for each of the following expressions. Make it as simple as you can.

16. $[(14x + 7) \div 7)] - 3$
17. $3(3x + 8) - 24$
18. $(n + n + n + n + n) \div 5$
19. $(4x - 4 + 12x + 20) \div 16$
20. $2x + 4x + 6x + 8x$

Solve each of the following equations. Check your solutions.

21. $2x + 7 = 37$
22. $2x - 7 = 37$
23. $85x + 100 = 950$
24. $4(x + 3) = 44$
25. $4(x - 3) = 44$

26. $2y + 7 = 37$
27. $85n + 100 = 950$
28. $4(w - 3) = 44$
29. $\frac{9}{5}C + 32 = 68$
30. $2C + 30 = 68$

31. The cost of natural gas in East Plainville is $30.00 per month plus 6¢ for each unit of gas used. Ms. Rivera's bill for the month of September was $36.66. How many units of gas did she use?

Enrichment: A Famous Number Series

Copy and complete this chart of different arrangements of nickels and dimes that form certain sums. Write *n* for *nickel* and *d* for *dime*. In this problem, an arrangement like *nd* is considered different from *dn*.

Sum	Different Arrangements of Nickels and Dimes	Number of Arrangements
5¢	*n*	1
10¢	*2n, d*	2
15¢	*3n, nd, dn*	3
20¢		
25¢		
30¢		
35¢		

You may use what you have learned about permutations in chapter 2 to help you find the numbers of different arrangements.

Now look at the numbers in the last column.

[1] Do you see a pattern?

[2] Can you predict what the number of arrangements for 40¢ will be?

The series of numbers that begins 1, 1, 2, 3, 5, 8, 13 is the Fibonacci series. This series is named after Leonardo Fibonacci of Pisa, who was born in 1175. Many of the patterns found in nature are related to the Fibonacci series.

Find out more about Fibonacci and the Fibonacci series. Learn how he first discovered this series and the many ways in which the series is useful.

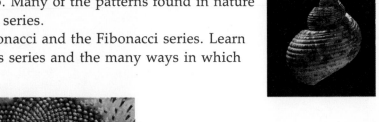

CHAPTER 3

PROBLEM
SOLVING

Solving a Problem

Catherine wants to know how many steps are showing on the "up" escalator at any given time.

When she tries to count them, they move. If she starts from the bottom, she knows that some steps disappear at the top before she can count them. If she starts at the top, some new steps appear at the bottom before she finishes.

Here are some ways Catherine tried to find out how many steps there are on the escalator.

A. She asked the store manager to stop the escalator so she could count the steps. The manager refused. Then she asked him how many steps there were. He said "About 60, I guess."

B. She measured the height of 1 step. It was about 31 centimeters high.

C. She tried to measure the height from the bottom of the escalator to the top of the escalator. With only a small ruler, and no way to go straight up or down, she couldn't get a very good measure. She estimated the distance to be about 8 meters but thought that her estimate might be off by as much as 1 meter.

D. She timed herself going up the escalator on a single step. It took her about 32 or 33 seconds.

E. She ran back down the steps. (No one else was on the escalator.) It took her 30 seconds to get down, and she counted 50 steps.

F. She walked back up the steps. It took her 20 seconds, and she counted 10 steps.

How many steps are there? Can you think of a way to solve this problem?

Problem solving is the most important use of mathematics. Some of the problems we solve with the help of mathematics are very practical: how to build a bridge or building so that it will stand, how to launch a space ship so that it will land on Neptune, how to predict the results of the next election, how to evaluate a new medical cure.

Some of the problems we solve with mathematics are solved simply to satisfy our curiosity and to develop our power to analyze a situation. The escalator problem is probably this kind of problem. Many puzzle problems are like this. Most of the problems we solve help us to understand mathematics itself better.

Solving problems out of curiosity or to gain a better understanding of mathematics should not be considered a waste of time. It makes us better problem solvers. Most people find that as they get good at solving problems they enjoy solving them and see great beauty and enjoyment in mathematics.

The best way to become good at solving problems is to solve a lot of problems. Sometimes it is useful to stop and look at the ways we solve problems and at the ways others solve problems. This helps us to think about ways we could improve our ability to solve problems.

If you have been studying Real Math for a long time, then you have been solving lots of different problems and you've been learning mathematics in a way that should help you do a better job of solving problems. In this chapter, we take time out to consider specific techniques some people use to solve some mathematical problems.

Here are some ways to solve problems:

A. Don't memorize rules for problem solving. Try to understand many different ways to solve problems, and use them intelligently and appropriately. Don't just apply rules blindly to try to solve problems.

B. Be sure you understand the problem. If it's written, reread it if necessary. State it in your own words. Act out the problem (or at least imagine the situation being acted out). Draw a picture. Pick out the important facts that are given. You can sometimes use "key words" to help you decide what operation to use, but be careful—key words can be misleading. (Try this problem: Yoshiko walked 20 meters north and then 15 meters west. After how many meters did she turn left? If your answer is 5 meters, you are misusing the key word *left*.)

C. Identify your goal. What kind of answer do you want? How will you recognize the answer when you get it? Keep your goal in mind as you work on the problem. It has been said that fanatics are people who, having lost sight of their goals, redouble their efforts. Don't be a fanatic.

D. Write the information in a notation that will be useful. Mathematical notation is often more concise and more helpful than words or other symbols. To see what a help good notation is, try multiplying 79 by 94 in Roman numerals and then in Arabic numerals. Be careful about the meaning of your symbols. Using the initial letter of a word to stand for a number related to that word is common and useful, but it can be misleading. If m stands for the number of meters in a length and c stands for the number of centimeters in the same length, c is certainly greater than m. But if you think m stands for meter rather than number of meters, you might think $m > c$. Remember that, in algebra, letters can stand only for numbers.

E. Use all the useful information you are given. If it isn't enough, try to get additional information (ask somebody, make measurements, check in a reference book, and so on). Sometimes you may have too much information. Ignore extra

pieces of information if they are irrelevant. If they contradict other information, try to find out why.

F. Organize the information so that it is easy to understand and use. Use a table, a chart, or a graph.

G. Look for patterns. Guess whether patterns will continue. Check to see if they do. Try to prove that they do (or don't).

H. If the problem is too complicated, try to separate it into smaller, simpler problems that you can solve. Often, solving a special case of the problem will suggest to you what the solution should be (if there is a solution).

I. Try to remember a similar problem you have solved, or try to solve a similar but simpler problem. Then apply the same process to your problem.

J. Decide on reasonable bounds for the answer. Make a reasonable estimate and check it. Sometimes, noticing how you check to see if your estimate is right will show you how to solve the problem.

K. Work backward. Guess the answer and see how close you can get to the given information from your guess. Keep revising your guess.

L. Use the "if only I knew" technique. Think: "If only I knew this fact, I could get this answer." Try to work out some way to get that fact. (Often, reasoning from the facts you already have will give it to you.) Sometimes you have to use this idea over and over to solve a problem.

M. Try to eliminate some possible answers. If there are 5 possible answers and you can eliminate 4, then you can be sure the fifth is correct. Even if you can only eliminate 2 or 3, you have simplified the problem.

N. If you think there's a chance that a general statement is untrue, try to find a counter-example. If somebody says all cats have tails and you can produce a cat that doesn't have a tail, you have shown that the statement is untrue. This may help you with strategy M, and it may help you avoid trying to answer a question that can't be answered or to prove something that isn't true.

O. Ask somebody. Probably the most common way of trying to solve a problem in real life is to ask somebody who, you hope, knows. Be careful about whom you ask. Many people who know less than you do will give you answers. Even when somebody you trust gives you an answer, check it. Is it reasonable? What evidence do you have that is correct?

P. Always check your answer. Is it reasonable? Does it satisfy all the conditions? Is it the only possible answer?

Q. After you have solved an interesting or difficult problem, think about how you solved it. You can probably use the procedure (or a similar one) in the future. Can you generalize the problem or the solution? Can you create new problems that are similar? Can you use the mathematical solution to solve other problems?

R. Bright ideas are often the key to solving a problem. A mathematics professor we know uses this method of solving a problem: Look at it until a solution occurs to you. You can help bright ideas to occur by studying the problem carefully and working on it very hard for a while, then going off to do something else while ideas percolate through your subconscious mind. When you come back to the problem, your mind will be filled with fresh ideas.

S. Be flexible. Try the problem from a different point of view. Sometimes you can even get a solution by apparently going in the wrong direction. A chicken inside a 3-sided fence with food on the other side finds it difficult to go away from the food to get to it. Don't be a chicken.

T. Be patient. Worthwhile problems require time, energy, flexibility, and many attempts before they are solved. The satisfaction of solving a really challenging problem after deep and careful thought is far greater than the satisfaction of solving a simple problem with little work.

U. Think. The ability to think about abstract things sets people apart from all other living things. Use your ability.

No 2 people would come up with the same set of methods for solving problems. Try to compare your own list with those of your classmates. Ask other people how they solve problems. Compare the suggestions in this book with your own and with other people's. Then make a new list of the strategies you find useful. As you solve more problems, in this course and in other parts of your life, keep revising your list to help you solve more problems.

What strategies did Catherine use to try to solve her escalator problem? What did *you* use when you solved that problem?

She probably understood the problem and knew what her goal was. She collected more information and tried to get still more. She asked the store manager for the answer.

Let's try to set reasonable bounds.

[1] **If each step is about 31 centimeters high, and the whole escalator is between 7 meters and 9 meters high, about how many steps might there be?**

[2] **Do you think the store manager's answer is likely to be right?**

[3] **What might he have been thinking about?**

Let's try to write the information using algebra. We want to know how many steps are showing at any given time. We'll let n be the number of steps showing. The speed at which the steps are moving is also important. They are appearing (at the bottom) at some number of steps per second. They are disappearing at the top at the same number of steps per second. And they go by any fixed point at the same rate. We'll let $r =$ the rate at which steps are passing any fixed point, so r is the number of steps that go by a point in 1 second.

Now, let's try to write some equations.

Since it took Catherine about 32 seconds to go from the bottom to the top of the escalator, the steps must have been disappearing at about the rate of $\frac{n}{32}$ steps per second, so $r \approx \frac{n}{32}$. (Remember that the $\approx$ sign means "about equal to.")

When she ran down the steps, it took her about 30 seconds and she counted 50 steps. She must have counted all the steps

showing at the beginning plus the 30 steps that appeared in the 30 seconds. So, $50 \approx n + 30r$.

When she walked up the steps, it took her 20 seconds and she counted only 10 steps. She must have counted all the steps showing minus those that disappeared in the 20 seconds. So, $10 \approx n - 20r$.

The last 2 equations can be changed to equivalent equations:

$$50 = n + 30r \text{ is equivalent to } 50 - 30r = n$$

$$10 = n - 20r \text{ is equivalent to } 10 + 20r = n$$

Since both $50 - 30r$ and $10 + 20r$ equal n, they must be equal to each other: $50 - 30r = 10 + 20r$. That equation is equivalent to $40 = 50r$, which is equivalent to $\frac{4}{5} = r$.

So, the steps are going by any fixed point at the rate of about $\frac{4}{5}$ of a step per second. To find the number of steps, we use $\frac{4}{5}$ for r in 1 of our equations. $n = 10 + 20r = 10 + 20\left(\frac{4}{5}\right) = 10 + 16 = 26$. So there are about 26 steps.

We're not finished yet. Let's check and reconsider what we've done.

[4] We estimated the number of steps to be between 22 and 29. Does 26 satisfy those bounds?

[5] The store manager said there were about 60 steps. Does his estimate conform to the bounds we set?

[6] Do you think he might have been talking about the total number of steps on the entire belt of steps going around in the escalator?

Try to find out how an escalator works. Think about it and then ask somebody or read.

Let's continue with our check. If there are 26 steps and they disappear at the rate of $\frac{4}{5}$ of a step per second, how long would it take all 26 to go by? (That is, how long would it take to ride up the escalator?)

If this problem seems too hard, try a problem with easier numbers.

[7] How long would it take 26 steps to disappear at the rate of 2 steps per second?

[8] Did you divide 26 by 2?

Divide 26 by $\frac{4}{5}$: $26 \div \frac{4}{5} = 26 \times \frac{5}{4} = 32\frac{1}{2}$. It should take about $32\frac{1}{2}$ seconds for somebody to ride up the escalator on one step. Does that agree with available information?

Catherine ran down the escalator in 30 seconds and counted 50 steps. In 30 seconds, at the rate of $\frac{4}{5}$ of a step per second, $\frac{4}{5}$ of 30 (or 24) steps should have appeared, and she should also have counted the 26 steps that were there.

[9] Check this answer. Is it correct?

In 20 seconds, at the rate of $\frac{4}{5}$ of a step per second, 16 steps should have disappeared.

[10] If she walked up in 20 seconds, how many steps should she have counted?

[11] Did she count that number?

[12] Were there other ways Catherine could have solved the problem?

Suppose she used the equations $r = \frac{n}{32}$ and $50 = n + 30r$. Replacing r in the second equation by $\frac{n}{32}$, we get:

$$50 = n + \frac{30n}{32}$$

$$50 = 1\frac{15}{16}n = \frac{31}{16}n$$

$$50 \div \frac{31}{16} = n$$

$$\frac{50 \times 16}{31} = n$$

$$\frac{800}{31} = n$$

$$n = 25\frac{25}{31}$$

[13] Is it reasonable to have $25\frac{25}{31}$ steps? Remember that this is an escalator, and we're talking about how many steps show at a time.

[14] What are some other ways Catherine could have figured out how many steps are on the escalator?

[15] What other problems can you think of that might be solved the same way?

Try to solve these problems. Get more information by reading or asking somebody (other than your teacher) when necessary. Work with classmates. Get help from other people if you like. Be prepared to defend your answers. Saying that somebody else said that an answer is right is not a defense.

1. Bill wanted to know how many steps there were showing at any given time for a certain escalator. He did the following research:

   • He rode up the escalator on 1 step. It took him 20 seconds to reach the top.
   • He ran back down the escalator and counted 30 steps. It took him 20 seconds to get down.
   • He ran up the escalator, counting only 12 steps. It took him 4 seconds to get back up.
   • He measured 1 of the escalator steps. It was about 30 centimeters tall.
   • He estimated the height of the escalator to be about 5 meters but thought that his estimate might be off by as much as 1 meter.

   How many steps were showing at a time?

2. Write an equation relating s, the number of students, and t, the number of teachers, if there are 30 students to each teacher. Use your equation to answer the following questions.
   a. If there are 30 teachers, how many students are there?
   b. If there are 10 teachers, how many students are there?
   c. If there are 600 students, how many teachers are there?
   d. If there are 30 students, how many teachers are there?
   e. If there are 10 students, how many teachers are there?

3. Out of every 12 customers, 5 ordered fish sandwiches and 7 ordered hamburgers. Write an equation relating f, the number of fish orders, and h, the number of hamburger orders. Use your equation to answer the following questions.
   a. If 10 people ordered fish, how many ordered hamburgers?
   b. If 25 people ordered fish, how many ordered hamburgers?

c. If 35 people ordered hamburgers, how many ordered fish?

d. If 10 people ordered hamburgers, how many ordered fish?

4. Manuela bought twice as many bottles of milk as boxes of cereal. Bottles of milk and boxes of cereal cost the same, $2 each. Manuela spent $30.

   She did the following computations. Let m stand for milk and c for cereal. Then $2m + 2c = \$30$. Since she bought twice as many milk bottles as cereal boxes, $m = 2c$. Replace m in $2m + 2c = \$30$ by $2c$:

$$2(2c) + 2c = \$30$$
$$4c + 2c = \$30$$
$$6c = \$30$$
$$c = \$5$$

So, cereal costs $5 a box.

   a. Is there anything wrong?

   b. Explain what is happening.

5. A sailor decided to reward the inhabitants of an island for saving her. There were 100 adults on the island. She offered the men $10 each and the women $20 each. All the men accepted but only half the women accepted. How much money did she give to the people of the island?

6. Which is heavier, a pound of gold or a pound of feathers? (Hint: A dictionary may help.)

7. One bus can take 36 people. How many buses will be needed to take 1050 people to a picnic?

8. Wilbur knows he has 40 animals on his farm. Some are ducks and the rest are dogs. Altogether they have 134 legs.

   a. Are there more dogs or more ducks?

   b. How many ducks are there?

Solve these problems.

1. Which is heavier, an ounce of gold or an ounce of feathers? (Hint: A dictionary may help.)

2. How many scruples are there in 2 typical aspirin tablets?

3. Which is heavier, an ounce of gold or an ounce of aspirin?

4. Rod measured his height in feet. He did a calculation on his calculator and announced, "There are 3 Rods in a rod." How tall is he?

5. The famous detective, Locksher House, knew that 1 of 12 pennies was a counterfeit. He also knew that the counterfeit was either heavier than a normal penny or lighter. By using a double-pan balance, he had to decide which penny was counterfeit and whether it was too heavy or too light. He had to pay $100 each time he used the scales, so he worked out a system to answer both questions (which penny, and whether it was too heavy or too light) in only 3 weighings. See if you can find such a system.

6. In a previous case, Mr. House had solved a similar problem with only 2 weighings. What is the maximum number of pennies he could have had then?

7. Try to generalize your answers to problems 5 and 6. How many coins could you handle with 4 weighings? With 5 weighings? With n weighings?

8. Assad knows he has 73 animals on his farm. Some of the animals are horses and the others are chickens. Altogether they have 264 legs. How many horses are there?

9. 1 bus can carry 40 adults or 60 children. (The children are seated 3 to a seat, and the adults are seated 2 to a seat.) 300 adults and 400 children are to be taken to a picnic by bus.

   a. How many buses will be needed?
   b. Can you put children and adults on the same bus?
   c. How many buses do you save by putting both children and adults on the same bus?
   d. Suppose 390 children are going with 300 adults. How do your answers to parts a, b, and c change?

10. A train and a strange, but very fast, fly started at the same spot moving toward a brick wall 100 kilometers away. The train traveled 100 kilometers per hour. The fly flew 200 kilometers per hour. When the fly reached the brick wall it turned around instantly and flew back to the train. Upon touching the train, the fly turned around instantly and flew back to the wall. The fly continued this strange behavior until it was crushed against the wall by the train. Before its flat finish, how far had the fly flown?

11. Augusto and Arnell are playing a game. The goal is to get to 100. The first player picks a whole number from 1 to 10, inclusive, and then the second player picks a whole number from 1 to 10 and adds it to the score so far. The first player repeats this move. They continue this way. The player who makes the score exactly 100 wins.

   a. Play the game and figure out a strategy for winning as first player.
   b. Change the rules so that the goal is 200 and numbers from 1 to 20 can be used.
   c. Change the rules so that the goal is 200 and numbers from 5 to 20 can be used.
   d. Change the rules so that the goal is 200 and numbers from 3 to 30 can be used.
   e. Give a general rule for winning the game if g is the goal and whole numbers from p to q ($p < q$) can be used.

Solve these problems.

1. Cecily is going to fly from New York to Los Angeles. Her plane leaves at 6:00 P.M. and is scheduled to arrive at 8:38 P.M. How long will the flight take (assuming it's on schedule)?

2. Her flight back to New York from Los Angeles is scheduled to leave at 9:00 A.M. and arrive in New York at 4:58 P.M. Which flight is scheduled to take a longer time? How much longer? Why do you suppose that is?

3. How can you give a friend 60¢ using only quarters, dimes, and nickels, but at least 1 of each?

4. How can you give a friend 60¢ using only quarters, dimes, nickels, and pennies, but at least 1 of each?

5. 3 men rented a hotel room for the night. The clerk charged them $30. Later she discovered that the room was supposed to rent for $25, so she sent a messenger to the room to return $5. The messenger decided that the men couldn't split $5 fairly, so he returned $3 ($1 for each) and kept $2. Thus the men paid $9 each for the room (or $27 altogether) and the messenger got $2, for a total of $29. What happened to the other dollar?

6. At 12:00 noon, the minute hand is directly over the hour hand of a clock. When, exactly, is the minute hand again directly over the hour hand of the clock?

7. Phyllis has a 5-liter container and a 3-liter container. She must get exactly 4 liters of water from the river. How can she do that? The containers are not marked. (Hint: She could get 2 liters by filling the 5-liter container and filling the 3-liter container from it, leaving 2 liters in the 5-liter container, but she cannot make 2 trips home from the river.)

8. On the island of Never Treasurer, there are truth-telling natives and lie-telling natives. The former *always* tell the truth, and the latter *never* tell the truth. There is also a path on the island that leads into the forest. About halfway into the forest the path splits. If you follow one route, you will get to a wonderful treasure. The other route leads to certain death. At the fork in the path there are always 2 natives—possibly from different tribes, possibly from the same tribe. They must each answer 1 question with yes or no, but as soon as they've answered the question they run away. You are at the fork in the path.

   a. What are your 2 questions? (The natives can recognize truth tellers and lie tellers.)
   b. Challenge: 1 question is enough. What is it?

9. All CD-4 airplanes can carry a 4-hour supply of fuel. These planes can land safely only at the initial and final points of their journeys. They can transfer fuel from one plane to another instantly. Thus, after 2 CD-4s fly together for 2 hours, the first can give the second 2 hours' worth of fuel, and the second can make a total trip of 6 hours. Unfortunately, the first is then out of fuel and crashes.

   a. How many CD-4s must start out for 1 to make a 6-hour trip and the others all to get back to the starting place safely?
   b. If 2 planes start out, how far (in hours) can 1 fly if the other is to return safely?
   c. Repeat part b for 3 planes, for 4 planes, for 5 planes, and for n planes.
   d. What is the maximum distance a CD-4 can fly from its home base if there are as many other CD-4s to support it as necessary (but all the other CD-4s must return safely to base)? (You may want to use a computer and look for a pattern as n gets large.)
   e. A CD-n plane can carry enough fuel for n hours of flight. A CD-6 can carry fuel for 6 hours of flight, a CD-10, for 10 (and so on). Repeat parts c and d for a CD-6, a CD-10, and a CD-n.

Some of these problems should be done with a calculator, but in all cases you should think carefully about whether to use a calculator and what to do with it if you do use it.

1. Use a calculator to decide what $11{,}111 \times 11{,}111$ is. Does your calculator show the right answer? Try 1111×1111. Try 111×111. Try 11×11. Do you see a pattern? What do you think $111{,}111 \times 111{,}111$ is?

2. What is $111{,}111 \times 999{,}999$?

3. What is $(999{,}999)^2$?

4. Using a calculator only (it's not fair to divide with pencil and paper), decide what the remainder is when you divide 843 by 76.

   a. Explain your method.
   b. Can you think of another method?
   c. Compare your method with other people's methods.

5. Wendy makes \$7.50 an hour. She worked for 5 hours and 40 minutes. She used her calculator to find that she had earned \$40.50. What are your comments about this?

6. A man had a fox, a goat, and a cabbage that he wanted to get across a river. Only 1 of the 3 would fit in the boat at a time with the man. If he left the goat and the cabbage alone together, the goat would eat the cabbage. If he left the goat and the fox alone together, the fox would eat the goat.

a. How can he get the fox, goat, and cabbage across the river without any of them being eaten?

b. How many extra trips are needed because of the unfortunate gluttonous tendencies of the animals?

7. Philip has a 9-liter bucket and a 4-liter bucket. He wants to bring exactly 6 liters of water home from the river in 1 trip. How can he do that?

If you have access to a computer, use it to help you solve the next 2 problems. If not, think about how you would use a computer to help you solve the problems.

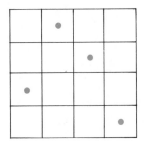

8. The blue dots in this form show 1 way to place 4 markers so that there is exactly 1 marker in each column, each row, and each of the 2 longest diagonals. How many different ways are there to put 4 markers on the form and satisfy these conditions?

9. There are 120 ways to arrange the digits 1, 2, 3, 4, and 5 as 5-digit numbers. Suppose you arrange them in numerical order. The first few numbers would be:

$$1 \ 2 \ 3 \ 4 \ 5$$
$$1 \ 2 \ 3 \ 5 \ 4$$
$$1 \ 2 \ 4 \ 3 \ 5$$
$$1 \ 2 \ 4 \ 5 \ 3$$

What will be the 60th number in the series?

This story appeared in a national newspaper. Read the story. See if you can make up some problems from the information provided.

Is there enough information to answer your questions? Sometimes newspaper stories provide so much information that the facts seem to contradict each other. Be on the lookout for that situation.

Here are some sample problems.

1. How many air controllers are there now? ("Now" means when the article was written.)
2. How many air controllers did not strike and get fired in 1981?
3. What does air controller safety mean?
4. According to the Federal Aviation Administration and to the other sources of information in the article, are there enough controllers now? Why do you think the number 14,141 is mentioned, and what do you think is its relationship to 14,300 (17,300 − 3000)?
5. What percentage of the controllers struck and were fired in August 1981?
6. There were 20 times as many airline fatalities in the first quarter of 1982 as in the first quarter of 1983. Do you think there were 20 times as many accidents? What are your comments about this statistic?

Dole lauds air controller safety record

By Ruth Hamel
USA TODAY

The USA's air traffic control system can safely handle the same level of traffic as before the 1981 controller's strike — even though there are 3,000 fewer controllers — Transportation Secretary Elizabeth Dole said Wednesday.

But flight restrictions remain at certain airports and airlines still cannot get all the peak-time flights they want.

As a result, travelers flying at busy hours to and from some major airports still must make reservations further in advance than before the strike, Bill Jackman of the Air Transport Association said.

Fred Farrar of the Federal Aviation Administration said Dole referred to "overall number of flights, not necessarily where they're going."

Airlines still can't get enough peak-time flights at Chicago O'Hare, New York LaGuardia, Denver Stapleton, Dallas/Fort Worth and Washington, D.C.'s National, Jackman said.

The FAA imposed the peak-time restrictions on 22 airports after 11,400 controllers struck and were fired in August 1981.

So far, the FAA has lifted restrictions at Boston, Minneapolis, Las Vegas, Nev.; and Kansas City, Mo. By summer's end, restrictions will be taken off Atlanta, San Francisco, Fort Lauderdale/Miami, Newark, N.J.; and John F. Kennedy International, New York City.

By year's end, only O'Hare and LaGuardia will have restrictions, Farrar said.

Before the strike, there were 17,300 controllers, but the Federal Aviation Administration says 14,141 are sufficient to operate the system now.

After the strike, remaining controllers and supervisors worked long hours. But FAA administrator Lynn Helms said that the average work week now is 40 hours.

The only exception is New York's Kennedy — the average work week: 44.6 hours.

Dole said USA airlines are enjoying a safe year so far — there were four fatalities in airline accidents during the first quarter of 1983, compared with 80 during the same period in 1982.

Make up some problems from this article. Try to get answers to your problems. Exchange problems with other students.

NEWSMAKERS

BEHIND THE SCENES WITH PEOPLE IN THE HEADLINES

Low-key sheriff takes crowding into own hands

By Robert Dunnavant, UPI

SHOWROOM JAIL: Morgan County, Ala., inmates sleep in Decatur auto showroom after sheriff refused them at his packed jail.

When Sheriff **Buford Burgess** spoke, Alabama state authorities were listening.

So were other county sheriffs in Alabama who are tired of seeing their jails swell with the overflow from crowded state prisons.

Burgess, 48, a first-term sheriff in north central Alabama's Morgan County, put his foot down Tuesday when a van carrying six new state prisoners pushed the population at his Decatur jail to 152 — 56 above its 96-inmate capacity.

He took the van, temporarily detained two state officers, hauled 32 prisoners to a makeshift jail in a vacant Buick dealership and threatened to bus them to a state prison.

By Wednesday, state officials agreed to move the 32 prisoners to other county jails, provided Burgess could work it out with the other jailers.

Burgess wasn't gloating over his victory, but in neighboring Cullman County, Sheriff **Wendell Roden** was. "I think it's fine," said Roden, whose 92-bed jail is "about at capacity."

"I'm a quiet, peace-loving fellow," said Burgess. "I try not to make waves, but I don't like to be pushed.

"I made my point. ... I hope I don't have to do it every day."

Alabama is under federal court order to remove a backlog of 1,500 inmates awaiting transfer to state institutions from county jails. A new 1,000-bed prison is scheduled to open June 1, and corrections officials plan to release another 500 inmates on supervised restitution programs.

Burgess has repeatedly complained about overcrowding. Two weeks ago, he asked the county commission to sue the state over the conditions.

Despite those complaints, Alabama prisons spokesman **Ron Tate** said the state wasn't expecting the reaction it got this week from Burgess, "one of the

SHERIFF BURGESS: '. . . I don't like to be pushed.'

most likable sheriffs in Alabama."

"If it had been somebody else, we wouldn't have been surprised, but we were literally astonished," Tate said.

Alabama's problem is far from unique. There are 412,303 prison inmates in the USA and 31 states are under court order to relieve overcrowding.

Burgess earned a reputation for steadiness and dependability in his 22 years as a state trooper. He was appointed sheriff in 1981 when then-Sheriff **Van Ward** resigned after his indictment in a scheme to discredit a local police chief.

Burgess was elected to a four-year term in January over a retired federal firearms agent in a Democratic primary runoff.

Even his former opponent, **Bobby Newsom**, praised Burgess for taking on the state penal system. "I can sympathize with him 100 percent. He is not being treated fairly by the state penal system."

Use other news articles to make up problems. Try to get answers. Exchange problems (and the articles) with other students.

Solve these problems.

1. Maya rode the escalator in the local store from bottom to top in 10 seconds (she did not climb any of the steps). The next day she walked up 6 of the steps, and the trip took only 6 seconds. How many steps of the escalator can be seen at any given time?

2. Write 5 rules that you think are useful in solving problems.

3. George raises rabbits and chickens. He knows that at the moment there are 800 legs on his farm and 275 animals.
   a. How many of the animals are rabbits?
   b. How many are chickens?

4. List all the ways there are to make 1 dollar using at least 1 half dollar, 1 quarter, 1 dime, 1 nickel, and 1 penny.

5. Estelle wants to bring exactly 6 liters of water home from the river in 1 trip. She has a 5-liter bucket and a 3-liter bucket. How can she do this?

6. Each link in a chain is 4 centimeters long and is made of metal that is 0.5 centimeter thick.
   a. How many links would it take to make a chain 28 centimeters long?
   b. To hang some shelves from the ceiling, Jane wants 4 lengths of chain, each 28 centimeters long. Any link that she cuts must be thrown out. What is the shortest length of chain she could buy in order to get the 4 chains she needs after cutting?
   c. The chain is sold by the tenth of a meter (rounded up to the nearest tenth of a meter), but you do not have to pay for the link that is cut in cutting off the amount you buy. Would it be cheaper for Jane to buy 1 length of chain and cut the 4 pieces herself or to buy the 4 lengths of 28 centimeters separately?

Enrichment: The Tower of Hanoi Problem

You'll need a dime, a penny, a nickel, a quarter, and a half dollar to do this problem. If you don't have the coins, you need 5 markers, each a different size.

Draw 3 circles on a piece of paper, as shown, numbering them 1, 2, and 3. In circle 1, place a stack of 5 coins or markers, with each coin smaller than the coin beneath it. (A dime, a penny, a nickel, a quarter, and a half dollar will work nicely.) See if you can move the stack so that it is in circle 3, in the same order as when you began. Sounds easy, doesn't it? But there is a catch. You can move a coin from a circle to any other circle, but only according to the following rules:

A. You can move only 1 coin at a time.
B. The coin you move must not have another coin on top of it.
C. You can only move it to an empty circle or else place it on a coin that is larger than it is.

Work on the problem awhile. If you don't seem to be making progress, check the list of strategies to see if any of them might apply. If you're still stuck, ask your teacher to suggest a strategy.

CHAPTER 4
PERMUTATIONS

Blaise Pascal

Did you ever notice that when people are not allowed to do something, it becomes even more interesting to them than before?

Blaise Pascal as a young boy was forbidden by his father to read or even think about mathematics. His father wanted him to concentrate on the study of ancient languages. But young Blaise was fascinated by geometry, and during his playtime he stayed in his room and secretly drew geometric figures with charcoal on the tiles. By reasoning about his drawings, he discovered many of the basic propositions of geometry. He found, for example, that the sum of the angles of a triangle equals 180°. He even made up terms for the figures he drew, calling circles *rounds* and lines *bars*. Without ever having seen a book on mathematics, when he was 11 he discovered 32 of the geometric propositions of the Greek mathematician Euclid.

When his father discovered his son's gift for mathematical reasoning, he encouraged him to follow his interest. Pascal attacked his studies, and at the age of 16 he published a book on conic sections (such as circles and ellipses) that astonished other French mathematicians.

Pascal continued to investigate mathematical ideas, and 2 years later he invented a calculating machine that added and subtracted English currency. Along with Pierre le Fermat, another French mathematician, Pascal discussed the odds of games of chance, such as dice and cards. In this way they began the branch of mathematics called probability.

Pascal's work was not limited to pure mathematics. He also experimented with the behavior of liquids in containers and made the observation that liquid in a container carries pressure equally in all directions. The hydraulic jacks, vacuum pumps, and air compressors we use today work on this principle.

Religion was always important to Pascal. He kept a diary, now known as the *Pensées*, which recorded both his spiritual and his scientific thoughts.

He recognized that his research was based on the discoveries of many other scientists. He wrote in the *Pensées*, "Let no one say that I have said something new. The arrangement of the subject is new. When we play tennis, we both play with the same ball, but one of us places it better."

Pascal was not a very healthy person, and he died in 1662 at the young age of 39. We have to wonder how many other branches of science he would have mastered had he lived longer. His many discoveries and inventions rank him as one of the greatest mathematicians and scientists of all time.

If you roll three 0–5 cubes, what is the probability that the 3 numbers will sum to 9?

You already know that there are 36 ways that 2 cubes can land. For each of those ways there are 6 ways that the third cube can land. So there are 6 × 36, or 216, ways for 3 cubes to land.

Making a list of the 216 ways would take a long time. Picking out those sets that sum to 9 would take even more time. And if you were not careful, you might miss some.

Let's try in some organized way to find those sets of numbers for the 3 cubes that sum to 9. To do this, we'll follow 3 rules:

A. Put the numbers on the cubes from left to right.
B. Always use the greatest possible number.
C. The numbers in each set may not increase going from left to right.

First set: We put 5 on the first cube. (5 is the greatest possible number.) We put 4 on the second cube. (We can't use another 5, because 5 + 5 = 10.) Then we put 0 on the third cube. (Anything else would make the sum greater than 9.)

5		
5	4	
5	4	0

Second set: We start with 5 again. Now we use 3 on the second cube. (We used 4 in the first set.) We put 1 on the third cube. (5 + 3 + 1 = 9)

5		
5	3	
5	3	1

Third set: We start with 5 again. Now we put 2 on the second cube and 2 on the third cube.

5		
5	2	
5	2	2

Fourth set: We can't start with 5 because that would give us 5, 1, 3, which would violate rule C, so we start with 4. Then we put 4 on the second cube and 1 on the third cube.

4		
4	4	
4	4	1

Fifth set: We start with 4. We put 3 next and then 2.

4		
4	3	
4	3	2

Sixth set: We can't start with 4, so we start with 3. We put 3 on the second cube and 3 on the third cube.

3		
3	3	
3	3	3

There aren't any more ways to arrange the cubes and still follow the rules.

So we have 6 sets of 3 numbers for the cubes:

`5` `4` `0`, `5` `3` `1`, `5` `2` `2`, `4` `4` `1`, `4` `3` `2`, and `3` `3` `3`.

They are all in descending order (each digit is less than or equal to the digit to its left).

We could rearrange the first set, 5, 4, 0, so that the 5 appears on the second or third cube, the 4 on the first or third, and so on.

[1] **How many different arrangements of the digits 5, 4, 0 can you find (including 5, 4, 0)?**

[2] **How many different arrangements of the digits 5, 3, 1 can you find?**

[3] **Is this the same number as your answer to the first discussion question?**

[4] **How many different arrangements of the digits 5, 2, 2 are there?**

[5] **Why is this number only half as great as the answers to the first 2 discussion questions?**

[6] **How many different arrangements of the digits 4, 4, 1 are there?**

[7] **How many different arrangements of 4, 3, 2 are there?**

[8] **How about 3, 3, 3?**

[9] **Are there 25 different ways in which three 0–5 cubes could produce the total 9?**

[10] **What is the probability of rolling a sum of 9 with 3 cubes?**

Making and Checking a Prediction

1. Suppose you roll three 0–5 cubes.

   a. What is the smallest sum you could get?
   b. What is the greatest sum you could get?

2. If you roll three 0–5 cubes, how many different ways are there to get each of the following sums?

   a. 0 j. 9
   b. 1 k. 10
   c. 2 l. 11
   d. 3 m. 12
   e. 4 n. 13
   f. 5 o. 14
   g. 6 p. 15
   h. 7 q. 16*
   i. 8

3. Use your answers to problem 2.

   a. What is the sum of the answers for all the parts of problem 2?
   b. Did you expect to get that number? (Look at the second paragraph of page 98.)

4. Use your answers to problems 2 and 3. Find the probability of getting each of the following sums by rolling three 0–5 cubes.

   a. 0 i. 8
   b. 1 j. 9
   c. 2 k. 10
   d. 3 l. 11
   e. 4 m. 12
   f. 5 n. 13
   g. 6 o. 14
   h. 7 p. 15

*Be careful.

5. If you rolled three 0–5 cubes 1080 times, about how many times would you expect to get a sum of

a. 0?   i. 8?
b. 1?   j. 9?
c. 2?   k. 10?
d. 3?   l. 11?
e. 4?   m. 12?
f. 5?   n. 13?
g. 6?   o. 14?
h. 7?   p. 15?

6. Record 1080 rolls of three 0–5 cubes. Work in groups of 3 or more. Use a form like the one below. Let each group do some of the 1080 rolls. Then combine the results. How do the data compare with your predictions?

Mrs. Alvarado has a collection of 10 antique thimbles. She just bought a display box for the thimbles.

[1] How many different ways do you think she can arrange the thimbles in the display box?

Finding the number of possible ways to arrange several objects in a row can be difficult. On page 99 you discovered that there are 6 ways to arrange 3 different numbers in a row. (You can think of the 3 numbers as 3 distinct objects.)

[2] How many ways are there to arrange 4 distinct objects in a row?

Try to find all the possible arrangements of the 4 letters a, b, c, and d. Here are some hints: If a is put in the first spot, how many ways are there to arrange b, c, and d? If b is put in the first spot, how many ways are there to arrange a, c, and d?

[3] Guess how many ways there are to arrange 5 objects (a, b, c, d, and e) in a row. See if you can give a convincing argument that you are right. Would you like to list all of them?

[4] Now can you figure out how many arrangements are possible for the 10 thimbles?

The number of arrangements (or permutations) of 5 objects in a row is 5 × 4 × 3 × 2 × 1, or 120. Products like this are common and require a lot of writing, so a shorter notation has been developed: 5! (5 with an exclamation point after it), called 5 factorial, is a short name for 5 × 4 × 3 × 2 × 1.

Do the following problems. Give both a factorial answer and the standard form. Use a calculator. The first problem has been done for you.

1. How many ways are there to arrange n objects in a row if n is:

   a. 5 5! (or 120)
   b. 2
   c. 3
   d. 6
   e. 7
   f. 8
   g. 9
   h. 10
   i. 11
   j. 12
   k. 13
   l. 14

   Here are some hints to help you with the last 3 problems:
   Does your calculator give you the answer for problem j? If not, try to figure out a way to change the calculation a bit so you can get the answer. If you divide 11! by 100, what's the answer? Suppose you multiply $\frac{11!}{100}$ by 12. What would you have to do to get 12!?
   Does 14! cause a problem? If you subtract 6,000,000,000 from 6,227,020,800 before multiplying by 14 and then add 14 × 6,000,000,000, can you solve the problem?

2. Try to calculate larger factorials with the help of either a calculator or a computer.

Sometimes you may want to permute a set of objects in which 2 or more of the objects are identical and not distinct. (Remember, *permute* means to arrange in different ways as many times as possible.)

When we were looking for the ways to get a sum of 9 with three 0–5 cubes, 1 set of numbers was 5, 2, 2. Since the 2s are identical, there are only 3 different ways to arrange these numbers: 5 2 2, 2 5 2, 2 2 5.

**[1] How many different ways can you arrange the letters of the word
    FOOT?**

Here is one way to do this problem. Label the Os with a 1 and a 2, and find all 24 arrangements ($4 \times 3 \times 2 \times 1$).

FO_1O_2T	FO_2O_1T	O_1TFO_2	O_2TFO_1
FTO_1O_2	FTO_2O_1	O_1FTO_2	O_2FTO_1
FO_1TO_2	FO_2TO_1	O_1O_2FT	O_2O_1TF
TO_1O_2F	TO_2O_1F	O_1O_2TF	O_2O_1FT
TO_1FO_2	TO_2FO_1	O_1TO_2F	O_2TO_1F
TFO_1O_2	TFO_2O_1	O_1FO_2T	O_2FO_1T

**[2] In each set of letters, how many different ways can the 2 Os be
    arranged?**

**[3] If you say that the Os are identical, how many different ways can
    you arrange the letters of FOOT?**

Now let's look carefully at a harder problem.

Rebecca wrote each letter of the word *TEEPEE* on a separate card. She put the 6 cards in a box and shook them up. She is going to pull out the cards 1 at a time without looking and put them on a table in the order she draws them. What is the probability that *TEEPEE* will be spelled correctly?

**[4] If the Es were labeled so that none were identical, how many
    permutations (different arrangements) would there be?**

Then, if we insisted that she draw the Es in the original order $(T\ E_1E_2P\ E_3E_4)$, the probability would be $\frac{1}{6!} = \frac{1}{720}$. But since there are 4! ways of arranging the Es in *TEEPEE*, the true probability that Rebecca will spell *TEEPEE* correctly this way is $\frac{4!}{6!} = \frac{1}{30}$.

Using the same reasoning, there are 4! ways to rearrange the letters E_1, E_2, E_3, and E_4 for any positions of T and P, so the total number of permutations (different arrangements) of the 6 letters is only $\frac{6!}{4!} = 30$.

The number of permutations of *DEEDED* would also be 6! if the Ds and Es were distinguished from each other: $D_1E_1E_2D_2E_3D_3$. But there are 3! ways to rearrange the Ds and still spell $DE_1E_2DE_3D$, and for each of those 6 permutations of Ds, there are 3!, or 6, ways to rearrange the Es. Altogether there are $3! \times 3!$ ways to rearrange for Ds and Es and still spell *DEEDED*. This statement is true for any arrangement of the 6 letters. So, there are $\frac{6!}{3! \cdot 3!} = \frac{6 \times 5 \times 4 \times 3 \times 2 \times 1}{3 \times 2 \times 1 \times 3 \times 2 \times 1} = 20$ permutations of the letters of *DEEDED*.

Practice with Permutations

In general, the way we found the number of permutations of *TEEPEE* and *DEEDED* will work for any set of objects in which there are subsets of identical objects.

You will be finding the number of permutations of each of the words in the problems below. We recommend canceling whenever possible, even if a calculator is available.

Example: *DEEDED* $\quad \dfrac{6!}{3! \cdot 3!} = \dfrac{6 \times 5 \times 4 \times 3 \times 2 \times 1}{3 \times 2 \times 1 \times 3 \times 2 \times 1} = 5 \times 4 = 20$

Since there will always be a whole number of permutations, the factors in the denominator should always reduce to 1.

1. For the following words, give the number of permutations in factorial form and in standard form.

   a. *ROPE*
   b. *ROLL*
   c. *LOLL*
   d. *RADIO*
   e. *RALLY*
   f. *RADAR*
   g. *OVENBIRD*
   h. *OVERDRAW*
   i. *OUTSHOOT*
   j. *LOLLYPOP*
   k. *SYPHON*
   l. *SYSTEM*
   m. *SYZYGY*
   n. *MISSISSIPPI*
   o. *OUTSHOUT*

2. List 20 permutations of *DEEDED*. Are there more permutations than you have listed?

3. List all the permutations of *ROLL*. Does the number of permutations on your list agree with your answer to problem 1a?

4. How many permutations are there of the following groups of letters:

   a. *HHH*?
   b. *HHT*?
   c. *HTT*?
   d. *TTT*?

5. If you toss 3 coins, how many ways are there to get the following combinations? (Does your answer to problem 4 help?)

   a. 3 heads
   b. 2 heads
   c. 1 head
   d. 0 heads

6. In chapter 1, you learned that when you toss 3 coins, there are $2 \times 2 \times 2 = 2^3 = 8$ possible ways for them to land. What is the relationship between that 8 and your answers to problem 5?

7. If you toss 4 coins, how many ways are there to get

   a. 4 heads?
   b. 3 heads?
   c. 2 heads?
   d. 1 head?
   e. 0 heads?
   f. 5 heads?
   g. any other number of heads?

8. From your work in chapter 1, what is the total number of different ways 4 coins can land? Is that the same as the total of your answers for problem 7?

9. If you toss 5 coins, how many ways are there to get

   a. 5 heads?
   b. 4 heads?
   c. 3 heads?
   d. 2 heads?
   e. 1 head?
   f. 0 heads?

10. What is the total number of ways 5 coins can land?

11. Assume that you toss 5 "honest" coins—that is, coins that are equally likely to fall heads or tails. What is the probability that you will get

    a. 5 heads?
    b. 4 heads?
    c. 3 heads?
    d. 2 heads?
    e. 1 head?
    f. 0 heads?

1. Michelle has forgotten the combination to her lock. The instructions for the combination were: Turn twice to the left and stop at ___. Make one complete turn to the right and continue until ___. Then turn left to ___. Michelle remembers that the 3 numbers are 12, 27, and 32, but she doesn't remember their order. How many different combinations might there be for Michelle's lock?

2. Marilee fixes computers. She has detached 5 wires from their terminals.

   a. How many different ways are there to attach each wire to a different terminal?
   b. If only 1 of those ways will make the computer work correctly, and Marilee has forgotten it, what is the probability that she will get the right set of connections by chance?

3. How many ways are there to arrange 8 children in a line?

4. Suppose some of the children in problem 3 are boys and some are girls, and you are interested *only* in whether a boy or a girl is in a particular position. How many arrangements are there if there are

   a. 5 boys and 3 girls?
   b. 4 boys and 4 girls?
   c. 6 boys and 2 girls?
   d. 7 boys and 1 girl?
   e. 8 boys and 0 girls?
   f. 5 girls and 3 boys?*
   g. 6 girls and 2 boys?
   h. 7 girls and 1 boy?
   i. 8 girls and 0 boys?

*How did you do this problem?

5. If you toss 8 coins, how many different ways could the coins land so that

    a. 8 are heads?   **f.** 3 are heads?

    b. 7 are heads?   **g.** 2 are heads?

    c. 6 are heads?   **h.** 1 is heads?

    d. 5 are heads?   **i.** none are heads?

    e. 4 are heads?

6. a. What is the sum of your answers to problem 5?

    b. How could you have determined that sum without adding the 9 numbers?

7. If you toss 8 coins, what is the probability of getting

    a. 8 heads?   **d.** 5 heads?   **g.** 2 heads?

    b. 7 heads?   **e.** 4 heads?   **h.** 1 heads?

    c. 6 heads?   **f.** 3 heads?   **i.** 0 heads?

8. Chuck and Connie Collins were just married. They think it might be interesting to have a family with 8 children. Assuming that it is equally likely that any one of the children will be a girl or a boy, what is the probability that they could have

    a. 8 girls?   **d.** 5 girls?   **g.** 2 girls?

    b. 7 girls?   **e.** 4 girls?   **h.** 1 girl?

    c. 6 girls?   **f.** 3 girls?   **i.** 0 girls?

The kind of thinking you used to solve permutation (arrangement) problems can be used to solve many sorts of problems. Here are some examples. Discuss them and their solutions.

[1] How many ways are there to choose 3 students from a class of 30 students to be class president, class vice president, and class secretary?

Solution: There are 30 possible choices for president. With each of these 30 possible presidents there are 29 possible vice presidents, so there are 30 × 29, or 870, ways to choose the president and vice president. With each of these 870 possibilities there are 28 ways to choose the secretary, so there are 30 × 29 × 28, or 24,360, ways to fill the 3 offices.

[2] How many ways are there to select the captain of the tennis team, the winner of the mathematics prize, and the editor of the paper from a class of 30 students?

Solution: With each of the 30 ways to choose the tennis captain there are 30 ways to choose the winner of the mathematics prize (since the same person might win both). With each of these 30 × 30, or 900, choices there would be 30 ways to choose the editor. So there are 30 × 30 × 30, or 27,000, ways to choose these 3 positions.

[3] How many different ways are there to choose 3 students to carry books from a class of 30?

Solution: This question is very much like the first discussion question, but we no longer care who was chosen first. Oralee as president, Eugene as vice president, and Mervin as secretary is different from Mervin as president, Oralee as vice president, and Eugene as secretary. But Oralee as book carrier, Eugene as book carrier, and Mervin as book carrier has exactly the same effect as Mervin as book carrier, Oralee as book carrier, and Eugene as book carrier.

So we can take the answer for the first discussion question and divide by 3!, or 3 × 2 × 1, to get:

$$\frac{30 \times 29 \times 28}{3 \times 2 \times 1} \times 4060.$$

Solve these problems.

1. From a class of 25 students, how many ways are there to choose
   a. a class president, vice-president, and secretary?
   b. a class "clown," "brain," and athlete?
   c. the class tennis team of 3 players?

2. In a certain state, the automobile license plates all have exactly 6 digits and no letters.

   a. If numbers like 003555 are possible, how many different license plates can the state make?
   b. If zeros are not allowed as the first digits, how many different license plates can the state make?
   c. If zeros are not allowed as the first digits, but numbers having 6, 5, 4, 3, 2, or 1 digits are allowed, how many different license plates can the state make?

3. In another state, the license plates all have 3 letters followed by 3 digits. Plates look like this: CEC 049. How many different license plates are possible in this state?

4. In Canada, the postal codes are made up of 3 letters and 3 digits. They look like this: N6G 2L5. How many different postal codes are possible in Canada?

5. The 7-digit telephone numbers in a certain town all start with 1 of the following 6 sets of 3 digits (in the given order): 531-, 552-, 622-, 629-, 661-, and 869-. The other 4 digits may be anything from 0 to 9. How many different telephone numbers are possible in that town?

Remember

An exponent tells how many times a number is multiplied by itself.

$$2^3 = 2 \times 2 \times 2 \qquad 3^2 = 3 \times 3$$

Raising 0 to any power gives 0.

$$0^5 = 0 \qquad 0^9 = 0$$

Raising any nonzero number to the zeroth power gives 1.

$$3^0 = 1 \qquad 10^0 = 1 \qquad 1^0 = 1$$

0^0 is impossible.

Calculate.

1. 0^0	16. 4^2	31. 10^3
2. 0^1	17. 2^4	32. 10^4
3. 0^2	18. 2^5	33. 10^5
4. 1^0	19. 2^6	34. 10^6
5. 2^0	20. 5^2	35. 2^7
6. 3^0	21. 6^2	36. 2^8
7. 1^1	22. 5^3	37. 2^9
8. 2^1	23. 3^4	38. 2^{10}
9. 3^1	24. 7^2	39. 3^4
10. 1^2	25. 8^2	40. 3^5
11. 2^2	26. 9^2	41. 4^4
12. 3^2	27. 10^2	42. 4^5
13. 1^3	28. 11^2	43. 14^2
14. 2^3	29. 12^2	44. 15^2
15. 3^3	30. 13^2	45. 16^2

EXPONENT GAME

Players: 2 or more
Materials: 0–5 cubes, 5–10 cubes, a calculator
Object: To make the largest number

Rules

1. Each player rolls two 0–5 cubes and uses the numbers rolled to make a number with an exponent. If you roll 2 zeros, roll again.
2. The player who has the larger number wins. Try to decide whose number is larger by estimating. Use the calculator if you have to.

Sample Game

Kevin and Pat played with two 0–5 cubes.

Kevin's Roll	His Number	Its Value	Pat's Roll	Her Number	Its Value	Winner of Round
3 0	3^0	1	4 5	5^4	625	Pat
1 2	1^2	1	1 2	2^1	2	Pat
2 4	2^4	16	2 4	4^2	16	tie
4 5	4^5	1024	3 4	4^3	64	Kevin

Other Ways to Play This Game

1. Roll one 0–5 cube and one 5–10 cube.
2. Keep score by adding the numbers made for 5 rounds. The player with the highest score wins.

Happy's Hamburgers is having a Great Giveaway Contest. Each customer gets a folded and sealed ticket. When opened, the ticket tells what the customer has won. Happy's Hamburgers printed 10,000 tickets for the contest.

The front of the ticket tells what the prizes are.

Win

$100
$10
$1

Free Happy's Cola

**Everyone
Is a Winner!**

Menu

Happy's Single	89¢
with Cheese	99¢
Happy's Double	$1.65
with Cheese	$1.85
Happy's Fries	
Small	47¢
Large	58¢
Happy's Cola	
Small 6 oz.	55¢
Medium 7 oz.	65¢
Large 8 oz.	75¢

The back of the ticket tells how many prizes there are.

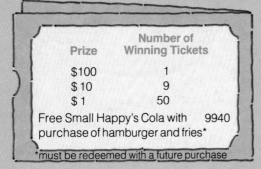

Prize	Number of Winning Tickets
$100	1
$10	9
$1	50
Free Small Happy's Cola with purchase of hamburger and fries*	9940

*must be redeemed with a future purchase

The inside of the ticket tells what the customer has won.

Congratulations!

You win $100!

*You must purchase a hamburger and fries to use this ticket on one of your next visits to Happy's.

Congratulations!

You win a small Happy's Cola!*

Work in groups to discuss and answer these questions. Use a calculator to do the calculations.

[1] On your first purchase at Happy's, what are your chances of winning

$100?
$10?
$1?
any money at all?

[2] What are your chances of winning any money in 3 visits? in 4 visits?

[3] Do you agree that everybody who makes a purchase and receives a ticket is a winner? You may have differences of opinion about this.

[4] Why do you think the rules say you can't use a winning cola ticket at the time you are making your first purchase?

[5] Sunny's Hamburgers, which is next door to Happy's, has an identical menu. Instead of having a contest to promote business, Sunny decided to give all customers a 30% discount. Which hamburger place, Happy's or Sunny's, gives the better buy?

Use the information on page 114. Make up your own problems and give them to a friend to solve. Here are some examples:

Which hamburger is the better buy—the single or double?

How many pieces of cheese do you think they put on the double hamburger?

Which size cola is the better buy?

Challenge: Does a store or restaurant in your town sometimes have similar contests? If so, try to figure out your chances of winning something worthwhile.

Tossing Coins

If you toss 1 coin, it can land either heads or tails. If you toss 2 coins, there is 1 way they could both land heads, 2 ways in which you could get 1 head and 1 tail (HT and TH), and 1 way to get 2 tails.

[1] **If you toss 3 coins, how many ways are there to get**

   3 heads?
   2 heads and 1 tail?
   1 head and 2 tails?
   3 tails?

[2] **If you toss 4 coins, how many ways are there to get**

   4 heads?
   3 heads and 1 tail?
   2 heads and 2 tails?
   1 head and 3 tails?
   0 heads and 4 tails?

We can make a chart of the information about tossing coins.

Number of Ways to Get *x* Heads When *y* Coins Are Tossed

y \ x	0 Heads	1 Head	2 Heads	3 Heads	4 Heads	5 Heads	6 Heads	7 Heads	8 Heads	Total
1 coin	1	1								2
2 coins	1	2	1							4
3 coins	1	3	3	1						8
4 coins	1	4	6	4	1					16
5 coins										
6 coins										
7 coins										
8 coins										

[3] **The number of ways to get 2 heads with 4 coins can be found using the formula** $\frac{4 \times 3 \times 2 \times 1}{2 \times 1 \times 2 \times 1} = 6$**. What is the number of ways to get 3 heads with 5 coins?**

[4] **What is the number of ways to get 5 heads with 8 coins?**

1. Copy and complete the chart on page 116.

2. Examine your chart for problem 1. Do you see any interesting patterns?

   a. What is the relation between each total and the previous one?

   b. Do you see an interesting connection between the numbers for 4 coins and the numbers for 5 coins?

   c. If you knew the numbers for the ways to get 3 heads with 6 coins and the ways to get 4 heads with 6 coins, how could you calculate the number for 4 heads with 7 coins (without calculating $\frac{7 \times 6 \times 5 \times 4 \times 3 \times 2 \times 1}{4 \times 3 \times 2 \times 1 \times 3 \times 2 \times 1}$)?

   d. Try your pattern on several other examples. Does it always work?

3. Use the pattern you found to extend your chart to 15 coins and 15 heads.

The pattern in the chart you developed in problems 1 and 3 is called *Pascal's Triangle*, or the *Arithmetic Triangle*. Each term in the arithmetic triangle can be found by adding the term above it and the term to the left of the one above it.

   Arithmetic triangles had been known and used for various things before Pascal's time, but he called attention to their connection with tossing coins and their other uses during his discussions with Fermat about gambling problems (see page 2 in chapter 1.)

4. Use your completed chart to tell how many ways there are to get

   a. 9 heads with 14 coins.
   b. 5 heads with 14 coins.
   c. 9 heads with 13 coins.
   d. 2 heads with 7 coins.
   e. 12 heads with 15 coins.
   f. 10 heads with 15 coins.
   g. 4 heads with 12 coins.
   h. 7 heads with 13 coins.

Suppose somebody told you that if you balance a U.S. 1-cent coin on a table and then tap the table gently until the coin falls, the coin will fall heads more often than tails.

[1] **How would you decide whether the statement is true?**

[2] **Suppose you tried the experiment with 15 pennies, and 8 fell heads. Would you be convinced?**

[3] **Suppose you tried the experiment with 15 pennies, and 15 fell heads. Would you be convinced?**

[4] **Suppose 13 fell heads. Would you be convinced?**

Most people will be convinced (or unconvinced) by how unusual they think the results are. Most people would say that getting 8 out of 15 heads is not unusual but that getting 15 out of 15 is unusual. 13 out of 15 heads also seems unusual to most people, but there might be some argument.

To help us decide what is unusual, we will say that any event that would occur by chance less than 1 time in 20 (that is, 5% of the time) is unusual. We will also say that any event that would occur by chance less than 1 time in 100 (1% of the time) is very unusual.

We must be careful to say *in advance* what we consider unusual. After the fact, many things can seem unusual. For example, suppose you toss a coin 15 times and it lands:

$$H\ T\ H\ H\ T\ H\ T\ T\ T\ H\ H\ T\ H\ H\ T$$

The probability of getting exactly this sequence of heads and tails is $\frac{1}{2^{15}} = \frac{1}{32,768}$. This outcome would be a most unusual event *if* you had predicted in advance that you would get this exact sequence of heads and tails. But since the coin had to land some way each time, it is not reasonable to look back and say the sequence was unusual unless you had predicted that sequence in advance.

Now let's return to the balanced pennies and the way they fall. We want to design an experiment with 15 U.S. pennies to see whether they fall heads more often than tails when balanced and then knocked down by gently tapping the thing on which they're balanced.

Here's one way to do it: We will balance 15 pennies on a table and tap it until they all fall. If more than a certain number fall heads, we'll say that's unusual, assuming that heads and tails are equally likely. In that case, we will conclude that heads and tails aren't equally likely.

What number shall we choose as an unusual number of heads? Assuming that heads and tails are equally likely,

$$\text{the probability of 15 heads is } \frac{1}{32{,}768}$$

$$\text{the probability of 14 heads is } \frac{15}{32{,}768}$$

$$\text{the probability of 13 heads is } \frac{105}{32{,}768}$$

$$\text{the probability of 12 heads is } \frac{455}{32{,}768}$$

$$\text{the probability of 11 heads is } \frac{1365}{32{,}768}$$

and so on.

Therefore, the probability of getting 11 or more heads is $\frac{1365 + 455 + 105 + 15 + 1}{32{,}768} = \frac{1941}{32{,}768}$, or about 0.0592. This outcome is not quite as unusual an event as we've defined it, since 0.0592, or 5.92%, is greater than 5%. Unusual events are those that are likely to occur by chance less than 5% of the time.

The probability of 12 or more heads is $\frac{455 + 105 + 15 + 1}{32{,}768} = \frac{576}{32{,}768}$, or about 0.0176. This outcome *is* unusual, since 0.0176, or 1.76%, is much less than 5%.

Therefore, if we get 12 or more heads, we will decide that such an outcome is unusual and that heads and tails are not equally likely.

If you have never done it, do the experiment in which you balance 15 U.S. pennies to see if they fall heads more often than tails. What's your conclusion?

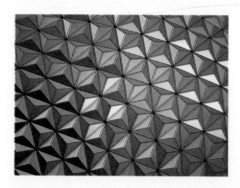

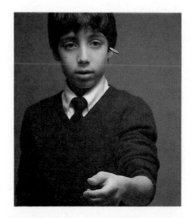

Use Pascal's Triangle (problem 3 on page 117) to help you solve these problems. Give your answers to problems 1–3, below, in 4 forms: a fraction, a decimal, a percentage, and a statement that the event is not unusual, is unusual, or is very unusual. Use a calculator.

1. If you toss 15 honest coins, what is the probability of getting 14 or more heads?

2. If you toss 15 honest coins, what is the probability of getting 10 or more heads?

3. If you toss 12 honest coins, what is the probability of getting

   a. 12 heads?   f. 12 or more heads?
   b. 11 heads?   g. 11 or more heads?
   c. 10 heads?   h. 10 or more heads?
   d. 9 heads?   i. 9 or more heads?
   e. 8 heads?   j. 8 or more heads?

4. Rudolph claims that you will get more heads than tails when you toss nickels. Design an experiment in which you toss some nickels to decide if Rudolph is right. How many heads are needed to call the results unusual if you toss

   a. 12 nickels?
   b. 10 nickels?
   c. 5 nickels?

5. a. Does it seem to you that the experiment becomes unfair to Rudolph as the number of tosses gets smaller?
   b. Why?

1. Extend Pascal's Triangle to 18.

2. If you toss 18 coins, what is the probability of getting each of the following outcomes (assuming heads and tails are equally likely)

   a. 18 tails?   **g.** 12 tails?
   b. 17 tails?   **h.** 15 or more tails?
   c. 16 tails?   **i.** 14 or more tails?
   d. 15 tails?   **j.** 13 or more tails?
   e. 14 tails?   **k.** 12 or more tails?
   f. 13 tails?

3. Enrique says that if you spin a U.S. penny it will land tails more often than heads. Spin a penny about 10 times on a smooth table to see if you think he might be right. Use a smooth surface like a table or floor without cracks. Don't count the spin if the penny hits anything else, such as another penny or a bump or crack. Count the spin only if the penny spins for at least 3 seconds (count slowly to 3).

4. Design an experiment to test Enrique's claim. Use 18 spins. How many tails must you get to consider this an unusual number of tails?

5. Do the experiment. Did you get an unusual number of tails?

6. Compare your results with other people's results.

   a. How many people got an unusual number of tails?
   b. How many people did not get an unusual number of tails?

7. Athena claims to have extrasensory perception (ESP). She says that she can sit in 1 room and tell whether the light is on in another room.

   a. Can you think of any way that she might be able to tell *without* having ESP?

   b. How could you design an experiment so that these things couldn't happen?

8. Design an experiment involving 18 trials for Athena to tell you whether the light is on. How many times would she have to be right for you to decide she guessed correctly an unusual number of times?

   a. If Athena was right 12 times, would that be unusual?

   b. If Athena was right 13 times, would that be unusual?

   c. If Athena was right 18 times, would that be unusual?

9. Billy's teacher has reason to believe that Billy was simply guessing on a true-false test. He got only 9 out of 15 correct answers.

   a. Is that an unusually high number of correct answers if Billy was just guessing?

   b. How many would he have had to get right to be unusual if he were just guessing?

10. An independent laboratory is setting up an experiment to see if people prefer Rocky Spring mineral water or Geyser Glory mineral water. If 17 people try both products, how many will have to prefer Rocky Spring for you to say that the outcome is unusual compared with the outcome you would expect if there were no difference between the 2 mineral waters?

Calculate.

1. Give the number of permutations in factorial form and in standard form of the letters in these words.

   a. *SASSARI*   c. *KIRKKILISSE*
   b. *SAAREMAA*   d. *STATISTICS*

2. How many permutations are there of each of the following sets of digits?

a.	55500	e.	55221	i.	54321	m.	44430	q. 43332
b.	55410	f.	54420	j.	54222	n.	44421	r. 33333
c.	55320	g.	54411	k.	53331	o.	44331	
d.	55311	h.	54330	l.	53322	p.	44322	

3. Suppose you rolled five 0–5 cubes.

   a. What is the total number of possible ways the cubes could land?
   b. Is that the same as $6 \times 6 \times 6 \times 6 \times 6$, or 6^5?
   c. How many different ways could the cubes land so that the sum of the numbers rolled is 15?

4. What is the probability of rolling the following sums with five 0–5 cubes?

   a. 15   b. 10   c. 20   d. 5

5. Copy and complete this table of probabilities for rolling certain sums with four 0–5 cubes.

	Sum	Probability		Sum	Probability
a.	10		d.	5	
b.	3		e.	15	
c.	17				

6. Copy and complete this table of probabilities for rolling certain sums with four 5–10 cubes.

	Sum	Probability		Sum	Probability
a.	35		c.	23	
b.	25		d.	40	

Solve for n.

1. $\frac{2}{3} + \frac{1}{4} = n$

2. $\frac{2}{3} - \frac{1}{4} = n$

3. $\frac{2}{3} \times \frac{1}{4} = n$

4. $\frac{2}{3} \div \frac{1}{4} = n$

5. $2\frac{2}{3} + 1\frac{1}{4} = n$

6. $2\frac{2}{3} - 1\frac{1}{4} = n$

7. $2\frac{2}{3} \times 1\frac{1}{4} = n$

8. $2\frac{2}{3} \div 1\frac{1}{4} = n$

9. $3\frac{1}{2} + 1\frac{1}{2} = n$

10. $3\frac{1}{2} - 1\frac{1}{2} = n$

11. $3\frac{1}{2} \times 1\frac{1}{2} = n$

12. $3\frac{1}{2} \div 1\frac{1}{2} = n$

13. $\frac{7}{8} - \frac{2}{3} = n$

14. $\frac{7}{8} \times \frac{2}{3} = n$

15. $\frac{7}{8} + \frac{2}{3} = n$

16. $\frac{7}{8} \div \frac{2}{3} = n$

17. $2\frac{3}{4} \div \frac{1}{4} = n$

18. $2\frac{3}{4} - \frac{1}{4} = n$

19. $2\frac{3}{4} \times \frac{1}{4} = n$

20. $2\frac{3}{4} + \frac{1}{4} = n$

21. $\frac{2}{3} \times 3\frac{1}{2} = n$

22. $\frac{2}{3} + 3\frac{1}{2} = n$

23. $3\frac{1}{2} \div \frac{2}{3} = n$

24. $3\frac{1}{2} - \frac{2}{3} = n$

25. $\frac{2}{3} \div 3\frac{1}{2} = n$

26. $3\frac{1}{2} + \frac{2}{3} = n$

27. $5 - \frac{2}{5} = n$

28. $\frac{2}{5} \div 5 = n$

29. $\frac{2}{5} \times 5 = n$

30. $5 \times \frac{2}{5} = n$

31. $5 \div \frac{2}{5} = n$

32. $\frac{2}{5} + 5 = n$

33. $\frac{1}{3} + \frac{1}{5} = n$

34. $\frac{1}{3} - \frac{1}{5} = n$

35. $\frac{1}{3} \div \frac{1}{5} = n$

36. $\frac{1}{3} \times \frac{1}{5} = n$

37. $\frac{2}{3} + \frac{2}{5} = n$

38. $\frac{2}{3} - \frac{2}{5} = n$

39. $\frac{2}{3} \times \frac{2}{5} = n$

40. $\frac{2}{3} \div \frac{2}{5} = n$

Chapter Review

1. Suppose you toss a penny, a nickel, and a dime. How many different ways can they land?

2. Suppose you roll three 0–5 cubes 1 at a time. How many different ways can they land?

3. Suppose you toss 10 coins 1 at a time. How many different ways can they land?

4. There are 6 different sets of numbers that make a total of 8 if you roll three 0–5 cubes at 1 time. List the 6 sets.

5. If you include the permutations, how many ways are there to make a total of 8 with three 0–5 cubes?

6. What is the probability of rolling 8 with three 0–5 cubes?

7. If you toss 10 coins, what is the probability of getting 4 heads?

8. How many permutations are there of the letters of SYZYGY?

9. The bicycle licenses in West Dingletown have a letter followed by 3 digits (for example, X 007). Assuming that all letters and all digits are allowed, how many different bicycle licenses are possible?

10. There are 30 pupils in Mr. MacLaurin's mathematics class. He goes over homework by having 3 students put their answers on the chalkboard. He chooses the students by drawing 3 slips of paper out of a box that has 30 slips of paper, each with a student's name on it. After drawing the 3 names each day, he puts the slips of paper back in the box. What is the probability that Serena will be asked to put her answers on the chalkboard today?

11. The Great Zo says he can predict the future—most of the time. He agrees to prove this by telling you how a coin will land the next 8 times you toss it. How many of those 8 times must he be right for you to agree that he has done something unusual? (Something unusual is something that would happen no more than 5% of the time if he were guessing.)

12. Robin is getting dressed in a dark room early one winter morning. She knows there are 5 white socks and 7 black socks in a drawer. How many does she have to take out to be sure she has a pair? (She has to walk to another room to see the socks.)

In the top drawer of Josephine's dresser, there are 6 white gloves (that make 3 pairs) and 8 black gloves (that make 4 pairs). They are the only things in the drawer but are all jumbled together. Josephine says that she can pull out a pair of gloves even if she is blindfolded. How many gloves does she have to take out to be sure she has a pair?

Chapter Test

1. Suppose you toss a penny, a nickel, a dime, and a quarter. How many different ways can they land?

2. Suppose you roll four 0–5 cubes 1 at a time. How many different ways can they land?

3. Suppose you toss 8 coins 1 at a time. How many different ways can they land?

4. There are 6 different sets of numbers that make a total of 7 if you roll three 0–5 cubes at 1 time. List the 6 sets.

5. If you include the permutations, how many ways are there to make a total of 7 with three 0–5 cubes?

6. What is the probability of rolling 8 with three 0–5 cubes?

7. If you toss 10 coins, what is the probability of getting 7 heads?

8. How many permutations are there of the letters of *ABRACADABRA*?

9. The bicycle licenses in East Dingletown have 2 letters followed by 2 digits (for example, XY 77). Assuming that all letters and all digits are allowed, how many different bicycle licenses are possible?

10. There are 25 pupils in Mrs. Ben-Horin's mathematics class. She goes over homework by having 5 students put their answers on the chalkboard. She chooses the students by drawing 5 slips of paper out of a box that has 25 slips of paper, each with a student's name on it. After drawing the 5 names each day, she puts the slips of paper back in the box. What is the probability that David will be asked to put his answers on the chalkboard today?

11. The Great Zo says he can predict the future—most of the time. He agrees to prove this by telling you how a coin will land the next 11 times you toss it. How many of those 11 times must he be right for you to agree that he has done something unusual? (Something unusual is something that would happen no more than 5% of the time if he were guessing.)

12. Reuben is getting dressed in a dark room early one winter morning. He knows there are 18 white socks and 30 black socks in a drawer. How many does he have to take out to be sure he has a pair? (He has to walk to another room to see the socks.)

Enrichment: Making Change for a $1 Bill

How many different ways can you make change for a $1 bill? You can use any of the U.S. coins (half dollar, quarter, dime, nickel, cent) in any amounts.

If you have a computer to use, write a program that gives you all the combinations as well as the number of combinations.

CHAPTER 5
GEOMETRY

5

More than $2\frac{1}{2}$ millennia (2500 years) ago Greek scholars visiting
Egypt noticed that land was measured officially to calculate the
taxes on the land. The Greeks called these procedures for
measuring land *geōmetria* from their words *gê* (earth) and *metreein*
(to measure). From that word came the word *geometry*, which we
use for the study of points, lines, angles, surfaces, and solids.

The Greeks were interested in what the Egyptians were doing.
When they returned to Greece they began to do their own work in
geometry. Both the Egyptians and the Greeks used various
instruments to help them solve problems in geometry. Some of
these instruments, with appropriate changes, are still used today.

4 instruments that you will use in geometry are a straightedge, a
compass, a ruler, and a protractor.

A. A straightedge is used to draw straight line segments through
2 points. The edge of a book, the edge of a ruler, or anything
with a straight edge can serve as a straightedge for drawing
lines.

B. A compass is used to draw a circle with a given point as center
and a given length as radius. Sometimes this instrument is
called *compasses* or *a pair of compasses*. A compass can also
be used to mark off a line segment of a given length.

C. A ruler is used for measuring lengths. The Greeks appear not
to have used rulers in doing geometry, but you will find rulers
useful. Our rulers commonly measure in centimeters and
inches.

D. A protractor is used for measuring angles in degrees. The Greeks and Egyptians apparently did not use protractors.

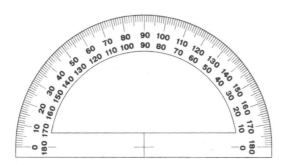

Use a compass and straightedge to do the following problems. (If you use a ruler for a straightedge, do not measure with it.) Be prepared to show how you did each of these problems.

1. Draw some interesting patterns or figures with straight line segments and circles.

2. To *bisect* means to cut in 2 equal-sized parts. Bisect a line segment.

3. Bisect an angle.

4. Construct 2 line segments that are perpendicular to each other. Remember that perpendicular lines meet at right angles.

The following figures may be of help in doing some of these problems.

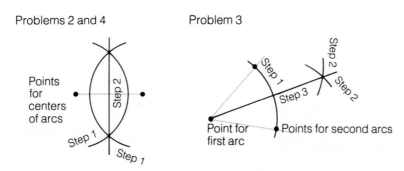

You can copy an angle using a straightedge and a compass.

Start with angle ABC ($\angle ABC$). Remember that the vertex, or corner point, is listed in the middle.

A. Draw an arc $\overset{\frown}{XY}$ with B as center. $\overset{\frown}{XY}$ crosses line AB at Y and line CB at X.

B. Choose (or draw) a vertex (Q) and one side (QR) of the new angle.

C. With Q as center, draw an arc with the same radius as $\overset{\frown}{XY}$, crossing QR at Z.

D. Using $\angle ABC$, set your compass so that one point is on X and the other on Y.

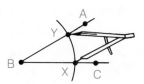

E. Using Z as center and the compass setting from step D, draw an arc that crosses the arc you drew in step C at W.

F. Draw a line QP that passes through W. $\angle PQR$ is the same size as $\angle ABC$.

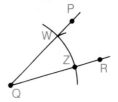

We say that angle ABC is equal to angle PQR if the angles have the same measure. This relationship is written $\angle ABC = \angle PQR$. Remember that we can refer to an angle by its vertex only when there is no doubt about which angle we mean. So we can also say that angle B is equal to angle Q, and we can write $\angle B = \angle Q$.

Steps A–F can be summarized on 1 figure showing the order of the steps. Start with $\angle ABC$.

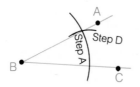 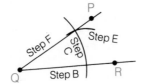

1. Draw any angle on your paper. Call it $\angle ABC$.
   a. Copy $\angle ABC$ somewhere else on your paper using this procedure.
   b. Use your protractor to measure each angle. Are they equal?

2. Repeat parts a and b of problem 1 for 5 more angles.

Constructing Similar Triangles

You can easily use a compass to copy a line segment without measuring.

A. Start with a line segment *AB*.

B. Set your compass so that the point is at *A* and the marker is at *B*.

C. Mark a point *C* on your paper. Place the point of the compass at *C* and make a small arc.

D. Draw a straight line from *C* to the arc. Call the point *D* where this line intersects the arc. *CD* = *AB*.

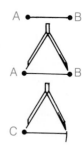

1. Draw a triangle. Call it △*EFG*.

2. You know how to copy an angle and a line segment. Try to draw △*HIJ* that would be an exact copy of △*EFG*.

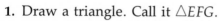

Remember

We say that 2 triangles are *congruent* if all the angles and sides of 1 triangle have the same measures as the corresponding angles and sides of the other triangle. △*EFG* ≅ △*HIJ* means triangle *EFG* is congruent to triangle *HIJ*.

---

3. Measure the angles and sides of both triangles. Are they congruent?

4. Now try to draw △*LMN* so that ∠*E* = ∠*L*, ∠*F* = ∠*M*, and ∠*G* = ∠*N*, but make *LM* twice as long as *EF*.

5. Measure all the angles in both triangles. Are the corresponding angles equal?

6. Measure all the sides in both triangles. What do you notice?

Remember

We say that 2 triangles are *similar* if all the angles of 1 triangle have the same measures as the corresponding angles of the other triangle. In similar triangles, the lengths of corresponding sides are in proportion. △*EFG* ~ △*LMN* means triangle *EFG* is similar to triangle *LMN*.

Proportions

Remember

A *proportion* shows a relation between number pairs. 2 pairs of numbers are said to be *in proportion* if the ratio of the numbers in 1 pair equals the ratio of the numbers in the other pair. For example, the number pairs (3, 6) and (5, 10) are in proportion because $\frac{3}{6} = \frac{5}{10}$. $\frac{3}{6} = \frac{5}{10}$ is a proportion.

If 1 number in a proportion is unknown, there are several ways you can find out what it is. For example:

$$\frac{3}{6} = \frac{2.4}{x}$$

Since 6 is 2×3, x must be 2×2.4, or 4.8, or, since 2.4 is 0.8×3, x must be 0.8×6, or 4.8.

Look at this proportion: $\frac{a}{b} = \frac{c}{d}$
Multiply both sides of the proportion by bd: $\frac{a}{b}(bd) = \frac{c}{d}(bd)$
Cancel where possible: $\frac{a}{\cancel{b}}(\cancel{b}d) = \frac{c}{\cancel{d}}(b\cancel{d})$
You get: $ad = cb$

If we use this procedure on the proportion $\frac{3}{6} = \frac{2.4}{x}$, we get $3x = 6 \times 2.4$, and $x = 4.8$. Thus we can always find 1 unknown number in a proportion if we know the other 3.

Find x in each of the following proportions.

1. $\frac{x}{5} = \frac{16}{8}$

2. $\frac{6}{x} = \frac{12}{4}$

3. $\frac{25}{10} = \frac{x}{2}$

4. $\frac{12}{3} = \frac{x}{5}$

5. $\frac{8}{24} = \frac{2}{x}$

6. $\frac{1}{2} = \frac{3}{x}$

7. $\frac{3}{x} = \frac{1}{5}$

8. $\frac{x}{4} = \frac{6}{24}$

9. $\frac{3}{7} = \frac{x}{10}$

10. $\frac{2}{5} = \frac{3}{x}$

11. $\frac{8}{16} = \frac{5}{x}$

12. $\frac{x}{5} = \frac{3}{1}$

13. $\frac{10}{2} = \frac{25}{x}$

14. $\frac{x}{3} = \frac{10}{7}$

15. $\frac{x}{5} = \frac{3}{2}$

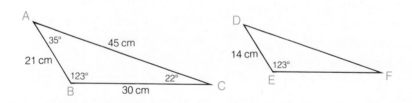

1. △ABC ~ △DEF

    a. What is the length of *EF*?
    b. What is the length of *DF*?
    c. What is the measure of ∠D?
    d. What is the measure of ∠F?

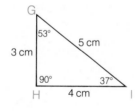
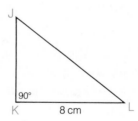

2. △GHI ~ △JKL

    a. What is the length of *JK*?
    b. What is the length of *JL*?
    c. What is the measure of ∠J?
    d. What is the measure of ∠L?

3. Try to construct a right angle using only a straightedge and compass. Remember: there are 90° in a right angle. (Hints: If you bisect a straight angle (180°), you produce 2 right angles. One method of bisecting a line segment produces perpendicular lines—lines that meet at right angles. See page 133.)

4. In $\triangle ABC$, $\angle A = 75°$, $\angle B = 80°$, $\angle C = ?$

5. In $\triangle DEF$, $\angle D = 10°$, $\angle E = 90°$, $\angle F = ?$

6. In $\triangle PQR$, $\angle Q = 73°$, $\angle R = 49°$, $\angle P = ?$

7. In $\triangle GHI$ and $\triangle JKL$, $\angle G = \angle J$ and $\angle H = \angle K$.

    a. What can you say about $\angle I$ and $\angle L$? Why?

    b. What can you say about $\triangle GHI$ and $\triangle JKL$?

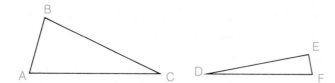

8. In triangle ABC, $\angle C = 90°$, $\angle A = 25°$, $AB = 100$ millimeters,
$BC = 42$ millimeters, and $AC = 91$ millimeters. In triangle DEF,
$\angle F = 90°$, $\angle D = 25°$.

    a. $\angle B = ?$ $\angle E = ?$

    b. If $DE = 50$ millimeters, how long is EF? How long is DF?

    c. If $EF = 84$ millimeters, how long is DE? DF?

    d. If $DF = 36.4$ millimeters, how long is EF? DE?

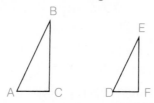

9. In $\triangle ABC$, $\angle C = 90°$, $\angle A = 40°$, $AB = 100$ millimeters, $BC = 64$
millimeters, and $AC = 77$ millimeters. In $\triangle DEF$, $\angle F = 90°$,
$\angle D = 40°$.

    a. $\angle B = ?$ $\angle E = ?$

    b. If $DE = 50$ millimeters, how long is EF? DF?

    c. If $EF = 25.6$ millimeters, how long is DE? DF?

Triangles are not the only figures that may be similar. Rectangles, hexagons, and many other figures may be similar.

In all similar figures, corresponding lengths are proportional and corresponding angles are equal.

Maps, blueprints, and other scale drawings are drawn to be similar to some other figure. A map of the United States, for example, is similar to the United States, and blueprints of parts of a house are similar to those parts of the house.

On a map of New Jersey the following scale appears:

Ms. Mollison measured the scale with her ruler and decided that 8 miles on the scale is 1 inch and 10 miles on the scale is $1\frac{1}{4}$ inches.

1. On the map, she measured the distance from Hamburg to Ewing in a straight line. It is about $7\frac{3}{4}$ inches. About how far is it from Hamburg to Ewing?

2. Can Ms. Mollison use her answer to problem 1 to decide exactly how many miles she would drive to go from Hamburg to Ewing? Why?

3. She estimated that the distance by road from Hamburg to Ewing on the map is about 9 inches. About how many miles would she have to drive?

4. If she can average 35 miles per hour for the trip, about how long will it take her?

5. The straight-line distance from Montague to Cape May on the map is about $20\frac{1}{2}$ inches. How many miles is that?

6. Following good highways, the distance on the map from Montague to Cape May is about $24\frac{1}{2}$ inches.

   a. How many miles is that?
   b. If Ms. Mollison can average 50 miles per hour for the trip, about how long will it take her?

7. Mr. Hopewell drove from Paterson to Atlantic City in 3 hours. He averaged 41 miles per hour. Following the roads he used, how long will the distance on the map be between Paterson and Atlantic City?

8. On a blueprint for the floor plan of a house, the following notation appears: 1 in = $1\frac{1}{2}$ ft. This means that 1 inch on the blueprint represents $1\frac{1}{2}$ feet in the real house.

   a. If a wall in the blueprint is 8 inches long, how long will the wall be in the house?
   b. A window of the house is supposed to be 36 inches wide. How wide should it be on the blueprint?
   c. The angle at which 2 walls meet in the house should measure 90°. What should the measure of the angle be on the blueprint?
   d. A door in the house is supposed to be 30 inches wide. How wide should the door be on the blueprint? (Remember, $1\frac{1}{2}$ feet = 18 inches.)

9. Make a scale drawing of the floor plan of your classroom. Start by measuring the length and width of the room, and choose a scale that will allow you to draw the entire figure on your paper. Measure windows, chalkboards, doors, the locations of tables, and so on. Draw—to scale—as many details as you can. If there are movable chairs and desks, you may want to cut out scale models of those so that you can move them around on your scale-drawing classroom.

10. Make scale drawings of the floor plans for 1 or more rooms in your house.

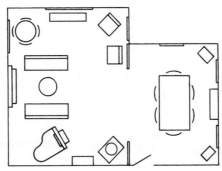

Transversals and Parallel Lines

Two lines are *parallel* if they go in the same direction and are always the same distance apart. In figure 1, line *AB* is parallel to line *CD*. We write this *AB* ∥ *CD*. In figure 2, line *IJ* is not parallel to line *KL*. We write this *IJ* ∦ *KL*.

If 2 lines are cut or crossed by a third line (called a transversal), angles in corresponding positions are called *corresponding angles*. In figure 2, the 4 pairs of corresponding angles are ∠*MOJ* and ∠*MPL*; ∠*JON* and ∠*LPN*; ∠*NPK* and ∠*NOI*; and ∠*KPM* and ∠*IOM*. In figure 1, the 4 pairs of corresponding angles are ∠*FHB* and ∠*FGD*; ∠*FHA* and ∠*FGC*; ∠*AHE* and ∠*CGE*; and ∠*BHE* and ∠*DGE*. If 2 parallel lines are cut by a transversal, the corresponding angles are equal.

Figure 1

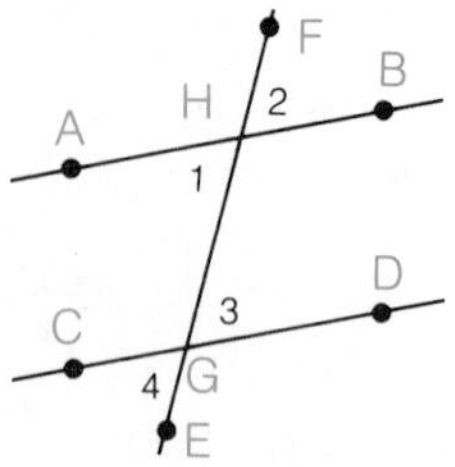

Figure 2

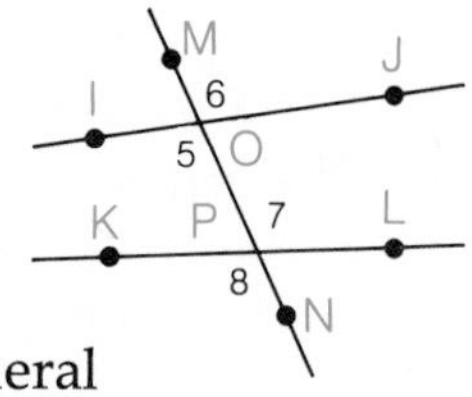

For simplicity, we sometimes label angles with a single numeral or other symbol. For example, ∠*AHE* could be called ∠1 and ∠*FHB* could be called ∠2. Angles that are formed by intersecting straight lines and are opposite each other, like ∠1 and ∠2, are called *vertical angles*. Vertical angles are equal.

1. List all the angles in figure 1 that you think are equal to ∠1. Explain why you think they are.

2. List all the angles you think are equal to ∠*AHF*.

3. If ∠1 = 50°, what is the measure of ∠*AHF*?

4. If ∠3 = 60°, what is the measure of ∠*AHF*?

5. In figure 2, suppose that ∠6 = 50° and ∠7 = 40°.

   a. Do you think lines *IJ* and *KL* could be parallel?
   b. If not, on which side of *MN* would they meet?

6. Suppose ∠5 = 40° and ∠7 = 41°

   a. Do you think lines *IJ* and *JK* could be parallel?
   b. If not, on which side of *MN* would they meet?

7. Suppose ∠5 = 37° and ∠7 = 37°.

   a. Do you think lines *IJ* and *KL* could be parallel?
   b. If not, on which side of *MN* do they meet?

8. Draw a line and a point outside the line. Construct another line that goes through the point and is parallel to the first line.

Sum of Angles of a Triangle

What is the sum of angles 1, 2, and 3? We can show that *the sum of the angles of any triangle is 180°*.

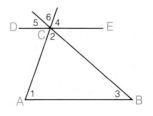

In $\triangle ABC$, draw line DE parallel to AB through C, and extend lines AC and BC past DE.

$\angle 1 = \angle 4$ and $\angle 3 = \angle 5$ because corresponding angles of parallel lines are equal.

$\angle 2 = \angle 6$ because vertical angles are equal. But $\angle 5 + \angle 6 + \angle 4 = 180°$, because DCE is a straight line. So, $\angle 3 + \angle 2 + \angle 1 = 180°$.

Use the following figure to do problems 1–12. $AB \parallel CD$.

1. If $\angle 6 = 80°$ and $\angle 7 = 60°$, $\angle 10 = ?$
2. If $\angle 5 = 120°$, $\angle 6 = ?$
3. If $\angle 5 = 120°$, $\angle 1 = ?$
4. If $\angle 5 = 130°$, $\angle 13 = ?$
5. If $\angle 12 = 110°$, $\angle 10 + \angle 7 = ?$
6. If $\angle 5 = 120°$, $\angle 10 + \angle 7 = ?$
7. If $\angle 8 = 150°$, $\angle 10 + \angle 6 = ?$
8. If $\angle 12 = 120°$, $\angle 6 = ?$
9. If $\angle 1 = 60°$ and $\angle 4 = 50°$, $\angle 10 = ?$
10. If $\angle 4 = 50°$ and $\angle 6 = 80°$, $\angle 12 = ?$
11. If $\angle 5 = 120°$, $\angle 13 = ?$
12. If $\angle 1 = 60°$ and $\angle 4 = 50°$, give the measure of each of the other numbered angles.

You know that the sum of the angles of any triangle is 180°. You can use that fact to find the sum of the angles of any polygon.

For example, let's find the sum of the angles of a pentagon (a figure with 5 sides). Consider any pentagon *ABCDE*. Draw *AD* and *AC,* making 3 triangles.

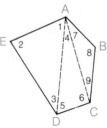

In $\triangle AED$, $\angle 1 + \angle 2 + \angle 3 = 180°$.
In $\triangle ADC$, $\angle 4 + \angle 5 + \angle 6 = 180°$.
In $\triangle ABC$, $\angle 7 + \angle 8 + \angle 9 = 180°$.
So $\angle 1 + \angle 2 + \angle 3 + \angle 4 + \angle 5 + \angle 6 + \angle 7 + \angle 8 + \angle 9 = 540°$.
But $\angle A = \angle 1 + \angle 4 + \angle 7$,
    $\angle B = \angle 8$,
    $\angle C = \angle 6 + \angle 9$,
    $\angle D = \angle 3 + \angle 5$,
and $\angle E = \angle 2$,
so $\angle 1 + \angle 2 + \angle 3 + \angle 4 + \angle 5 + \angle 6 + \angle 7 + \angle 8 + \angle 9$
    $= \angle A + \angle B + \angle C + \angle D + \angle E = 540°$.

[1] Do you see a relationship that you can use to work out the sum of the angles of a pentagon?

[2] How could you work out the sum of the angles of any polygon?

1. What is the sum of the angles of a quadrilateral (4-sided polygon)?
2. What is the sum of the angles of a hexagon (6-sided polygon)?
3. What is the sum of the angles of a heptagon (7-sided polygon)?

The formal names of polygons are Greek in origin. To avoid having to remember and say or write these names, we sometimes refer to a heptagon as a 7-gon, an octagon as an 8-gon, and so on. It is quite useful to be able to refer to a polygon with *n* sides as an *n*-gon.

4. What is the sum of the angles of a 12-gon?
5. What is the sum of the angles of an *n*-gon?

Regular Polygons

Remember

A *regular polygon* is a polygon in which all the angles are equal and all the sides are equal. An *equiangular polygon* is one in which all angles are equal. An *equilateral polygon* is one in which all sides are equal.

1. What is the measure of each angle in a regular triangle? Draw a regular triangle. A regular triangle is usually called an *equilateral triangle* and is sometimes called an *equiangular triangle*.

2. Can you draw an equilateral or an equiangular triangle that is not a regular triangle?

3. What is the measure of each angle of a regular quadrilateral? Draw a regular quadrilateral. What is the more common name for a regular quadrilateral?

4. Draw an equiangular quadrilateral that is not a regular quadrilateral. What is an equiangular quadrilateral usually called?

5. Draw an equilateral quadrilateral that is not a regular quadrilateral. An equilateral quadrilateral is usually called a *rhombus*.

6. What is the measure of an angle of a regular pentagon (5-gon)? Draw a regular pentagon. (Use a protractor to help if you like.)

7. Draw an equiangular pentagon that is not regular.

8. Draw an equilateral pentagon that is not regular.

9. Draw a regular hexagon. What is the measure of each of its angles?

10. What is the measure of each of the angles of a regular
    a. 7-gon?   c. 12-gon?
    b. 8-gon?   d. *n*-gon?

One of the problems the ancient Egyptians had to solve was how to make a right angle when they were working out in the field. Then someone made an amazing discovery. A triangle with sides of 3, 4, and 5 units of length will have a right angle between the 3-unit side and the 4-unit side. After that, Egyptian surveyors carried ropes with them that had 12 knots spaced to make 12 equal lengths.

When surveyors needed a right angle, they would have 3 people hold a rope at appropriate knots and stretch the rope so that it became straight line segments of lengths 3, 4, and 5. Then they would have a right triangle (a triangle with a 90° angle, or a right angle).

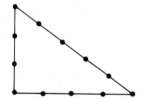

1. Get a piece of string. Tie knots in it so that you have 12 equal lengths. Try to make a right triangle the way the Egyptians did.

2. If a triangle with sides 3 centimeters, 4 centimeters, and 5 centimeters (a 3-4-5 triangle) is a right triangle, do you think a 6-8-10 triangle would also be a right triangle? Draw a 6-8-10 triangle.

3. List 4 other sets of 3 measurements that would be the sides of a right triangle.

4. You can construct a right angle with a straightedge and compass. (See problem 3, page 138.) Construct a right angle. Measure 6 centimeters from the vertex along 1 side and 8 centimeters along the other side. Connect these 2 end points. How long do you think the connecting lines will be? Measure to check.

5. Construct an isosceles right triangle.

6. Using only a straightedge and compass, construct a trapezoid.

7. Construct an isosceles trapezoid.

Remember that similar figures have the same shape. Congruent figures have exactly the same size as well as the same shape. You could think of congruent figures as being similar figures in which distances are in the ratio 1 to 1.

In congruent polygons, corresponding sides are equal and corresponding angles are equal.

8. Draw any triangle. Construct a congruent triangle by copying an angle, then a side, then an angle, and so on. How many parts of the triangle did you have to copy before the new triangle was determined?

9. Repeat problem 8, but start with a side. Then copy an angle, then a side, and so on.

POLYGON GAME

Players: 2 or more
Materials: Two 0–5 cubes, two 5–10 cubes
Object: To get the greater total score

Rules

1. Roll all 4 cubes.

2. Use 3 of the numbers rolled as sides of a triangle, or use all 4 as sides of a quadrilateral.

3. Calculate your points from this table. Be prepared to draw the figure if you are challenged.

Polygon Formed	Points
Any quadrilateral	1
Isosceles trapezoid	2
Parallelogram or rectangle	3
Rhombus or square	4
Any triangle	2
Isosceles triangle	3
Right triangle	4
Equilateral triangle	4
No possible polygon	5

4. Play 5 rounds. The player with the highest score is the winner.

Sample Game

Janice		Frederick	
Rolled	**Scored**	**Rolled**	**Scored**
1 2 5 7	1	3 4 5 9	4
1 5 5 9	3	3 5 6 10	2
4 5 7 8	2	1 2 5 5	3
4 5 7 7	2	0 4 7 9	2
1 1 5 7	5	1 4 6 7	2
	13		13

Janice and Frederick tied.

Compute. Write answers as whole numbers, mixed numbers, or proper fractions. Reduce completely.

1. $\frac{3}{8} + \frac{1}{4}$

2. $\frac{3}{8} \times \frac{1}{4}$

3. $\frac{3}{8} \div \frac{1}{4}$

4. $\frac{3}{8} - \frac{1}{4}$

5. $4\frac{1}{2} + \frac{3}{4}$

6. $4\frac{1}{2} \div \frac{3}{4}$

7. $4\frac{1}{2} \times \frac{3}{4}$

8. $4\frac{1}{2} - \frac{3}{4}$

9. $6\frac{3}{5} \times 1\frac{9}{11}$

10. $6\frac{3}{5} \div 1\frac{9}{11}$

11. $6\frac{3}{5} - 1\frac{9}{11}$

12. $6\frac{3}{5} + 1\frac{9}{11}$

13. $\frac{6}{5} + \frac{5}{6}$

14. $\frac{6}{5} - \frac{5}{6}$

15. $\frac{6}{5} \times \frac{5}{6}$

16. $\frac{6}{5} \div \frac{5}{6}$

17. $2\frac{2}{3} - 2\frac{1}{4}$

18. $2\frac{2}{3} \times 2\frac{1}{4}$

19. $2\frac{2}{3} \div 2\frac{1}{4}$

20. $2\frac{2}{3} + 2\frac{1}{4}$

21. $1\frac{2}{5} + \frac{5}{7}$

22. $1\frac{2}{5} \times \frac{5}{7}$

23. $1\frac{2}{5} - \frac{5}{7}$

24. $1\frac{2}{5} \div \frac{5}{7}$

25. $\frac{1}{3} + \frac{1}{4}$

26. $\frac{1}{3} - \frac{1}{4}$

27. $\frac{1}{3} \times \frac{1}{4}$

28. $\frac{1}{3} \div \frac{1}{4}$

29. $\frac{3}{4} + \frac{2}{3}$

30. $\frac{3}{4} - \frac{2}{3}$

31. $\frac{3}{4} \times \frac{2}{3}$

32. $\frac{3}{4} \div \frac{2}{3}$

33. $3\frac{1}{2} - \frac{2}{7}$

34. $3\frac{1}{2} \times \frac{2}{7}$

35. $3\frac{1}{2} + \frac{2}{7}$

36. $3\frac{1}{2} \div \frac{2}{7}$

37. $2\frac{1}{4} \times 1\frac{3}{4}$

38. $2\frac{1}{4} + 1\frac{3}{4}$

39. $2\frac{1}{4} - 1\frac{3}{4}$

40. $2\frac{1}{4} \div 1\frac{3}{4}$

The Egyptians discovered that a 3-4-5 triangle is always a right triangle. A more general statement about right triangles says that, for any right triangle, the area of a square drawn on the side opposite the right angle is equal to the sum of the areas of squares drawn on the other 2 sides. Conversely, if the sides of any triangle have this relationship, the triangle is a right triangle and the right angle is opposite the longest side. The longest side of a right triangle is called the hypotenuse.

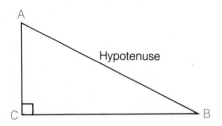

$\triangle ABC$ is a right triangle. $\angle C$ is the right angle. AB is the hypotenuse.

Measure the 3 sides.

   AC is about 22 millimeters.
   BC is about 44 millimeters.
   AB is about 49 millimeters.

Now we'll draw a square on each side of $\triangle ABC$.

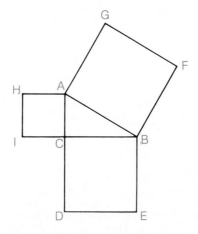

AC squared gives the area of *ACIH*: (22 millimeters)^2 = 484 millimeters^2
BC squared gives the area of *BCDE*: (44 millimeters)^2 = 1936 millimeters^2
AB squared gives the area of *ABFG*: (49 millimeters)^2 = 2401 millimeters^2

[1] What is the sum of the areas of the 2 smaller squares?

[2] Is that sum about equal to the area of the largest square?

So, within the limits of accuracy of our measurements, the sum of the first 2 areas equals the third.

A Greek mathematician named Pythagoras is given credit for first proving this statement, and the statement is generally called the Pythagorean Theorem. It is usually expressed in this way: in a right triangle, the square on the hypotenuse equals the sum of the squares on the other 2 sides.

A Proof of the Pythagorean Theorem

To work out a mathematical proof, start with statements that you believe to be true. Then proceed step by step, using only those true statements to show that something else is true.

Since the time of Pythagoras, many mathematicians have worked out proofs that the Pythagorean Theorem is true. Here is 1 such proof.

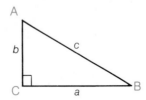

Here is the way we set up the problem.

Start with any right triangle ABC. Let $\angle C$ be the right angle. Let a, b, and c be the lengths of the sides opposite points A, B, and C respectively. $\angle A + \angle B + \angle C = 180°$, so $\angle A + \angle B = 90°$. The hypotenuse is c.

We want to prove that $c^2 = a^2 + b^2$.

So we begin by finding some relations based on things we believe to be true.

Extend CB a length equal to b and construct a right angle. Complete a new triangle congruent to $\triangle ABC$ as shown. Call the angle equal to $\angle A$ in this triangle $\angle 1$. Extend that side a distance of b, make a right angle, and continue in the same manner until you have completed the figure below with 4 congruent right triangles.

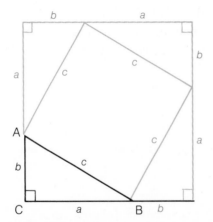

The larger figure is a square because the sides have equal length $(a + b)$ and its angles are right angles.

The quadrilateral inside the figure is also a square, since its sides have equal length and its angles are right angles. (Remember, $\angle A + \angle B = 90°$, the sum of the 3 angles at B is 180°, and $\angle 1 = \angle A$, so the angle of the inside quadrilateral is 90°.)

These are the final steps of the proof:

$$
\begin{aligned}
\text{I} = \text{area of the large square} &= (a + b) \times (a + b) \\
&= a(a + b) + b(a + b) \\
&= a^2 + ab + ab + b^2 \\
&= a^2 + 2ab + b^2
\end{aligned}
$$

We can also show this geometrically:

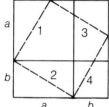

area of 1 $= a^2$
area of 2 $= ab$
area of 3 $= ab$
area of 4 $= b^2$
area of the large square $= a^2 + 2ab + b^2$

Notice that both algebra and geometry give the same answer.

$$\text{II} = \text{area of } \triangle ABC = \tfrac{1}{2}ab$$

$$\text{area of the 4 congruent triangles} = 4\left(\tfrac{1}{2}ab\right)$$

$$= 2ab$$

$$\text{III} = \text{area of the small square} = c^2$$

It is clear that the area of the large square is equal to the area of the 4 triangles and the small square.

$$\text{I} = \text{II} + \text{III}$$
$$a^2 + 2ab + b^2 = 2ab + c^2$$
$$a^2 + b^2 = c^2$$

We have shown that what we wanted to prove is true. For any (right) triangle, the square on the hypotenuse is equal to the sum of the squares on the other 2 sides.

We do not need to think of the Pythagorean Theorem in terms of area. The equation $a^2 + b^2 = c^2$ gives us a relation between lengths. In this way, the Pythagorean Theorem is used to solve various problems. Here is an example:

About how long a wire will be needed to stretch from the top of a 36-foot pole to a point on the ground 50 feet from the base of the pole?

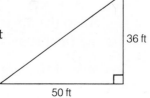

36 ft

50 ft

You can assume that the angle between the pole and the ground is a right angle. The squares on the 2 short sides of the triangle are 2500 and 1296, so the square on the hypotenuse is 2500 + 1296, or 3796.

Now, you must find a number that when multiplied by itself equals 3796. This number is called the *square root* of 3796. The square root of any number n is a number that multiplied by itself equals n. The symbol for the square root of n is $\sqrt{n}$. A calculator is helpful in finding square roots.

Let's try to find $\sqrt{3796}$. You know that $60^2 = 3600$. Try 61^2 (that's 3721) and 62^2 (that's 3844). So the answer is between 61 and 62. For practical purposes, that would be close enough. If you want a more precise answer, you can keep trying as follows: $61.6^2 = 3794.56$, $61.7^2 = 3806.89$, $61.61^2 = 3795.7921$, $61.62^2 = 3797.0244$, and so on.

There are more efficient ways of calculating square roots to great precision, but you will seldom need them. Probably the most efficient procedure is to use a calculator, if your calculator has a square root key. Enter 3796 in your calculator, push the square root key, and get 61.61168.

The length of the wire from the top of the pole to the ground would be a little longer than 61 feet. Because the wire would sag in the middle, some extra length might be needed.

For each of the following right triangles, determine the length of the side that isn't given. Round answers to 1 decimal place.

1.

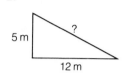

5 m

12 m

?

2.

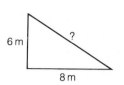

6 m

8 m

?

3.

1 m

1 m

?

4. *

5 m

4 m

?

5.

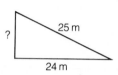

25 m

24 m

?

6.

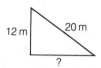

12 m

20 m

?

7.

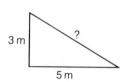

3 m

5 m

?

8.

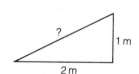

?

2 m

1 m

9.

3 m

2 m

?

10.

2 m

2 m

?

11. Cube *ABCDEFGH* is 1 centimeter on a side. How long is diagonal *AG*?†

12. Cube *ABCDEFGH* is 2 centimeters on a side. How long is diagonal *AG*?

13. A door is 203 centimeters high and 75 centimeters wide. A large piece of plate glass is 215 centimeters by 230 centimeters. Will the piece of glass fit through the door? Explain your answer.

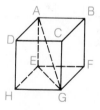

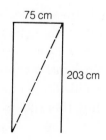

75 cm

203 cm

*Hint: The hypotenuse is opposite the right angle, and the square on the hypotenuse is the largest square, so you should *not* add 25 and 16.
†Hint: It may help to find how long EG is.

We live in a 3-dimensional world. Things in our world have height, width, and depth. The geometry we have done up to now in this chapter is 2-dimensional. It is useful because we live and move about on a 2-dimensional surface and much of our communication is done on 2-dimensional surfaces (pictures on paper, on television, on movie screens, and so on). Because of the importance of both 2- and 3-dimensional objects in our lives, we should understand both 2- and 3-dimensional geometry.

Here are some common objects in our world of 3 dimensions:

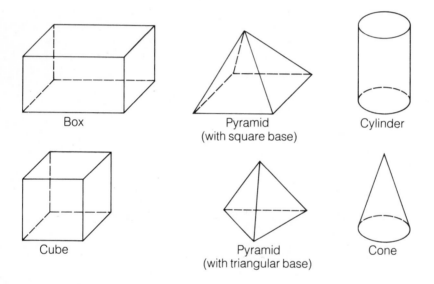

Box	Pyramid (with square base)	Cylinder
Cube	Pyramid (with triangular base)	Cone

Sometimes these objects are surfaces in 3 dimensions, and sometimes they are solids. When we say *cylinder* in ordinary conversation, we can mean the roll of aluminum foil, the box of salt, or the rung of a chair. We use the same word to refer to open, closed, or solid forms of a cylinder, just as we use *circle* to mean either the line that makes the circle or the space inside the circle.

Let's say that the figures on page 156 are hollow but have tops and bottoms. If we were to cut the cylinder so that it would lie flat, it would look something like the figure below.

This figure could also be a pattern for making a cylinder. If you cut out this pattern and included small flaps for gluing at one end of the rectangle and at several places on the circles, you could roll up the rectangle and attach the top and bottom to get a cylinder.

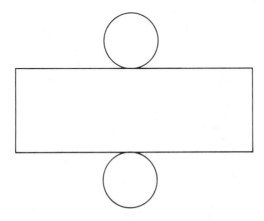

1. Show what each of the other 5 figures on page 156 would look like if it were cut so that it would lie flat. Each figure should be "cut" as little as possible. The box, the 2 pyramids, and the cube should each still be 1 continuous piece with folds.

2. The figure shown at right is a sphere, or ball. Can you draw a picture of how it would look if it were cut to lie flat? Discuss the answer to this question with others.

A *polyhedron* is a figure made up of polygons (called *faces*). Boxes, cubes, and pyramids all are *polyhedra* (or *polyhedrons*). You can spell the plural either way. the *vertices* (singular: *vertex*) are the points at the corners, and the straight line segments joining the vertices (the sides of the polygons) are called *edges*.

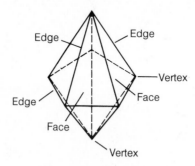

A *regular polyhedron* is a polyhedron in which all the faces are congruent to each other, all edges have the same length, and all angles have the same measure.

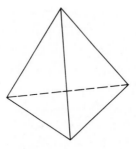

The regular polyhedron with the smallest number of faces is the regular *tetrahedron* (or 4-hedron), which has 4 equilateral triangles for its faces.

The figure below is a pattern for making a regular tetrahedron. Cut this figure out of cardboard. Score the folds on what will be the outside of the final figure. Notice that there are 3 flaps. Tuck those in as you fold the tetrahedron, and glue them to the inside of the adjacent face. The resulting model will stay together and will be quite strong. You may prefer not to use the flaps but to simply tape the edges together.

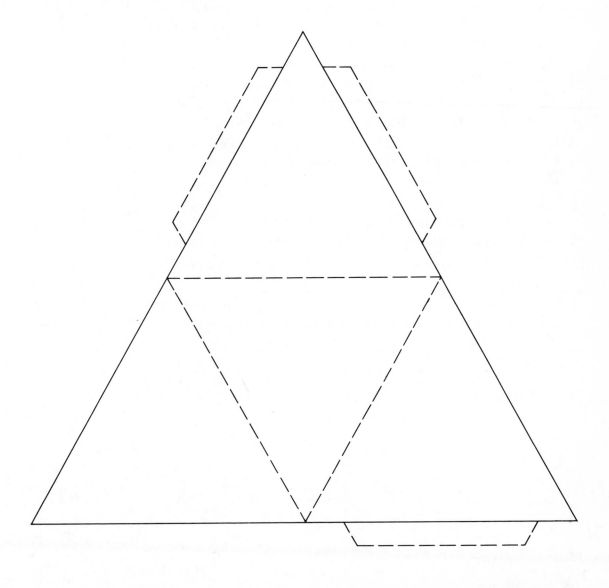

1. Look at your model of a tetrahedron. In a regular tetrahedron, there are 3 equilateral triangles meeting at each vertex. What is the sum of the angles at each vertex?

2. Would it be possible to have 4 equilateral triangles meet at a vertex of a regular polyhedron? If you put 4 equilateral triangles together at a point, could you fold the resulting pattern into a vertex? What is the sum of the angles at each vertex?

3. Would it be possible to have 5 equilateral triangles meet at a vertex? If you put 5 together at a point, could you fold that pattern? What is the sum of the angles at each vertex?

4. Would it be possible to have 6 equilateral triangles meet at a vertex? If you put 6 together at a point, could you fold that pattern? What would be the sum of the angles at each vertex?

5. Would it be possible to have more than 6 equilateral triangles at a vertex?

6. Could 3 squares meet at a vertex of a regular polyhedron? What would be the sum of the angles at a vertex? What is the common name of the regular polyhedron with 3 squares at a vertex?

7. Could 4 squares meet at a vertex of a regular polyhedron? Explain.

8. What is the measure of an angle of a regular pentagon (5-gon)? Could 3 regular pentagons meet at the vertex of a regular polyhedron? Explain.

9. Could more than 3 regular pentagons meet at the vertex of a regular polyhedron? Explain.

10. Could 3 regular hexagons (6-gons) meet at the vertex of a regular polyhedron? Explain.

11. Could 3 regular n-gons meet at the vertex of a regular polyhedron if n is greater than 6? Explain.

If we assume that the number of and the shape of regular polygons meeting at a vertex determines the polyhedron, then your answers to problems 1–11 should convince you that there are at most 5 regular polyhedra. There are, in fact, exactly 5 regular polyhedra. Patterns for those polyhedra appear on pages 162 and 163. Copy those patterns (with the flaps) on cardboard, score the folds on what will be the outsides of the finished figures, and glue the flaps inside the figures to make the 5 regular solids. If you copy them without the flaps, you can use tape to hold the edges together. There are other possible patterns from which you could construct the figures.

Patterns for the 5 Regular Polyhedra

Regular Tetrahedron (4-hedron)
(triangular pyramid)

Regular Hexahedron (6-hedron or cube)

Regular Octahedron (8-hedron)

Regular Dodecahedron (12-hedron)

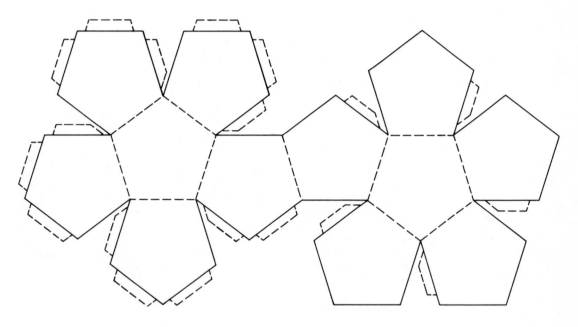

Regular Icosahedron (20-hedron)

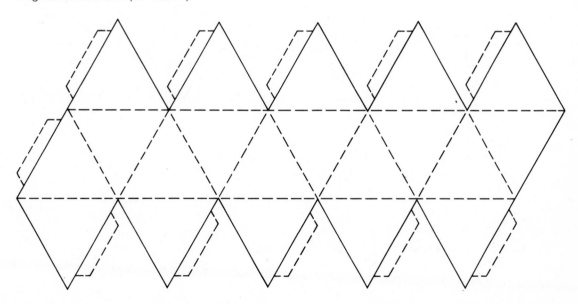

The prisms and the pyramids are 2 important classes of polyhedra. There are many different prisms and pyramids.

A *prism* is a polyhedron with congruent polygons lying in parallel planes as top and bottom and with sides formed by parallel straight line segments that join the corresponding vertices of the polygons and are perpendicular to the polygons.

These polyhedra are prisms:

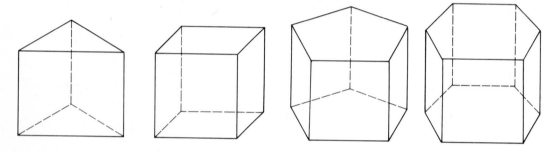

A *pyramid* is a polyhedron with a polygon as its base and triangles that meet at a single vertex as faces.

These polyhedra are pyramids:

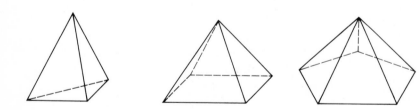

Look for more information about prisms and pyramids.

Use your models of the 5 regular polyhedra and the drawings in this chapter to help you with this seminar. If you count the faces, the edges, and the vertices of several polyhedra, an interesting pattern emerges. See if you can discover the pattern as you complete the following table.

Name of Figure	Number of Faces	Number of Vertices	Number of Edges
Box (see page 156)	6	8	12
Square pyramid (see page 164)	5		
Decahedron (see page 158)			
Regular tetrahedron			
Regular hexahedron			
Regular dodecahedron			
Regular icosahedron			
Pyramid with pentagon as base (see page 164)			
Prism with square base (see page 164)			
Prism with triangular base (see page 164)			
Prism with pentagon as base (see page 164)			

Now let f be the number of faces, v the number of vertices, and e the number of edges of a polyhedron. Write a formula that relates the 3 numbers.

Find or make models or drawings of other polyhedra. Does your formula still work?

1. Draw a straight line on your paper and label it *AB*. About an inch above the line mark a point and label it *P*. Using only a straightedge and compass, construct a line parallel to *AB* through *P*. Leave any lines or arcs you draw on your paper to indicate how you did your construction.

2. △*ABC* is similar to △*DEF*, with ∠*A* = ∠*D* and ∠*B* = ∠*E*. *AB* = 6 centimeters, *BC* = 5 centimeters, *AC* = 7 centimeters, and *DE* = 10 centimeters.

   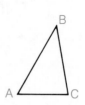

   a. How long is *EF*?
   b. How long is *DF*?
   c. If ∠*A* = 50° and ∠*C* = 60°, what is the measure of ∠*D*?
   d. If ∠*A* = 50° and ∠*C* = 60°, what is the measure of ∠*E*?

3. Find *x* in each of the following proportions.

   a. $\frac{3}{x} = \frac{7}{14}$ b. $\frac{1}{7} = \frac{6}{x}$ c. $\frac{3}{8} = \frac{x}{5}$ d. $\frac{x}{2} = \frac{3}{4}$

4. Frank was making a scale drawing of his living room floor. He let 1 centimeter represent $\frac{1}{2}$ meter. His living room is 3 meters wide and 4 meters long. His couch is 2 meters long. On the scale drawing, what should be the measurement of

   a. the width of the living room?
   b. the length of the living room?
   c. the length of the couch?
   d. the height of the living room?

5. In this figure, *AB* ∥ *CD*, ∠1 = 60°, and ∠4 = 40°. Find the measures of all the other numbered angles.

   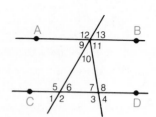

6. What is the measure of an angle of a regular pentagon (5-gon)?

7. Draw a pattern for making a regular octahedron (8-hedron). Include the necessary flaps for gluing.

8. In right triangle ABC, $\angle C = 90°$. Do the following problems. Round answers to 1 decimal place.

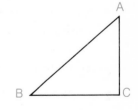

   a. If $\angle B = 40°$ and $AC = 30$ centimeters, $\angle A = $?
   b. If $AB = 50$ centimeters and $AC = 30$ centimeters, $BC = $?
   c. If $AC = 9$ centimeters and $BC = 40$ centimeters, $AB = $?
   d. If $AB = 4$ centimeters and $BC = 3$ centimeters, $AC = $?
   e. If $AB = 10$ centimeters and $AC = 5$ centimeters, $BC = $?

Enrichment: Probability with Polyhedra 1

Make models of the 5 regular polyhedra and use them to make number-hedrons. You'll make a 0–3 tetrahedron, a 0–5 hexahedron, a 0–7 octahedron, a 0–11 dodecahedron, and a 0–19 icosahedron.

With the number-hedrons, you'll use the number that is facing *down* after the number-hedron is tossed. If you toss the 0–3 tetrahedron in the air, what is the probability that it will land with the 2 facing down?

Calculate the probability of each of the number-hedrons landing with the 2 down after being tossed in the air. Then estimate how many times each of the number-hedrons will land with the 2 down if you toss each of them 100 times. Finally, do the experiment and see how close your results are to your estimates.

Save your number-hedrons for the enrichment activity on page 169.

1. Draw a straight line on your paper and label it *AB*. About an inch above the line mark a point and label it *P*. Using only a straightedge and compass, construct a line perpendicular to *AB* through *P*. Leave any lines or arcs you draw on your paper to indicate how you did your construction.

2. △*ABC* is similar to △*DEF*, with ∠*A* = ∠*D* and ∠*B* = ∠*E*. *AB* = 6 centimeters, *BC* = 5 centimeters, *AC* = 7 centimeters, and *EF* = 10 centimeters.

   a. How long is *DE*?
   b. How long is *DF*?
   c. If ∠*A* = 45° and ∠*C* = 65°, what is the measure of ∠*D*?
   d. If ∠*A* = 45° and ∠*C* = 65°, what is the measure of ∠*E*?

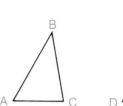
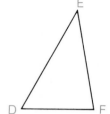

3. Find *x* in each of the following proportions.

   a. $\frac{4}{x} = \frac{7}{21}$ b. $\frac{1}{6} = \frac{7}{x}$ c. $\frac{3}{5} = \frac{x}{15}$ d. $\frac{x}{4} = \frac{5}{8}$

4. Fran was making a scale drawing of her kitchen. She let 1 centimeter represent $\frac{1}{3}$ meter. Her kitchen is 2 meters wide and 3 meters long. Her stove is 1 meter wide. On the scale drawing, what should be the measurement of

   a. the width of the kitchen?
   b. the length of the kitchen?
   c. the height of the kitchen?
   d. the width of the stove?

5. In this figure, *AB* ∥ *CD*, ∠1 = 45°, and ∠4 = 55°. Find the measures of all the other numbered angles.

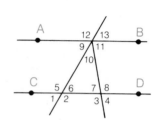

6. What is the measure of an angle of a regular heptagon (7-gon)?

7. Draw a pattern for making a regular hexahedron (6-hedron). Include the necessary flaps for gluing.

8. In right triangle ABC, $\angle C = 90°$. Do the following problems. Round answers to 1 decimal place.

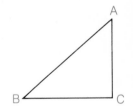

a. If $\angle B = 50°$ and $AC = 50$ centimeters, $\angle A = ?$
b. If $AB = 100$ centimeters and $AC = 60$ centimeters, $BC = ?$
c. If $AC = 8$ centimeters and $BC = 36$ centimeters, $AB = ?$
d. If $AB = 4$ centimeters and $BC = 2$ centimeters, $AC = ?$
e. If $AB = 12$ centimeters and $AC = 6$ centimeters, $BC = ?$

Enrichment: Probability with Polyhedra 2

For this activity, you should work with 1 or more friends. You'll need the number-hedrons you made earlier (see page 167).

Use 2 of the same number-hedrons. Choose a sum and calculate the probability of getting that sum by tossing the 2 number-hedrons. With the number-hedrons, remember to use the number that is facing *down* after the number-hedron is tossed. Choose the number of times you want to toss the 2 number-hedrons, and estimate how many times you'll get the sum you chose. Then toss the number-hedrons to check your estimate.

You can make this activity as simple or as complicated as you like.

CHAPTER 6

MATHEMATICS IN EVERYDAY LIFE

Thinking mathematically helps you to understand and to control the world around you. It can help you as you earn and spend money, and it can help you understand the daily news, take tests, learn about computers and how to use them, and so on. You have many opportunities to think mathematically and thus to be more efficient and make your life easier or more understandable. Often these opportunities involve more than simply doing some obvious arithmetic. They always require thinking carefully.

This chapter shows some ways in which you may be able to use mathematical thinking in your everyday life. Try to find others.

Think about each of these problems. Discuss them with other people.

1. Vantania was offered 2 jobs. One pays $4.50 an hour. The other pays $175 per week.

   a. Which job pays better?

   b. Is there anything else you'd like to know about either job? What?

   c. Make some assumptions about the answers to your questions in part b. Tell what your assumptions are and answer question a again.

2. Leon was offered 2 jobs. One pays $200 per week. The other pays $825 per month.

   a. Which pays better?

   b. Think about and discuss these jobs as in parts b and c of problem 1.

3. Leon was offered a third job that pays $10,000 per year. Compare the third job with the jobs in problem 2.

Different employers often have different definitions of a work week, a work year, and so on. Before you compare salaries, it is important to find out exactly what is expected and what is being paid for.

[1] Horacio works from 8 to 5 and gets 1 hour off for lunch. How many actual hours per day does he work? How many hours per week?

Do the following problems. Assume that people paid by the hour are paid only for hours actually worked (that they get no pay for lunch hours or holidays), that people paid by the week are paid for working 5 days (8 hours per day), and that people paid by the month get $\frac{1}{12}$ of their yearly pay (which is based on 52 weeks, including 2 weeks of vacation and 10 holidays a year).

4. At $5.00 an hour, how much will Sara earn in 50 weeks if she works 40 hours each week?

5. At $4.50 an hour, how much will Richard earn in 48 weeks if he works 40 hours each week?

6. At $175 per week, how much will Jamie earn in 40 weeks?

7. At $200 per week, how much will Rita earn in 48 weeks?

8. At $825 per month, how much will Isabel earn in 1 year?

Some people get "time-and-a-half" for overtime work. That means they are paid $1\frac{1}{2}$ times their usual rate when they work overtime.

9. If Lou's usual salary is $5.00 an hour and he works 3 extra hours at time-and-a-half, how much extra money does he earn?

10. If Jim's usual salary is $4.50 an hour and he works 6 extra hours at time-and-a-half, how much extra money does he earn?

[2] What factors other than salary and number of working hours should a person consider in choosing a job?

Abigail's paycheck deposit statement looks like this:

THE SLAG STEEL COMPANY							DEPOSIT DATE: 10/15/85			

EMPLOYEE NUMBER		HOURS				EARNINGS				
	REGULAR	OVERTIME	HOLIDAY	SPECIAL	REGULAR	VACATION	SICK			
112358	30.3				214.93		53.20			
SOCIAL SECURITY NUMBER	VACATION	SICK	TOTAL HOURS		OVERTIME	HOLIDAY	SPECIAL			GROSS PAY
011-23-5813		7.5	37.8							268.13

TAXES					DEDUCTIONS					
FICA		STATE WITH.	CITY WITH.	SAV. BOND	LOAN					TOTAL DEDUCTIONS
18.42										
FEDERAL WITH.		STATE	TOTAL TAXES	SAV. ACCT.						TOTAL DEDUCTED TAXES
39.20										57.62

YEAR TO DATE							PAY PERIOD	NET PAY
GROSS	FICA	FED. WITH. TAX			STATE TAX	CITY WITH. TAX		
10,092.26	678.18	1494.64					10/09/85	210.51

Abigail has often thought that there is a lot of information on the paycheck deposit statement. Let's look at what is there.

Give your best answers to the following questions. Discuss them with other people.

1. How much money was actually deposited in Abigail's bank account according to this statement?
2. When was the money deposited?
3. How many hours did Abigail work in the period ending 10/09/85?
4. In writing dates, some people write the month first and some people write the day of the month first.
   a. From this stub, how can you tell which procedure is being used?
   b. In what month is the date 10/09/85?
5. For how many hours of sick time did Abigail get paid?
6. For how many total hours was she paid?

7. What is Abigail's hourly wage (before taxes)?

8. F.I.C.A. is the abbreviation used for social security. Try to find out what the letters stand for.

9. How much of Abigail's pay was withheld for social security?

10. How much of Abigail's pay was withheld for federal income taxes?

11. How much of Abigail's pay was withheld for other taxes or other deductions?

12. Name at least 3 possible deductions other than taxes that might be withheld from somebody's salary.

13. Abigail doesn't expect to get a raise until the beginning of 1986. This paycheck is an average one for Abigail.

    a. About how much will Abigail earn for the entire year (1985)?

    b. About how much will Abigail pay for social security for the year?

    c. About how much will be withheld from Abigail's salary for federal income tax?

    d. About what percentage of her total yearly salary (gross pay) will be withheld from Abigail's salary for social security and federal income taxes?

14. So far this year (year to date), what percentage of Abigail's salary has been withheld in social security and federal income taxes?

Bruce is in high school. Last summer he worked as a lifeguard. Even though he is a student, federal withholding tax was deducted from his pay. Now he must file a 1040EZ tax form to get a refund. He has to do so before April 15. His social security number is 1 of the items called for on the tax form.

[1] Do you know your social security number?

Bruce earned a total of $968.64 last summer. Of this amount, $83.00 was withheld for federal income tax.

[2] On page 177 is a copy of form 1040EZ. What will Bruce enter on lines 1–8?

The tax tables show that a single person with a taxable income less than $2300 does not have to pay any tax.

[3] What will Bruce enter on line 9?

[4] How will Bruce fill out the rest of the tax form?

Department of the Treasury - Internal Revenue Service
Form 1040EZ Income Tax Return for
Single filers with no dependents (0)

OMB No. 1545-0675

Name & address

If you don't have a label, please print:

Write your name above (first, initial, last)

Present home address (number and street)

City, town, or post office, state, and ZIP code

Please write your numbers like this.

1234567890

Social security number

Presidential Election Campaign Fund
Check box if you want $1 of your tax to go to this fund. ▶

Dollars   Cents

Figure your tax

1 Wages, salaries, and tips. Attach your W-2 form(s).   1

2 Interest income of $400 or less. If more than $400,
   you cannot use Form 1040EZ.   2

Attach Copy B of Form(s) W-2 here

3 Add line 1 and line 2. This is your **adjusted gross income.**   3

4 Allowable part of your charitable contributions. Complete
   the worksheet on page 19. Do not write more than $25.   4

5 Subtract line 4 from line 3.   5

6 Amount of your personal exemption.   6

   1 000 00

7 Subtract line 6 from line 5. This is your **taxable income.**   7

8 Enter your Federal income tax withheld. This should be
   shown in Box 9 of your W-2 form(s).   8

9 Use the tax table on pages 29-34 to find the **tax** on your
   taxable income on line 7. Write the amount of tax.   9

Refund or amount you owe

10 If line 8 is larger than line 9, subtract line 9 from line 8.
    Enter the **amount of your refund.**   10

11 If line 9 is larger than line 8, subtract line 8 from line 9.
    Enter the **amount you owe.** Attach check or money order
    for the full amount, payable to "Internal Revenue Service."   11

Attach tax payment here

Sign your return

I have read this return. Under penalties of perjury, I declare
that to the best of my knowledge and belief, the return is true,
correct, and complete.

Your signature   Date

X

For IRS Use Only—Please
do not write in boxes below.

For Privacy Act and Paperwork Reduction Act Notice, see page 38.

The table on page 179 is part of a tax table. You can look up what the tax is if you know the taxable income and the filing status. For example, if Mikela's taxable income is $15,458 and she is single, her tax is $2211.

1. Use the copy of form 1040EZ and the tax tables to show what should be entered on lines 1–11 of form 1040EZ for each of these people.

    a. Jason Roebuck had wages of $9508.37, federal income tax withholding of $897.54, and interest income of $168.27 from a savings and loan institution but no dividends from stock.

    b. Martha Wilson had wages of $11,127.56, federal withholding of $1097.56, and interest income of $84.96. She is able to deduct $20.00 for her charitable contributions.

    c. Charles Lui had wages of $13,942.76, federal withholding of $2038.40, and interest income of $391.82.

    d. Wanda Kolowski had wages of $17,002.36, federal withholding of $2732.16, and interest income of $256.87. She is able to deduct $25.00 for her charitable contributions.

    The same tax table is used by persons who use form 1040A. Form 1040EZ is used only by single taxpayers. Form 1040A can be used by all taxpayers, whether married, single, or in some other filing status.

2. Use the tax table to find the tax in these situations.

    a. Martin and Mercedes Lopez, a married couple filing jointly, with taxable income of $13,452.16

    b. Gina Schmidt, a widow filing as head of household, with taxable income of $8967.35

    c. Rafael Jacobson, married but filing separately, with taxable income of $15,859.00

    d. Nora Jumblat, a single person, with taxable income of $16,157.32

Tax Table

If 1040A, line 19, OR 1040EZ, line 7 is—		And you are—			
At least	But less than	Single	Married filing jointly	Married filing separately	Head of a household
		Your tax is—			
8,000					
8,000	8,050	795	568	928	733
8,050	8,100	802	575	937	740
8,100	8,150	810	583	947	748
8,150	8,200	817	590	956	755
8,200	8,250	825	598	966	763
8,250	8,300	832	605	975	770
8,300	8,350	840	613	985	778
8,350	8,400	847	620	994	785
8,400	8,450	855	628	1,004	793
8,450	8,500	862	635	1,013	800
8,500	8,550	870	643	1,023	808
8,550	8,600	879	650	1,032	815
8,600	8,650	887	658	1,042	823
8,650	8,700	896	665	1,051	830
8,700	8,750	904	673	1,061	839
8,750	8,800	913	680	1,070	848
8,800	8,850	921	688	1,080	857
8,850	8,900	930	695	1,089	866
8,900	8,950	938	703	1,099	875
8,950	9,000	947	710	1,108	884
9,000					
9,000	9,050	955	718	1,118	893
9,050	9,100	964	725	1,127	902
9,100	9,150	972	733	1,137	911
9,150	9,200	981	740	1,146	920
9,200	9,250	989	748	1,156	929
9,250	9,300	998	755	1,165	938
9,300	9,350	1,006	763	1,175	947
9,350	9,400	1,015	770	1,184	956
9,400	9,450	1,023	778	1,194	965
9,450	9,500	1,032	785	1,203	974
9,500	9,550	1,040	793	1,213	983
9,550	9,600	1,049	800	1,222	992
9,600	9,650	1,057	808	1,232	1,001
9,650	9,700	1,066	815	1,241	1,010
9,700	9,750	1,074	823	1,251	1,019
9,750	9,800	1,083	830	1,260	1,028
9,800	9,850	1,091	838	1,270	1,037
9,850	9,900	1,100	845	1,279	1,046
9,900	9,950	1,108	853	1,289	1,055
9,950	10,000	1,117	860	1,298	1,064
10,000					
10,000	10,050	1,125	868	1,308	1,073
10,050	10,100	1,134	875	1,317	1,082
10,100	10,150	1,142	883	1,328	1,091
10,150	10,200	1,151	890	1,339	1,100
10,200	10,250	1,159	898	1,351	1,109
10,250	10,300	1,168	905	1,362	1,118
10,300	10,350	1,176	913	1,374	1,127
10,350	10,400	1,185	920	1,385	1,136
10,400	10,450	1,193	928	1,397	1,145
10,450	10,500	1,202	935	1,408	1,154
10,500	10,550	1,210	943	1,420	1,163
10,550	10,600	1,219	950	1,431	1,172
10,600	10,650	1,227	958	1,443	1,181
10,650	10,700	1,236	965	1,454	1,190
10,700	10,750	1,244	973	1,466	1,199

If 1040A, line 19, OR 1040EZ, line 7 is—		And you are—			
At least	But less than	Single	Married filing jointly	Married filing separately	Head of a household
		Your tax is—			
10,750	10,800	1,253	980	1,477	1,208
10,800	10,850	1,262	988	1,489	1,217
10,850	10,900	1,271	995	1,500	1,226
10,900	10,950	1,281	1,003	1,512	1,235
10,950	11,000	1,290	1,010	1,523	1,244
11,000					
11,000	11,050	1,300	1,018	1,535	1,253
11,050	11,100	1,309	1,025	1,546	1,262
11,100	11,150	1,319	1,033	1,558	1,271
11,150	11,200	1,328	1,040	1,569	1,280
11,200	11,250	1,338	1,048	1,581	1,289
11,250	11,300	1,347	1,055	1,592	1,298
11,300	11,350	1,357	1,063	1,604	1,307
11,350	11,400	1,366	1,070	1,615	1,316
11,400	11,450	1,376	1,078	1,627	1,325
11,450	11,500	1,385	1,085	1,638	1,334
11,500	11,550	1,395	1,093	1,650	1,343
11,550	11,600	1,404	1,100	1,661	1,352
11,600	11,650	1,414	1,108	1,673	1,361
11,650	11,700	1,423	1,115	1,684	1,370
11,700	11,750	1,433	1,123	1,696	1,379
11,750	11,800	1,442	1,130	1,707	1,388
11,800	11,850	1,452	1,138	1,719	1,397
11,850	11,900	1,461	1,145	1,730	1,406
11,900	11,950	1,471	1,153	1,742	1,416
11,950	12,000	1,480	1,162	1,753	1,425
12,000					
12,000	12,050	1,490	1,170	1,765	1,435
12,050	12,100	1,499	1,179	1,776	1,444
12,100	12,150	1,509	1,187	1,788	1,454
12,150	12,200	1,518	1,196	1,799	1,463
12,200	12,250	1,528	1,204	1,811	1,473
12,250	12,300	1,537	1,213	1,822	1,482
12,300	12,350	1,547	1,221	1,835	1,492
12,350	12,400	1,556	1,230	1,848	1,501
12,400	12,450	1,566	1,238	1,861	1,511
12,450	12,500	1,575	1,247	1,874	1,520
12,500	12,550	1,585	1,255	1,887	1,530
12,550	12,600	1,594	1,264	1,900	1,539
12,600	12,650	1,604	1,272	1,913	1,549
12,650	12,700	1,613	1,281	1,926	1,558
12,700	12,750	1,623	1,289	1,939	1,568
12,750	12,800	1,632	1,298	1,952	1,577
12,800	12,850	1,642	1,306	1,965	1,587
12,850	12,900	1,651	1,315	1,978	1,596
12,900	12,950	1,661	1,323	1,991	1,606
12,950	13,000	1,672	1,332	2,004	1,615
13,000					
13,000	13,050	1,682	1,340	2,017	1,625
13,050	13,100	1,693	1,349	2,030	1,634
13,100	13,150	1,703	1,357	2,043	1,644
13,150	13,200	1,714	1,366	2,056	1,653
13,200	13,250	1,724	1,374	2,069	1,663
13,250	13,300	1,735	1,383	2,082	1,672
13,300	13,350	1,745	1,391	2,095	1,682
13,350	13,400	1,756	1,400	2,108	1,691
13,400	13,450	1,766	1,408	2,121	1,701
13,450	13,500	1,777	1,417	2,134	1,710

If 1040A, line 19, OR 1040EZ, line 7 is—		And you are—			
At least	But less than	Single	Married filing jointly	Married filing separately	Head of a household
		Your tax is—			
13,500	13,550	1,787	1,425	2,147	1,720
13,550	13,600	1,798	1,434	2,160	1,729
13,600	13,650	1,808	1,442	2,173	1,739
13,650	13,700	1,819	1,451	2,186	1,748
13,700	13,750	1,829	1,459	2,199	1,758
13,750	13,800	1,840	1,468	2,212	1,767
13,800	13,850	1,850	1,476	2,225	1,777
13,850	13,900	1,861	1,485	2,238	1,786
13,900	13,950	1,871	1,493	2,251	1,796
13,950	14,000	1,882	1,502	2,264	1,805
14,000					
14,000	14,050	1,892	1,510	2,277	1,815
14,050	14,100	1,903	1,519	2,290	1,824
14,100	14,150	1,913	1,527	2,303	1,834
14,150	14,200	1,924	1,536	2,316	1,843
14,200	14,250	1,934	1,544	2,329	1,853
14,250	14,300	1,945	1,553	2,342	1,862
14,300	14,350	1,955	1,561	2,355	1,872
14,350	14,400	1,966	1,570	2,368	1,881
14,400	14,450	1,976	1,578	2,381	1,891
14,450	14,500	1,987	1,587	2,394	1,900
14,500	14,550	1,997	1,595	2,407	1,910
14,550	14,600	2,008	1,604	2,420	1,919
14,600	14,650	2,018	1,612	2,433	1,929
14,650	14,700	2,029	1,621	2,446	1,938
14,700	14,750	2,039	1,629	2,459	1,948
14,750	14,800	2,050	1,638	2,472	1,957
14,800	14,850	2,060	1,646	2,485	1,967
14,850	14,900	2,071	1,655	2,498	1,976
14,900	14,950	2,081	1,663	2,511	1,986
14,950	15,000	2,092	1,672	2,525	1,995
15,000					
15,000	15,050	2,103	1,680	2,540	2,005
15,050	15,100	2,115	1,689	2,555	2,016
15,100	15,150	2,127	1,697	2,570	2,026
15,150	15,200	2,139	1,706	2,585	2,037
15,200	15,250	2,151	1,714	2,600	2,047
15,250	15,300	2,163	1,723	2,615	2,058
15,300	15,350	2,175	1,731	2,630	2,068
15,350	15,400	2,187	1,740	2,645	2,079
15,400	15,450	2,199	1,748	2,660	2,089
15,450	15,500	2,211	1,757	2,675	2,100
15,500	15,550	2,223	1,765	2,690	2,110
15,550	15,600	2,235	1,774	2,705	2,121
15,600	15,650	2,247	1,782	2,720	2,131
15,650	15,700	2,259	1,791	2,735	2,142
15,700	15,750	2,271	1,799	2,750	2,152
15,750	15,800	2,283	1,808	2,765	2,163
15,800	15,850	2,295	1,816	2,780	2,173
15,850	15,900	2,307	1,825	2,795	2,184
15,900	15,950	2,319	1,833	2,810	2,194
15,950	16,000	2,331	1,842	2,825	2,205
16,000					
16,000	16,050	2,343	1,851	2,840	2,215
16,050	16,100	2,355	1,860	2,855	2,226
16,100	16,150	2,367	1,870	2,870	2,236
16,150	16,200	2,379	1,879	2,885	2,247
16,200	16,250	2,391	1,889	2,900	2,257

Percents

Percent means "per hundred." So 100 percent, written 100%, means 100 per hundred, or everything. 10% means 10 per hundred, or $\frac{10}{100}$, or $\frac{1}{10}$.

1. a. What does 50% mean?
    b. What completely reduced fraction equals 50%?

2. a. What does 25% mean?
    b. What completely reduced fraction equals 25%?
    c. What decimal is equal to 25%?

3. Give a completely reduced fraction and a decimal equal to each of the following percents.

    a. 20%   c. 60%   e. 150%
    b. 75%   d. 100%   f. 37.5%

4. Give a percent and a decimal equal to each of the following fractions.

    a. $\frac{1}{2}$ c. $\frac{3}{8}$ e. $\frac{3}{2}$ g. $\frac{4}{5}$
    b. $\frac{1}{4}$ d. $\frac{5}{8}$ f. $\frac{5}{2}$

   You can always take a percent of a number by changing the percent to a decimal (moving the point 2 places to the left) and multiplying. For example, 25% of 40 = 0.25 × 40 = 10. But there are sometimes easier ways. For example, 25% of 40 = $\frac{1}{4}$ × 40 = 10.
   Sales tax rates are given as percents. If the rate is 4%, it means that you pay 4¢ tax for every 100¢ an object costs.

5. Tell what the tax would be for the following prices and sales tax rates.

    a. $10 at 4%   e. $1.25 at 4%   i. $7 at 5%
    b. $100 at 4%   f. $100 at $7\frac{1}{2}$%   j. $0.20 at 5%
    c. $1 at 4%   g. $1 at $7\frac{1}{2}$%*   k. $7.20 at 5%
    d. $43 at 4%   h. $2 at $7\frac{1}{2}$%   l. $4.60 at 5%

*Be careful.

Discounts are often figured as percents. A 25% discount means that you pay 25¢ less for every 100¢ an object costs.

6. Tell what the cost of the following items would be. Assume that there is no sales tax.
   a. A $40 chair with a 25% discount
   b. A $250 television set at 20% off
   c. A $79 table at 30% off
   d. An $18.98 basketball with a 10% discount

7. How much should you pay for a $100 tape deck with a 5% discount *and* a 5% tax?

8. Give the cost of the following sale items.
   a. $19.98 jeans with $3 off
   b. $19.98 jeans with a 20% discount
   c. A $50 radio with $5 off
   d. A $50 radio with a 5% discount
   e. A $98 mixer with $10 off
   f. A $98 mixer with 10% off

9. In each case, tell which is the better buy.
   a. A $20 videotape at $10 off or at 10% off
   b. A $40 tennis racket at $10 off or at 10% off
   c. $60 hiking boots at $10 off or at 10% off
   d. An $80 sweeper at $10 off or at 10% off
   e. A $100 desk at $10 off or at 10% off

10. Which is the better bargain—$10 off or 10% off?

To find what percent a number is of another, divide the first by the second, and change the decimal to a percent.

Example: Mike earned $386, but $83 was withheld for taxes and social security. What percent of Mike's earnings went for taxes and social security?

$$\frac{83}{386} \approx 0.2150259, \text{ or about } 0.215 = 21.5\%$$

Example: Sandi got 7 hits in 30 times at bat. What is her batting average?

$$\frac{7}{30} \approx 0.2333333 \approx 0.233.$$

As a percent, this is 23.3%, but batting averages are usually reported in thousandths, so 0.233 or .233 is correct. (People usually leave off the point and just say "a two-thirty-three" batting average.)

11. Becky earned $400. $125 was withheld for taxes, social security, and her savings plan. What percent was withheld?

12. Edward got 12 hits in 60 times at bat.
    a. What is his batting average (in thousandths)?
    b. What percent of the times at bat did he get a hit?
    c. If he continues to hit at that rate, how many hits will he get in his next 100 times at bat?

13. Fred's sales goal for this week is $3392. But he has sold only $3004 worth of his product. Last year in the same week he sold $2434 of the product.
    a. What percent of his sales goal has Fred made?
    b. For the week, what percent of his sales last year are his sales this year? (Hint: Since he has sold more this year than last year, the answer must be greater than 100%.)

TIPS GAME

Players: 20 or more
Materials: Two 0–5 cubes, two 5–10 cubes
Object: To make the most money on tips

Rules

1. Each player is waiting on customers in a restaurant and will get 5 tips. 1 tip will be 10%, 3 tips will be 15%, and 1 tip will be 20%.

2. Roll all 4 cubes. Find the bill for 1 of the customers by making an amount of money in dollars and cents.

3. Decide which tip you'll get from this customer. Then calculate the tip. Keep a record of your tips.

4. After 5 rounds, add the tips.

5. The player with the most money from tips wins.

Sample Game

	Round 1	Round 2	Round 3	Round 4	Round 5
Kent rolled:	8 3 7 3	1 5 5 6	1 6 4 10	4 5 5 8	10 0 8 2
Kent made:	$87.33	$65.51	$106.41	$85.54	$108.20
Kent chose:	15%	15%	20%	10%	15%
Kent's tip:	$13.10	$9.83	$21.28	$8.55	$16.23
Claire rolled:	3 5 0 10	8 5 8 4	3 9 6 2	8 10 1 5	9 0 5 2
Claire made:	$105.30	$88.54	$96.32	$108.51	$95.20
Claire chose:	20%	15%	15%	15%	10%
Claire's tip:	$21.06	$13.28	$14.45	$16.28	$9.52

Kent's total was $68.99. Claire's total was $74.59. Claire was the winner.

Calculating Percents Quickly

Certain percents can be calculated or estimated without use of a calculator or pencil and paper.

Here are some hints for calculating some percents quickly.

10% of $28   (Multiply by 0.1) Move the decimal point 1 place to the left. Answer is 2.8, or $2.80.

1% of $28   (Multiply by 0.01) Move the decimal point 2 places to the left. Answer is 0.28, or $0.28, or 28¢.

You may have to round when doing this kind of calculation in real situations.

1% of $37.98	$0.3798, but should be rounded to $0.38, or 38¢.
20% of $39	Twice 10%. 10% is 3.9, and 20% is 7.8, or $7.80.
5% of $39	Half of 10%. Half of 3.9 is 1.95, or $1.95.
15% of $39	10% + 5%. 3.90 + 1.95 = $5.85.
$7\frac{1}{2}$% of $39	Half of 15%. 2.925, or $2.93 (maybe $2.92). Or $\frac{3}{4}$ of 10%. $\frac{3}{4}$ of 3.9 = 2.925.
18% of $39	20% − 2%. 7.80 − 0.78 = $7.02.
25%, 50%, or 75%	Take $\frac{1}{4}$, $\frac{1}{2}$, or $\frac{3}{4}$ of the number.

Do the following calculations in your head. Just write the answers. Round to the nearest cent. (Round up when there is no nearest cent.)

1. 10% of $36	9. 75% of $36	17. 2% of $47
2. 10% of $47	10. 50% of $47	18. 100% of $47
3. 5% of $36	11. 25% of $36	19. 100% of $37.84
4. 5% of $47	12. 2.5% of $36	20. 10% of $37.84
5. 15% of $36	13. 18% of $47	21. 1% of $37.84
6. 15% of $47	14. 5% of $19.98	22. 5% of $37.84
7. 20% of $47	15. 5% of $29.98	23. 15% of $37.84
8. $7\frac{1}{2}$% of $36	16. 5% of $39.98	24. 20% of $37.84

BIG SALE   ALL ITEMS SOLD AT 25% OFF MARKED PRICE

Sales tax is 6%. We round up whenever we get the chance.

1. How much would Thelma actually pay for the hat?
2. How much would Edna spend for the dress, the hat, and the shoes?
3. How much would Tom spend for the jacket, the slacks, and the shoes?
4. Make up 3 more problems from this advertisement. Find the answers to your problems. Then let a friend try to do your problems.
5. Look through the advertisements in your local paper. Find some that tell about sales or that show discounts. Make up some problems from those advertisements.

Play the Tips Game. Try to estimate who has won without actually doing the calculations.

Many people write checks to pay their bills. When you write a check, you are telling the bank to pay someone with money from your account. Checks differ somewhat in appearance, but they tend to be very similar.

Your bank will cash (or honor) your check only if you write the check correctly. The drawing below shows a typical check and the 5 parts that must be completed.

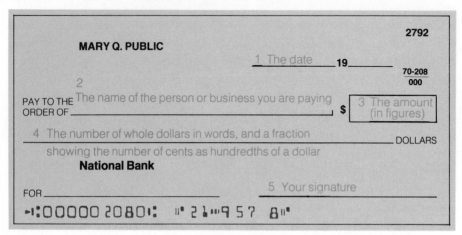

You may make a note in the space marked "FOR" to show what the payment was for. The strange looking numbers at the bottom are for use by the computer and include your account number and other information.

In writing the number of dollars in words, it is customary to use the word *and* between the dollars and cents (where the decimal point would be): For example, Two hundred twenty-five *and* $\frac{73}{100}$.

For problems 1–15 on page 187, write each of the amounts in words as you would on a check. If you are not sure how to spell a word or where to put a hyphen, use a dictionary.

Example: $1743.18

One thousand, seven hundred forty-three and $\frac{18}{100}$, or Seventeen hundred forty-three and $\frac{18}{100}$ (either answer is correct).

1. $73.15 4. $99.99 7. $7.04 10. $128.09 13. $1050.00
2. $26.84 5. $14.12 8. $1000 11. $1312.11 14. $1.42
3. $47.71 6. $100.00* 9. $50 12. $1415.16 15. $67.89

For problems 16–24, write the 5 pieces of information needed for correctly writing a check. Use today's date and sign your name.

Example: $77.84 to Mabel's Telephone Co. If the date today were 29 February 1984, you would write:

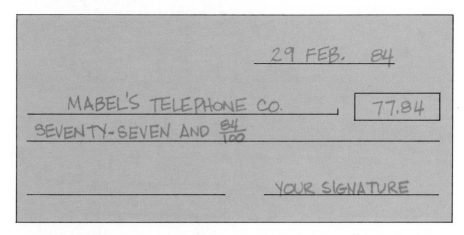

16. $247.81 to Beansprout Natural Gas Co.
17. $1000 to Thrifty Savings and Loan Corp.
18. $74.06 to Semi-Bright Electric Co.
19. $47.16 to Peabody's Department Store
20. $60 to Jonas K. Marshall, M.D.
21. $143.17 to Shortrisk Insurance Co.
22. $40 to Richard C. Winnoker
23. $90 to Tammy R. Smith
24. $50 to get cash from the bank (Usually people write "cash" in the name blank.)

25. Choose amounts between $1 and $2000 and write checks to 5 people you know.

*Hint: We usually write amounts under 10¢ as 2 digits: $\frac{00}{100}$ (or $\frac{no}{100}$, but not $\frac{0}{100}$), $\frac{04}{100}$ (not $\frac{4}{100}$), and so on.

Checking Accounts

People with checking accounts keep records of the number of each check, the date, the person to whom the check was made, and the amount of the check. They subtract the amount of each check from the balance and add the amount of any deposit in order to know how much money is in the account at any time. Different forms are used for check records. A typical form is shown here.

BE SURE TO DEDUCT ANY PER ITEM CHARGES, SERVICE CHARGES, OR FEES THAT MAY APPLY.

NUMBER	DATE	TRANSACTION DESCRIPTION	(+ OR −) OTHER	✓ T	(+) AMOUNT OF DEPOSIT	(−) AMOUNT OF PAYMENT OR WITHDRAWAL	BALANCE FORWARD 528 64
765	11/20	THIRD FEDERAL SAVINGS & LOAN (MORTGAGE)				348 15	348 15 / 180 49
766	11/30	LONGRISK INSURANCE CO. (HOUSE INSURANCE)				117 44	117 44 / 63 05
767	12/1	CASH			2145 60 (MONTHLY SALARY)	100 00	+2045 60 / 2108 65
768	12/1	BEANSPROUT NATURAL GAS CO.				162 55	162 55 / 1946 10
769	12/1	JONAS K. MARSHALL, M.D. (OFFICE VISIT. NOV.10)				45 00	45 00 / 1901 10
770	12/3	SEMI-BRIGHT ELECTRIC CO.				72 45	72 45 / 1828 65
771	12/8	PEABODY'S DEPARTMENT STORE (GIFTS)				229 74	229 74 / 1598 91
772	12/10	REMARKABLE CREDIT CARD CO.				315 80	315 80 / 1283 11
773	12/15	CASH				200 00	200 00 / 1083 11
774	12/15	PHILUP BAKERY			40 00 (FROM DICK W.)	43 81	3 81 / 1079 30
775	12/18	FANDANGLE DECORATIONS				37 84	37 84 / 1031 56

REMEMBER TO RECORD ALL DEPOSITS AND WITHDRAWALS AS WELL AS PRE-AUTHORIZED TRANSACTIONS.

Do these problems. Use a calculator.

1. What is the total of payments between 20 November and 18 December?

2. What is the total of the deposits in that time?

3. Add the deposits to the original balance ($528.64) and subtract from that sum the total payments. Do you get the final balance ($1031.56)? Should you?

4. Find the error or errors in the record shown here.

Once a month, most banks send their checking account customers a statement for the month. This includes the checks that have been cashed and other records that help to identify and correct errors. A monthly statement covering the checks listed in the record on page 188 might look like this:

DATE	CHECKS			DEPOSITS	BALANCE
11/21	BEGINNING BALANCE				528.64
11/24	348.15				180.49
12/2	117.44	100.00		2145.60	2108.65
12/5	162.55	72.45			1873.65
12/15	229.74	315.80		40.00	1168.11
	200.00				
12/20	37.84				1130.27

BALANCE LAST STATEMENT	NO. OF CHECKS	TOTAL AMOUNT OF CHECKS	NO. OF DEPOSITS	TOTAL AMOUNT OF DEPOSITS	BALANCE THIS STATEMENT
528.64	9	1583.97	2	2185.60	1130.27

Do these problems. Use a calculator.

5. Does the bank write the month or the day of the month first?

6. Why do the dates listed by the bank sometimes differ from the records on page 188?

7. Which 2 checks that were written have not yet been cashed? Give the number, the date, the person to whom it was written, and the amount.

8. In order to "balance the checkbook," compare the balance in the checkbook (page 188) with the closing balance shown by the bank. How would you handle the 2 checks that were not cashed? Do the arithmetic. Does the checkbook balance? If not, why not?

Ms. Welty's last gas bill looked something like this:

				Billing Period		Next
				From	To	Reading
				11/16/85	12/15/85	1/15/86

PREVIOUS READING	CURRENT READING	BILLING DATE	METER NUMBER			
340	372	12/22/85	302594	PREVIOUS BALANCE		39.78
(100 CU FT)				PAYMENT		39.78
				BALANCE FORWARD		00.00
				GAS AMOUNT		31.66
ACCOUNT NUMBER 2191 00400				AMOUNT DUE		31.66

1. How many cubic feet of gas were used during the billing period?

2. About how much did the gas company charge for each cubic foot of gas?

3. When was the meter to be read again?

On the day for the meter to be read, Ms. Welty looked at the meter. It looked like this:

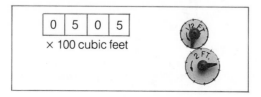

4. How many cubic feet of gas were used since the last bill?

5. About how much will she owe the gas company for that?

6. The pointers on the 2 dials spin around very quickly. Which one do you think turns more quickly?

7. If the "half-foot" pointer makes a complete circle (turns 360°), how far would you expect the "two-foot" pointer to turn?

8. How many times would you expect the "two-foot" pointer to make a complete circle between the time the meter first reads 0505 and the time it first reads 0506?

Mr. and Mrs. Pothier's last electricity bill looked something like this:

	BILLING	PERIOD		METER	READING	KILOWATT
METER #	FROM	TO	DAYS	PREVIOUS	CURRENT	HOURS USED
47006670	AUG 16	SEPT 15	30	81476	82884	1408

```
SERVICE CHARGE                                    7.350000
ENERGY CHARGE        1408 x 0.075200            105.881600
FUEL ADJUSTMENT      1408 x 0.002710 CR           3.815680 CR
GU ADJUSTMENT        1408 x 0.001230 CR           1.731840 CR
OC ADJUSTMENT        1408 x 0.000376              0.529408
                                              $108.213488

NEXT READING ON/ABOUT OCT 14    AMOUNT NOW DUE $108.21
```

On October 14, Mrs. Pothier looked at the electricity meter. It looked like this:

9. If Mrs. Pothier had not used any electricity at all for 1 month, what would she be charged?

10. The rate for adjustments depends on the cost of fuel and other factors. What effect did the 3 adjustments, taken together, have on the bill this month?

11. From looking at the drawing of the meter, determine what the reading was on October 14.

12. How much electricity was used between September 15 and October 15?

13. About what do you think the bill is likely to be for the period September 15 to October 15? Explain how you got your answer.

14. Find the utility meters for your apartment, house, or school. Try to read them. Draw pictures that show what they look like and write your reading below the picture.

Manufacturers of food products are required to list all the ingredients of a product on its package in the order of the amount used, from greatest to smallest. For example, if the ingredients were listed as flour, sugar, butter, vanilla, and salt, you would know that there is at least as much flour as any other 1 ingredient, at least as much sugar as butter, and so on.

It is interesting to try to analyze a list of ingredients to see how much of each ingredient there might be. Since many people like to avoid eating too much sugar, a way to decide what the greatest percentage of sugar might be in a product is useful to know. Because a little salt goes a long way, you can usually assume that there is very little of any ingredient that comes after salt on the list.

Work in groups to discuss and answer both parts of this question. Look up ingredients you aren't sure of in a dictionary. For sugar, count honey, molasses, corn syrup, corn sweetener, and anything else that the dictionary says is a form of sugar.

How much sugar might there be in these products:

Fitness Flakes:

Wheat, rye, barley and oat flour; corn syrup; sugar; malt; salt; artificial flavor.

Goodness Granola Bars:

Granola (rolled oats, brown sugar, coconut oil, honey, sesame seeds, salt, soy lecithin, natural flavor), sugar, nonfat milk, malto dextrin, dextrose, coconut oil, whey, salt, soy lecithin, natural flavor.

After you work out an answer, read the explanation on page 193.

The list of ingredients for Fitness Flakes seems to allow the possibility that almost 67% $\left(\text{or } \frac{2}{3}\right)$ of the cereal is sugar (or corn syrup). Even though there are apparently 4 kinds of flour, the first ingredient is flour, not wheat flour. The manufacturer has apparently tried to give the impression that there is at least 4 times as much flour as corn syrup and sugar, even though it is possible that all the flour together is scarcely more than the amount of corn syrup.

An extreme interpretation of the Goodness Granola Bar ingredients could allow you to argue that there is almost 70% sugar in one of these granola bars. The granola itself has brown sugar and honey listed among the first 4 ingredients, so it could be almost $\frac{1}{2}$ sugar. The first 5 ingredients of the granola bar are Granola, sugar, nonfat milk, malto dextrin, and dextrose. The last 2 are forms of sugar. Of the first 5 ingredients, 3 are sugar and 1 might be $\frac{1}{2}$ sugar, so it is possible for the bars to be 70% sugar. In fact, there are quite a few sesame seeds in the granola and probably quite a bit of coconut oil in the bar, but there could easily be 40% sugar in the granola and more than 50% sugar in the granola bars.

Now do these problems on your own.

1. Determine from the ingredients listed what the greatest possible percentage of sugar could be in each of the following packaged products.
   a. Strawberry Preserves: strawberries, sugar, corn syrup, fruit pectin, citric acid.
   b. Mint Jelly with Mint Leaves: apple juice, corn sweetener, sugar, fruit pectin, citric acid, mint leaves, sodium citrate, mint flavoring, and artificial color.
   c. Pears: pears, water, sugar, corn sweetener.
   d. Creamy Yogurt-Garlic Salad Dressing: nonfat yogurt, corn syrup, water, soybean oil, distilled vinegar, sugar, salt, food starch, egg yolks, natural flavors, xanthan gum, artificial color, polysorbate 60, red bell pepper, potassium sorbate, spices, disodium EDTA.

2. Do you think there is any garlic in the dressing listed in problem 1d? If so, under which ingredient do you think it is?

3. Copy the lists of ingredients from 5 different packaged foods. Look up in a dictionary any ingredient you don't recognize. Decide what the greatest and smallest percentages of various kinds of ingredients (such as meat, sugar, starch, vegetable oil, flavorings, colors, preservatives, and so on) might be.

Do these problems.

1. 5% of $4400
2. 10% of $4400
3. 15% of $4400
4. 20% of $4400
5. 50% of $4400

6. 50% of 440
7. 5% of 880
8. 5% of 1320
9. 5% of 1760
10. 25% of $11,000

11. 25% of $1100
12. 25% of $110
13. 25% of $11
14. 1% of $17.68
15. 2% of $17.68

16. 5% of $17.68
17. 10% of $17.68
18. 50% of $17.68
19. 50% of 12,358
20. 25% of 12,358

21. 12.5% of 12,358
22. 6.25% of 12,358
23. 3% of 300
24. 3% of 330
25. 3% of 333

26. 4% of 1200
27. 4% of 1212
28. 4% of 2424
29. 4% of 4848
30. 4% of 9696

31. 10% of 92,000
32. 11% of 92,000
33. 12% of 92,000
34. 22% of 92,000
35. 20% of 5000

36. 21% of 5000
37. 19% of 5000
38. 50% of 5000
39. 0.5% of $100
40. 0.5% of $110

41. 0.5% of $200
42. 1% of $100
43. 1% of $110
44. 1.5% of $100
45. 1.5% of $110

46. $66\frac{2}{3}$% of $300
47. $33\frac{1}{3}$% of $300
48. 30% of $300
49. 75% of $300
50. 50% of $500

Sometimes you can use mathematical thinking to help when you are taking a test. If you are taking a multiple-choice test and you don't know the answer to a question, you have to decide whether to guess. To do this, think about the penalty for making a wrong guess. In many multiple-choice tests, extra points are taken off for each wrong answer.

[1] Suppose there are 5 possible answers listed for each question and only 1 is correct. What fraction of a point should be taken off for a wrong answer? Discuss this question with other students.

[2] If there are 60 questions on the test and you guess randomly at all 60 questions, about how many would you expect to get right by chance? Would you expect to get $\frac{4}{5}$ of 60, or 48, wrong?

[3] If you *did* guess randomly at all the questions on the test, would zero be a fair grade for you on the test?

[4] Does your answer to the first discussion question produce a test score of zero for 12 right and 48 wrong? If not, try again.

[5] Suppose you are taking a 60-item test on which there are 5 choices for each question. You are able to decide for sure that 2 of the answers are wrong for each question but can't decide which of the other 3 answers is correct. Should you guess if the grade is determined by the formula $G = R - \frac{1}{4}W$, where G is the grade, R is the number right, and W is the number wrong?

[6] In the fifth discussion question, about how many correct answers would you expect to get if you guessed randomly from among the 3 possibly correct answers for each item? About what would your final score be? Is that better than the 0 you would get if you didn't guess at all?

Do these problems.

1. Abraham guessed randomly among the 4 possible alternatives on a 60-item multiple-choice test.

   a. What fraction of the problems would you expect him to get right?

   b. How many of the 60 problems would you expect him to get right?

c. What is a fair formula for giving a grade on the test if R stands for the number of correct answers and W stands for the number of wrong answers?

2. On a 100-item multiple-choice test, each item has 4 alternatives.
   a. What is a fair formula for grading the test?
   b. Does the number of questions make a difference in the formula?

3. If there are 3 choices on each item of a multiple-choice test, what is a fair formula for assigning grades?

4. On a true-false test, what is a fair formula for calculating grades?

For problems 5 and 6, use the appropriate grading formula from problems 1–4 and the discussion questions on page 196.

5. On a 100-item, 5-choice test, Maxwell was able to eliminate 1 choice for each item, and he guessed randomly among the other 4. About what would you expect his final grade on the test to be if the appropriate grading formula is used?

6. Wanda took a 10-item true-false test and guessed randomly at all 10 answers.
   a. About how many correct answers would she expect to get?
   b. Would you be surprised if she didn't get exactly 5 right answers?
   c. What is the probability that she would get all 10 correct? (See chapter 1 if you have trouble with this problem.)
   d. What is the probability that she would get all 10 wrong?
   e. What is the probability that she would get a grade of exactly 1 (using the proper grading formula)?
   f. What is the probability that she would get a grade of 1 or −1?

People who make up multiple-choice tests sometimes follow procedures that allow people who take the tests to guess intelligently, even if they know nothing about the subject matter. Not everyone who makes up tests does these things, so if you want to do very well on a test, you should look at other tests made by the same test maker. Only if you do this should you try to use any of the following ideas on an important test. It is always much better to have the expected knowledge when you take a test.

Here are some ideas to consider if you find that you must guess on a test.

A. On social science, language, and other items with word answers, longer answers tend to be correct more often than shorter answers because more explanation is often needed to be correct.

B. Grammatically incorrect answers are likely to be wrong. Such answers often result when the test maker has forgotten precisely how the question was asked.

C. Correct numerical answers for nonmathematics items may be near the middle of the given answers because the test maker tends to cluster the listed answers around the correct answer to avoid having to list obviously wrong answers. For example, if the possible answers are a. 1810, b. 1750, c. 1812, d. 1815, and e. 1848, probably a, c, or d is correct, and c seems most likely.

D. The answer "none of the above" is seldom correct, but this matter depends on the test maker. It is best to check other tests written by the test maker before choosing this answer.

E. On mathematics questions, the correct answer is likely to be 1 of several answers that are similar mathematically. (Wrong answers are often derived by making just 1 error in the derivation.) For example, if 3 answers have square root symbols ($\sqrt{}$) and 2 do not, the right answer probably has a square root symbol. If 3 have fractions and 2 do not, the correct answer probably has a fraction.

1. Use suggestions A–E on page 198 as you take the following test. Only the answers are given. Choose the correct answer. If 2 answers seem equally likely, list both and circle the one you would choose on a test.

   1. . . .
      a. be unconcerned with what is happening around him.
      b. be continually aroused by wrongs.
      c. slight the work of writing.
      d. welcome aggression.
      e. accept criticism gladly.

   2. . . . means
      a. "Many times the coward is almost caught in his misdeeds."
      b. "The coward is frequently seriously ill."
      c. "The coward's frequent fears are often as bad as death."
      d. "Cowards many times wish they were dead."
      e. "The coward has several lines."

   3. . . . is inclined to
      a. cooperation with each other.   d. fight.
      b. be forgetful much of the time.   e. trust.
      c. believe in their immortality.

   4. . . .
      a. $\frac{\sqrt{3}}{2}$ b. $\frac{3}{2}$ c. $\sqrt{2}$ d. $\sqrt{3}$ e. $\frac{2}{3}$

   5. . . .
      a. 1   b. $1\frac{1}{3}$ c. $1\frac{2}{3}$ d. 2   e. $\frac{2}{3}$

   6. . . .
      a. $\frac{1}{3}$ b. $\frac{1}{9}$ c. 27   d. 3   e. 9

   7. . . .
      a. $\frac{1}{7}$ b. $\frac{1}{5}$ c. $\frac{1}{3}$ d. $\frac{2}{3}$ e. $\frac{4}{5}$

2. Analyze a test from a magazine or other source to see if suggestions A–E on page 198 work for the test. If you get a better score using the suggestions than if you just guessed randomly, then the suggestions work.

Blue Ribbon Taxi

Rates

90¢, plus 10¢ for each 1/10 of a kilometer or part thereof
Luggage: 25¢ per bag
Rates apply 24 hours per day.

Red Ribbon Taxi

Rates

$2.00, plus 10¢ for each kilometer or part thereof
(Rates apply within the city limits only.)
More than 3 people: 50¢ surcharge
Night rates: $2.00 surcharge 8:00 P.M. to 6:00 A.M.

Use the information on this page. Work in small groups to solve
and discuss the following problems.

1. Which taxi company would be less expensive for a group of 4
   traveling 10 kilometers at 9:00 P.M.?

2. Mr. Marks wants a taxi to take him to the airport, which is 30
   kilometers from his house. He has a 4:00 P.M. flight, and he has
   4 pieces of luggage. Which taxi company would be less
   expensive?

3. Tina and Ron want to see a movie in the city. The movie
   begins at 7:00 P.M. They live 1 kilometer away. Which taxi
   should they choose to take them there? Should they choose the
   same one to come home?

4. Three business people need to go to the train station downtown. The train leaves at 8:00 P.M. Their hotel is 3 kilometers from the station. Which company would be less expensive?

5. Is there a distance for which both companies would charge the same amount during the day? (Hint: Make a chart comparing the 2 companies for given distances from less than 1 kilometer to 20 kilometers.)

6. How does the comparison in problem 5 change if passengers are traveling at night?

7. Within what range of distances are the companies competitive with each other?

8. Why does Red Ribbon Taxi have different rates for driving outside the city limits?

9. Jake Smith is a taxi driver for the Blue Ribbon Taxi Company. He gets a percentage of the fares. Here is a section from his order book for 1 evening.

   a. Complete his list of fares.

Time	Number of People	Distance Traveled (km)	Luggage	Fare
7:30 P.M.	2	1.5	–	
7:42	4	2.7	–	
7:51	1	1.8	2	
8:02	3	1.2	–	
8:15	2	1.4	4	

   b. Would Jake have made more money working for the Red Ribbon Taxi Company if he had the same entries in his order book?

1. Yolanda has a choice of 2 jobs. For 1 she would be paid $6 per hour for 40 hours' work each week and she would get time-and-a-half for overtime work. For the other job she would be paid $300 per week. She expects to work about 45 hours a week in either job.

   a. In which job would she make more money per week?

   b. How much more?

2. Sylvester has accepted a job in which he will work 40 hours per week and will get 2 weeks of yearly vacation with pay. He will be paid the fair amount on Friday of every second week. Which of the following systems of payment would give him the most money?

   a. $7 per hour   **c.** $280 per week   **e.** $14,400 per year

   b. $56 per day   **d.** $1215 per month

3. Miss Sohm's bill in a restaurant comes to $48. She wants to leave a 15% tip. How much should she leave for the tip?

4. What will a $140 coat cost when it is on sale for 20% off? (There is no sales tax.)

5. What will a $140 coat cost with a 5% sales tax?

6. What will a $140 coat cost when it is on sale for 20% off and there is a 5% sales tax?

7. What is 100% of $873.56?

8. What (to the nearest cent) is 1% of $873.56?

9. Write each of the following amounts in words as you would on a check. Remember to write the number of cents as a fraction of a dollar.

   a. $73.00   **b.** $54.71   **c.** $40.00   **d.** $14.75   **e.** $2576.07

10. Last month when the meter reader came, Mr. Ahonian's gas meter showed | 0 | 7 | 4 | 2 | × 100 cubic feet. This month, it showed | 0 | 7 | 9 | 1 | × 100 cubic feet. The company charges Mr. Ahonian about $1.50 per 100 cubic feet of gas used and a $10.00 service charge. About how much will his gas bill be?

11. What is a fair grading formula on a multiple-choice test in which

    a. each item has 4 possible answers listed?

    b. each item has 10 possible answers listed?

    c. each item is a true-false question?

12. Marta took a 5-item true-false test. A fair formula was used for grading.

    a. What are the possible scores she can get?

    b. What is the probability that her final grade on the test will be exactly 0 if she guessed randomly at all 5 questions?

1. Hank has a choice of 2 jobs. For 1 he would be paid $8 per hour for 40 hours' work each week and he would get time-and-a-half for overtime work. For the other job he would be paid $400 per week. He expects to work about 48 hours a week in either job.

   a. In which job would he make more money per week?

   b. How much more?

2. Harriet has accepted a job in which she will work 40 hours per week and will get 2 weeks of yearly vacation with pay. She will be paid the fair amount on Friday of every second week. Which of the following systems of payment would give her the most money?

   a. $9 per hour   **c.** $360 per week   **e.** $18,700 per year
   b. $75 per day   **d.** $1560 per month

3. Ms. Hayakawa's bill in a restaurant comes to $42. She wants to leave a 15% tip. How much should she leave for the tip?

4. What will a $180 stereo cost when it is on sale for 20% off? (There is no sales tax.)

5. What will a $180 stereo cost with a 5% sales tax?

6. What will a $180 stereo cost when it is on sale for 20% off and there is a 5% sales tax?

7. What is 10% of $975.42?

8. What (to the nearest cent) is 1% of $975.42?

9. Write each of the following amounts in words as you would on a check. Remember to write the number of cents as a fraction of a dollar.

   a. $62.00   **b.** $43.60   **c.** $20.00   **d.** $25.86   **e.** $3467.03

10. Last month when the meter reader came, Mr. Burton's gas meter showed | 0 | 6 | 3 | 1 | × 100 cubic feet. This month, it showed | 0 | 6 | 9 | 9 | × 100 cubic feet. The company charges Mr. Burton about $2.00 per 100 cubic feet of gas used and an $8.00 service charge. About how much will his gas bill be?

11. What is a fair grading formula on a multiple-choice test in which
    a. each item has 5 possible answers listed?
    b. each item has 8 possible answers listed?
    c. each item is a true-false question?

12. Carlo took an 8-item true-false test. A fair formula was used for grading.
    a. What are the possible scores he can get?
    b. What is the probability that his final grade on the test will be exactly 1 if he guessed randomly at all 8 questions?

A group of 6 monkeys had collected a pile of coconuts. The monkeys agreed to take turns guarding them so that they would not be stolen.

The first monkey to stand guard stole half the coconuts and threw 1 of the remaining coconuts into the ocean. The second monkey to stand guard did the same—stole half the coconuts that were left and threw 1 of the remaining coconuts into the ocean. The third, fourth, and fifth monkeys did likewise. When the sixth monkey came to take its turn at standing guard, it found that there was only 1 coconut left.

1. How many coconuts were there to start with? See if you can find 1 of the problem-solving strategies that applies to this problem. If you find you can't get anywhere with the problem, ask your teacher to suggest a strategy.

2. Once you have solved the problem, try solving this variation of it. See how much faster you can solve a problem once you have a method of going at it! This problem is the same as the preceding one except that each monkey throws 1 coconut in the ocean *before* removing half the coconuts. How many coconuts were there to start with?

The first of these problems can be done simply by thinking about it. For the other, you will probably need to use a calculator or a computer.

1. Use the digits 0, 1, 2, . . ., 9 once and only once each to make several numbers. Can you arrange these numbers so that the sum is 100?

2. Some numbers are divisible by the sum of their digits. Here are some examples:

Number	Sum of Digits	Number ÷ Sum of Digits
27	9	3
84	12	7
42	6	7
54	9	6

   a. How many 2-digit numbers are divisible by the sum of their digits?

   b. How many 3-digit numbers are divisible by the sum of their digits?

   c. How many 4-digit numbers are divisible by the sum of their digits?

CHAPTER 7

FUNCTIONS AND GRAPHING

ALGEBRA

Words come into our language by the strangest routes. The origin of the word *algebra* is a good example.

In Baghdad about A.D. 825, an Arab mathematician named Mohammed ibn-Musa al-Khowarizmi wrote a book on equations with the title *Hisab al-jabr w'al-muqabalah*. Understandably, this title was shortened to *Al-jabr*. When the book was later translated into Latin, it became *Algebra*. There is some dispute concerning the meaning of the original Arabic title. Most scholars do agree that it can be translated as "the science of reunion and opposition," referring to the method of solving an equation by subtracting the same thing from both sides of the equation and putting together what is left. An additional sidelight about the word *algebra* is that the Spanish word for a person who sets broken bones (reunites them) is *algebrista*, which comes from the same Arabic root word.

The earliest known manuscript that deals with algebraic equations is called the Rhind Papyrus and dates from 1700–1600 B.C. This scroll presents a trial-and-error method for solving equations with such practical examples as finding the volume of a round storage silo.

Cuneiform tablets provide evidence that the Babylonians knew some of the principles of algebra, and documents from India show that Hindu mathematicians also used this knowledge. The ancient Greeks were interested mainly in geometry, but they used geometric drawings to make "pictures" of the solutions to certain equations. For example, the idea of the square root was symbolized by the diagonal of a square.

During the Dark Ages in Europe, much of the knowledge of the Greeks about mathematics was lost. The Arab world, however, translated Greek mathematical books into its own language and thereby preserved ideas about algebra that otherwise would have been lost. The Arabs also knew of the work that had been done in India and other parts of Asia. One of the Arabs' most important contributions was the introduction of the Hindu symbols for numbers, which were much easier to use than the clumsy Roman numerals. (These symbols are now commonly called Arabic numerals, even though they originated in India.)

Knowledge of algebra came back to Europe with the translation into Latin of al-Khowarizmi's book. Mathematicians began to use the Hindu-Arabic symbols, and the invention of movable type and the printing press made mathematical information much more available. The increase in trade and travel also made the exchange of ideas easier, and for these reasons, knowledge of algebra flourished.

It took a long time for algebraic notation to develop into the system we use today. For example, the equals sign (=) was introduced only in 1557. And each mathematician had his own peculiar ways of writing equations. In Italy, in the 1500s, you might have seen an equation written like this: I. p. $\overset{6}{8}$ Eguale à 20. In modern notation, this would be: $x^6 + 8x^3 = 20$.

By the end of the seventeenth century, the knowledge of elementary algebra was complete, and mathematicians began to investigate other, more advanced systems.

Graphing

Audrey's parents measured her height every year on her birthday, starting when she was 2 years old. Here are their measurements:

Age (years)	Height (cm)
2	85
3	94
4	102
5	109
6	115
7	120
8	125
9	132
10	140
11	146
12	152
13	159
14	162
15	163
16	163

Audrey graphed the measurements. She plotted her age in years along the horizontal axis of the graph and her height along the vertical axis. She had to choose her scale of measurements carefully so that all the points would fit on her graph.

Here is Audrey's graph.

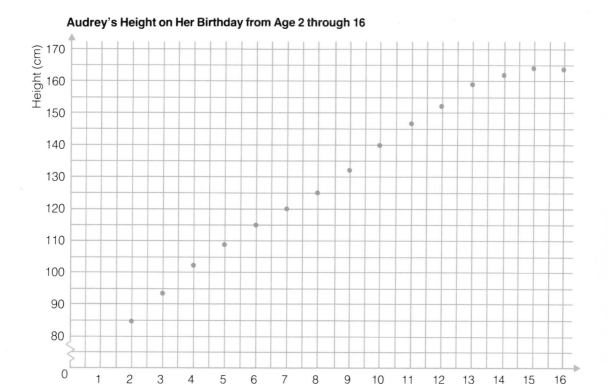

Audrey's Height on Her Birthday from Age 2 through 16

An *axis* of a graph is a line with measurements indicated on it that is used for reference. The plural of axis is axes (pronounced ak'sēz).

The broken line in the height axis between 0 and 80 shows that numbers for some measurements are left out. Look carefully at the graph. Notice that each axis, and the graph itself, is labeled.

1. Copy the graph on page 213, including the labels and the broken height axis.

2. Audrey measured herself when she was $10\frac{1}{2}$ years old and decided that she was 54 centimeters tall.

   a. Do you think she was right?

   b. Why?

   c. What mistake might she have made?

3. On your graph, draw a straight line from the point showing Audrey's height when she was 2 to the point for her height at age 13. Are most of the dots close to that line?

4. When Audrey was 13 she drew a line like the one you have just drawn. Then she used that line to try to predict how tall she'd be when she was 17 years old. She guessed that she would be 188 centimeters tall.

   a. Does this seem reasonable?

   b. Explain your answer.

5. Terry's parents measured his height every year on his birthday too. Here are their measurements.

Age (years)	Height (cm)
2	90
3	96
4	104
5	111
6	116
7	122
8	129
9	135
10	140
11	147
12	156
13	165
14	171
15	175
16	179
17	180
18	180

a. Make a graph showing Terry's height on his birthday from age 2 through age 18.

b. Draw as smooth a line as you can connecting the points of your graph. Does the line you drew look reasonably straight for most of its length? About when does it appear to stop being reasonably straight?

c. Terry measured himself when he was $12\frac{1}{2}$ and decided that he was 164 cm tall. Put a point on your graph to show that measurement. Does the point fall on or very near the line you have just drawn? Do you think Terry measured correctly?

d. When Terry was $14\frac{1}{2}$ he measured his height as 173 cm. Put this point on your graph. Is it on or very near your line? Do you think Terry measured correctly?

1. Audrey and Terry (and their parents) kept records of their weights in kilograms on their birthdays. Sometimes they weighed themselves between birthdays as well. Then they wrote their ages as mixed numbers. These are their records.

Terry

Audrey

Audrey		Terry	
Age (years)	Weight (kg)	Age (years)	Weight (kg)
2	11	2	12
3	15	3	14
4	16	4	17
5	16	5	17
6	19	6	17
7	24	6½	20
8	26	7	25
9	28	8	29
10	30	8½	30
11	35	8¾	32
12	40	9	31
12½	39	10	36
13	41	11	40
13½	47	11½	44
14	51	12	49
14½	49	13	55
15	53	14	61
16	55	15	67
16½	52	16	72
17	53	17	75

a. Make a graph of Audrey's weight.
b. Make a graph of Terry's weight.
c. Look at the weight Audrey recorded for age 12½.
   Can this be correct? Explain. Compare your answer for this question with your answer to problem 2 on page 214.
d. About how much do you think Audrey will weigh when she is 20? How confident are you that your guess will be within 2 or 3 kilograms of her actual weight?

e. About how much do you think Terry will weigh when he's 20? How confident are you that your guess will be within 2 or 3 kilograms of his actual weight?

f. Discuss any differences in your confidence in parts d and e.

2. Kuo-bing rode her bicycle for 6 hours. She kept a record of how many kilometers the odometer showed at the end of each hour.

time (hr)	0	1	2	3	4	5	6
distance (km)	0	18	37	55	72	89	108

a. Make a graph for these distances and times.

b. Describe the graph in part a.

c. About how many kilometers per hour was Kuo-bing traveling?

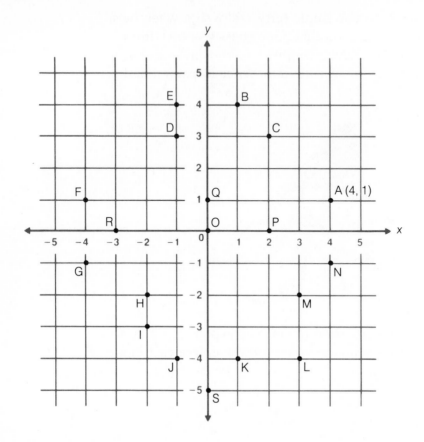

We often graph functions to help us get a better picture of the function. In the graph on page 213, Audrey's height is a function of her age. Some functions have graphs that are common geometric figures. The simplest of these are straight lines. Others have more complicated graphs. In this chapter we will study some functions and their graphs.

Function rules often involve 2 variables. 1 variable is an independent variable. We can give it any reasonable value we choose. The other variable is called a dependent variable because its value depends on the value of the independent variable. Any letters or symbols can be used for variables. We often use x for the independent variable and y for the dependent variable.

We usually agree to plot the independent variable, or x, sideways and the dependent variable, or y, up or down. When we draw the axes for a graph, we label the horizontal axis x or whatever we are calling the independent variable, and we label the vertical axis y or whatever we are calling the dependent variable. The point where the axes cross is called the *origin*.

We also usually write the value of x (the *x-coordinate*) first and the value of y (the *y-coordinate*) second. So, the ordered pair of numbers (4, 1) locates the point where $x = 4$ and $y = 1$. This point is 4 steps to the right of the *origin* and 1 step up. It is point A on the graph on page 218. M is 3 steps to the right and 2 steps down, or (3, −2), I is (−2, −3), and so on.

Use the graph on page 218 to answer these questions.

1. What are the coordinates of the origin?
2. Give the coordinates of each of the following points: A, B, E, F, G, J, K, N.
3. Name the point for each of the following coordinates: (4, 1), (1, 4), (2, 3) (−1, 4), (−1, 3), (−4, 1), (−1, −4), (−2, −3), (−2, −2), (3, −4), (3, −2), (2, 0), (0, 1), (−3, 0), (0, −5).

GET THE POINT

Players: 2
Materials: Graph paper, crayons or markers (4 colors), black pen or pencil
Object: To find the coordinates of the secret point

Rules

1. Decide what size "playing field" will be used. Each player makes a playing field by drawing coordinate axes on a sheet of graph paper.

2. The first player chooses a secret point with integer coordinates and draws 2 straight lines through the point, at 45° angles to the axes. (See the sample game.) This separates the playing field into 4 parts. The first player then colors each of the 4 parts a different color.

3. Without seeing what the first player has done, the second player guesses a point by calling out its coordinates. Then the first player tells the color of that point. A point on 1 of the 2 dividing lines is described as black.

4. The second player keeps guessing points until he or she gets the secret point.

Sample Game

Lynda and Stuart decided on a playing field that goes from −5 to 5 on each axis. Lynda was the first player. She chose (3, −2) as the secret point, drew 2 lines, and colored the sections as shown.

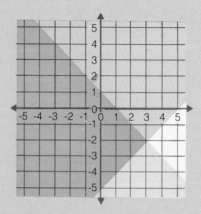

Stuart made a playing field just like Lynda's but without the lines and colors. On his field, Stuart kept a record of each move.

A. Stuart said, "(0, 0)." Lynda said, "Red." Stuart circled the point (0, 0) in red.

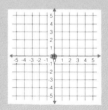

B. Stuart said, "(1, 1)." Lynda said, "Green." Stuart circled the point (1, 1) in green. He knew there was a line between (0, 0) and (1, 1). He drew this line so that he could remember where it was.

C. Stuart said, "(4, −2)." Lynda said, "Yellow." Stuart circled that point in yellow. Then he knew that the other line lay between (1, 1) and (4, −2).

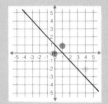

D. Stuart said, "(2, 0)." Lynda said, "Green." Stuart circled that point in green. Then he knew that the other line was between (2, 0) and (4, −2).

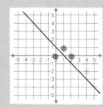

E. Stuart said, "(4, −1)." Lynda said, "Black." Stuart circled that point in black. Then he knew where the line was. He drew it to find the point where the 2 lines intersected.

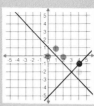

F. Stuart said, "(3, −2)." Lynda said, "That's the point I chose. You got it in 6 moves."

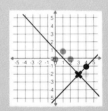

Coordinates as a Code

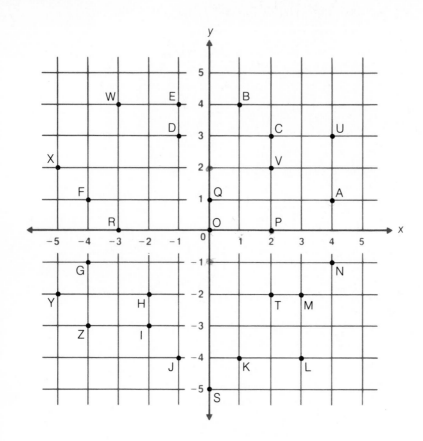

Use the graph on this page. Find the labeled point for each pair of coordinates to decipher the messages below.

1. (3, −2)(4, 1)(2, −2)(−2, −2), (−1, 4)(3, −2)(4, 1)(2, −2)(−2, −3)(2, 3)(0, −5)
   (−2, −3)(0, −5)
   (4, 3)(0, −5)(−1, 4)(−4, 1)(4, 3)(3, −4).

2. (2, −2)(−2, −2)(0, 0)(0, −5)(−1, 4)
   (−3, 4)(−2, −2)(0, 0)
   (−1, 3)(−2, −3)(0, −5)(−3, 0)(−1, 4)(−4, −1)(4, 1)(−3, 0)(−1, 3)
   (2, −2)(−2, −2)(−1, 4)
   (2, 0)(4, 1)(0, −5)(2, −2)
   (4, 1)(−3, 0)(−1, 4)
   (1, 4)(0, 0)(4, 3)(4, −1)(−1, 3)
   (2, −2)(0, 0)
   (−3, 0)(−1, 4)(2, 0)(−1, 4)(4, 1)(2, −2)
   (−2, −3)(2, −2).

3. (3, −2)(−5, −2)
   (−4, 1)(−3, 0)(−2, −3)(−1, 4)(4, −1)(−1, 3)(0, −5)
   (−3, 4)(−1, 4)
   (−2, −2)(4, 1)(2, 2)(−1, 4)
   (4, −1)(0, 0)(2, −2)(−2, −2)(−2, −3)(4, −1)(−4, −1)
   (2, −2)(0, 0)
   (−4, 1)(−1, 4)(4, 1)(−3, 0)
   (1, 4)(4, 3)(2, −2)
   (−4, 1)(−1, 4)(4, 1)(−3, 0)
   (−2, −3)(2, −2)(0, −5)(−1, 4)(3, −4)(−4, 1).
   —(−4, 1).
   (−1, 3).
   (−3, 0)(0, 0)(0, 0)(0, −5)(−1, 4)(2, 2)(−1, 4)(3, −4)(2, −2).

4. Make up your own messages and trade with other students.

KEEPING SHARP SIGNED NUMBERS

Solve for n.

1. $9 + 6 = n$
2. $9 - 6 = n$
3. $-9 + 6 = n$
4. $-9 - 6 = n$
5. $-9 + (-6) = n$
6. $9 + (-6) = n$
7. $9 - (-6) = n$
8. $-9 - (-6) = n$
9. $9 \times 6 = n$
10. $-9 \times 6 = n$
11. $9 \times (-6) = n$
12. $-9 \times (-6) = n$
13. $21 \div 7 = n$
14. $-21 \div 7 = n$
15. $21 \div (-7) = n$
16. $-21 \div (-7) = n$
17. $-21 - (-7) = n$
18. $21 - (-7) = n$
19. $-21 - 7 = n$
20. $21 + (-7) = n$
21. $21 \times 7 = n$
22. $21 - 7 = n$
23. $-21 + 7 = n$
24. $-21 + (-7) = n$
25. $7 - (-21) = n$
26. $42 + 7 = n$
27. $42 \div 7 = n$
28. $42 - 7 = n$
29. $42 - (-7) = n$
30. $42 \div (-7) = n$
31. $-42 + (-7) = n$
32. $-42 \div (-7) = n$
33. $42 \times 7 = n$
34. $42 \times (-7) = n$
35. $-42 \div 7 = n$
36. $-42 - (-7) = n$
37. $-42 \times (-7) = n$
38. $7 - 14 = n$
39. $-7 \times 14 = n$
40. $-7 \div 14 = n$
41. $-14 \div (-7) = n$
42. $-14 \div 7 = n$
43. $-14 + 7 = n$
44. $-14 - (-7) = n$
45. $14 \div 7 = n$
46. $14 \times 7 = n$
47. $-14 + (-7) = n$
48. $-7 - (-14) = n$
49. $-7 - 14 = n$
50. $-7 \div (-14) = n$

Linear Equations

$3x - 2y - 5$ is a function of 2 independent variables. This idea may be new to you. We will call the value of this function z, and we can write an equation $3x - 2y - 5 = z$. Here x and y are independent variables and z is the dependent variable. If you choose values for x and y, they determine a value for z. For example, let $x = -5$ and $y = 5$. Then $z = 3(-5) - 2(5) - 5 = -15 - 10 - 5 = -30$. Or, for $x = 4$ and $y = 5$, $z = 3(-4) - 2(5) - 5 = -12 - 10 - 5 = -27$.

1. Make a table like the one below.

2. Fill in all the values for z when x and y are whole numbers from -5 through 5. Look for patterns to help you. Be sure to do some of the calculations to check your patterns.

z-values for $z = 3x - 2y - 5$

y-values

5	−30	−27	−24	−21	−18	−15	−12	−9	−6	−3	0
4	−28	−25									
3		−23									
2											
1											
0											
−1											
−2											
−3											
−4											
−5	−10										20
	−5	**−4**	**−3**	**−2**	**−1**	**0**	**1**	**2**	**3**	**4**	**5**

x-values

3. Draw a pair of axes and label them like those below.

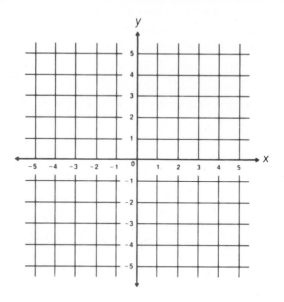

Locate on the graph each of the 121 ordered pairs (x, y) you found in problem 2 on page 225. Color a point red if the corresponding value of z is negative, blue if the value of z is positive, and black if z is 0. For example, $(-5, 5)$ is red, $(5, -5)$ is blue, and $(5, 5)$ is black.

4. Look at your graph.
   a. Do you think the point $\left(-3\frac{1}{2}, 3\frac{1}{2}\right)$ should be red, blue, or black?
   b. How about the point $\left(3\frac{1}{2}, -3\frac{1}{2}\right)$?
   c. Check by putting these values for x and y into the equation.

5. Find 5 more points that are black ($z = 0$).
   a. Where do you think all such points are?
   b. Where are all the red points?
   c. Where are all the blue points?

The region with the red points is called a *half plane*. In this half plane the values for z are negative. All the blue points are in a half plane in which the values of z are positive.

Solve for n.

1. $25 \times 10 = n$
2. $25 \times 100 = n$
3. $25 \div 10 = n$
4. $25 \div 100 = n$
5. $25 \div 1000 = n$

6. $25 \times 1000 = n$
7. $50 \times 2 = n$
8. $50 \times 20 = n$
9. $50 \times 200 = n$
10. $50 \div 2 = n$

11. $50 \div 200 = n$
12. $50 \div 20,000 = n$
13. $2.5 \times 4 = n$
14. $2.5 \times 40 = n$
15. $2.5 \times 400 = n$

16. $2.5 \times 40,000 = n$
17. $2.5 \times 0.4 = n$
18. $2.5 \times 0.04 = n$
19. $3 \times 30 = n$
20. $3 \div 30 = n$

21. $3 \times 300 = n$
22. $3 \times 30,000 = n$
23. $3 \div 300 = n$
24. $3 \div 3 = n$
25. $3 \times 0.03 = n$

26. $5.5 \times 10 = n$
27. $5.5 \div 10 = n$
28. $5.5 \times 100 = n$
29. $5.5 \div 100 = n$
30. $5.5 \times 1000 = n$

31. $5.5 \div 1000 = n$
32. $0.5 \times 10 = n$
33. $0.5 \times 100 = n$
34. $0.5 \times 1000 = n$
35. $0.5 \div 10 = n$

36. $0.5 \div 100 = n$
37. $0.5 \div 1000 = n$
38. $75 \div 100 = n$
39. $7.5 \div 100 = n$
40. $0.75 \div 100 = n$

41. $0.75 \times 100 = n$
42. $0.075 \div 1000 = n$
43. $0.075 \times 1000 = n$
44. $325 \div 100 = n$
45. $32.5 \div 100 = n$

46. $3.25 \div 100 = n$
47. $0.325 \div 100 = n$
48. $0.325 \times 100 = n$
49. $0.0325 \times 100 = n$
50. $0.0325 \times 10,000 = n$

Consider the equation $3x - 2y - 5 = 0$.

What will the graph of $3x - 2y - 5 = 0$ look like? That is, where are all the points with coordinates (x, y) that make $3x - 2y - 5 = 0$?

From your work on pages 225 and 226, you know that $(5, 5)$, $(3, 2)$, $(1, -1)$, and $(-1, 4)$ satisfy the conditions. You also know that you can draw a straight line through those 4 points.

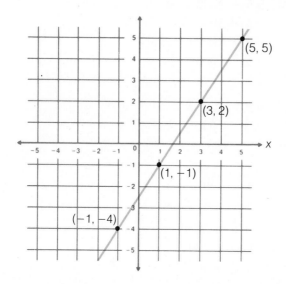

[1] **Do you think that every point on the line has coordinates that make $3x - 2y - 5$ equal 0?**

[2] **Do you think that all pairs of numbers (x, y) that make $3x - 2y - 5$ equal to 0 are coordinates of points on the line?**

Check each of the following number pairs (x, y) to see if it satisfies the equation $3x - 2y - 5 = 0$ (that is, if it makes $3x - 2y - 5$ equal 0). Graph each of the points to see if it is on the line.

1. $\left(0, -\frac{5}{2}\right)$ 6. $\left(2\frac{1}{3}, 1\right)$ 11. $(2, 1)$

2. $\left(2, \frac{1}{2}\right)$ 7. $\left(3\frac{2}{3}, 3\right)$ 12. $(2, 0)$

3. $\left(4, 3\frac{1}{2}\right)$ 8. $\left(4\frac{1}{3}, 4\right)$ 13. $(4, 3)$

4. $\left(-1\frac{2}{3}, 5\right)$ 9. $\left(\frac{1}{3}, -2\right)$ 14. $(4, 4)$

5. $\left(\frac{5}{3}, 0\right)$ 10. $\left(-\frac{1}{3}, -3\right)$ 15. $(-1, -3)$

Remember

Every straight line can be described by an equation of the form

$$Ax + By + C = 0$$

where A, B, and C are numbers. Equations of this form always describe straight lines (except when $A = B = 0$) and are called linear equations. When A or $B = 1$, then we simply write x or y, not $1x$ or $1y$.

Equivalent Equations

Here are 2 equations:

A. $3x + y - 6 = 0$ B. $y = 6 - 3x$

Before you discuss these questions with the whole class, work in small groups to find the answers.

[1] For each equation, find 3 ordered pairs that satisfy the equation.

[2] On the same set of axes, graph the lines for each of the equations.

[3] What did you find out about equations A and B?

Equations like $3x + y - 6 = 0$ and $y = 6 - 3x$ are called *equivalent equations.* When equations are equivalent, they will have the same straight line graph.

You can also show algebraically that 2 equations are equivalent. Let's look again at equations A and B.

Start with equation A:	$3x + y - 6 = 0$
Add 6 to both sides:	$3x + y - 6 + 6 = 0 + 6$
This gives:	$3x + y = 6$
Now subtract $3x$ from both sides:	$3x + y - 3x = 6 - 3x$
This gives:	$y = 6 - 3x$

Since $y = 6 - 3x$ is the same as equation B, equations A and B are equivalent.

Use both algebra and graphing to determine whether the equations in each set below are equivalent.

1. $2x + 2y = 4$
   $x + y = 2$

2. $2x + y = 5$
   $x + 2y = 5$

3. $3y - 2x = 12$
   $3y - 12 = 2x$

4. $x - 3y + 9 = 0$
   $9x + 2 = 3y$

5. $x + 2y = 5$
   $2x = 10 - 4y$

6. $x = 4$
   $y = 4$

Solve for n.

1. $\frac{2}{5} + \frac{1}{5} = n$

2. $\frac{2}{5} - \frac{1}{5} = n$

3. $\frac{2}{5} \times \frac{1}{5} = n$

4. $\frac{2}{5} \div \frac{1}{5} = n$

5. $1\frac{2}{5} + \frac{4}{5} = n$

6. $1\frac{2}{5} - \frac{4}{5} = n$

7. $1\frac{2}{5} \times \frac{4}{5} = n$

8. $1\frac{2}{5} \div \frac{4}{5} = n$

9. $\frac{2}{3} - \frac{1}{6} = n$

10. $\frac{2}{3} + \frac{1}{6} = n$

11. $\frac{2}{3} \div \frac{1}{6} = n$

12. $\frac{2}{3} \times \frac{1}{6} = n$

13. $\frac{2}{3} - \frac{4}{6} = n$

14. $\frac{2}{3} \div \frac{4}{6} = n$

15. $\frac{2}{3} \times \frac{4}{6} = n$

16. $\frac{2}{3} + \frac{4}{6} = n$

17. $1\frac{2}{3} + 3\frac{1}{2} = n$

18. $1\frac{2}{3} \div 3\frac{1}{2} = n$

19. $1\frac{2}{3} \times 3\frac{1}{2} = n$

20. $3\frac{1}{2} - 1\frac{2}{3} = n$

21. $\frac{3}{4} + \frac{2}{3} = n$

22. $\frac{3}{4} - \frac{2}{3} = n$

23. $\frac{3}{4} \times \frac{2}{3} = n$

24. $\frac{3}{4} \div \frac{2}{3} = n$

25. $\frac{3}{4} + \frac{1}{3} = n$

26. $1\frac{1}{4} - \frac{1}{4} = n$

27. $1\frac{1}{4} + \frac{1}{4} = n$

28. $1\frac{1}{4} \div \frac{1}{4} = n$

29. $1\frac{1}{4} \times \frac{1}{4} = n$

30. $2\frac{2}{3} - \frac{2}{3} = n$

31. $2\frac{2}{3} + \frac{2}{3} = n$

32. $2\frac{2}{3} \div \frac{2}{3} = n$

33. $2\frac{2}{3} \times \frac{2}{3} = n$

34. $\frac{2}{3} + \frac{2}{3} = n$

35. $\frac{2}{3} - \frac{2}{3} = n$

36. $\frac{2}{3} \times \frac{2}{3} = n$

37. $\frac{2}{3} \div \frac{2}{3} = n$

38. $1\frac{1}{4} + 1\frac{1}{4} = n$

39. $1\frac{1}{4} \times 1\frac{1}{4} = n$

40. $1\frac{1}{4} \div 1\frac{1}{4} = n$

41. $1\frac{1}{4} - 1\frac{1}{4} = n$

42. $1\frac{1}{2} - \frac{2}{3} = n$

43. $1\frac{1}{2} \times \frac{2}{3} = n$

44. $1\frac{1}{2} \div \frac{2}{3} = n$

45. $1\frac{1}{2} + \frac{2}{3} = n$

46. $2 - \frac{3}{4} = n$

47. $2 + \frac{3}{4} = n$

48. $2 \div \frac{3}{4} = n$

49. $2 \times \frac{3}{4} = n$

50. $\frac{3}{4} + 2 = n$

You know that equations of the form $Ax + By + C = 0$ have straight line graphs (unless both A and B are 0). If you can write an equivalent equation for an equation in the form $Ax + By + C = 0$, you know that the equation has a straight line graph. For example, since $2x = 3y + 4$ can be rewritten as $2x - 3y - 4 = 0$, it has a straight line graph.

Because 2 points of a straight line determine the line, you can graph a straight line after finding the coordinates of 2 points. Usually, it is a good idea to check by finding a third point.

Example: Graph $y = 3x - 7$.

First find the coordinates of 2 points.

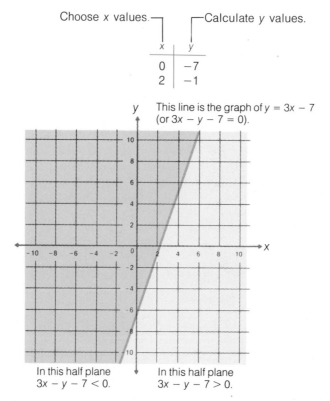

Choose x values.   Calculate y values.

x	y
0	−7
2	−1

This line is the graph of $y = 3x - 7$ (or $3x - y - 7 = 0$).

In this half plane $3x - y - 7 < 0$.

In this half plane $3x - y - 7 > 0$.

Graph these points and draw the line. Then find the coordinates of another point. If $x = 4$, $y = 5$. Check to see that (4, 5) is on the line.

If you now want to know on which side of the line $3x - y - 7$ has values greater than 0, you can take any point not on the line. Let's take $(0, 0)$. $3(0) - 0 - 7 = -7$.

Since this result is negative, all the points in the half plane with $(0, 0)$ will satisfy the inequality $3x - y - 7 < 0$. The points in the half plane on the other side of the line satisfy the inequality $3x - y - 7 > 0$.

We show the half plane by writing its inequality and shading the graph.

For each item, graph the given equations or inequalities on the same pair of axes.

1. $2x - 3y - 4 = 0$
   $2x - 3y - 4 > 0$

2. $2x - 3y + 3 = 0$
   $2x - 3y + 3 < 0$

3. $4x - 5y = 0$
   $4x - 5y + 2 = 0$
   $4x - 5y - 7 = 0$
   $4x - 5y + 5 = 0$

4. $y = 3x - 7$
   $y > 3x - 7$

5. $x + 8 = 0$
   $x + 8 > 0$

6. $y = 4$
   $y > 4$

7. $x + y + 1 > 0$

HIT THE LINE

Players: 2 or more
Materials: Blank graph paper with x and y axes from -10 to 10, two 0–5 cubes, two 5–10 cubes
Object: To hit (or get closest to) the line with a point

Rules

1. The lead player rolls a 0–5 cube 3 times (if 0 is rolled, the player rolls again). The first number rolled is A, the second B, and the third C in the equation $Ax - By + C = 0$. Then the players graph the line on axes marked from -10 to 10.

2. The players take turns rolling all 4 cubes and choosing 2 of the numbers rolled as the coordinates of a point. Negative signs may be used for 1 or both coordinates.

3. The player whose point is closest to the line wins. If there is disagreement, substitute the coordinates into $Ax - By + C = z$. The player with the z value closest to 0 wins.

Sample Game

1. As lead player, Inga rolled ⁤4⁤ ⁤0⁤ ⁤2⁤ ⁤4⁤
   She drew the graph of the equation
   $4x - 2y + 4 = 0$.

2. Inga rolled ⁤2⁤ ⁤5⁤ ⁤7⁤ ⁤7⁤ and chose the point $(-5, -7)$. Gareth rolled ⁤1⁤ ⁤2⁤ ⁤5⁤ ⁤7⁤ and chose $(2, 5)$. Ariel rolled ⁤1⁤ ⁤2⁤ ⁤8⁤ ⁤9⁤ and chose $(-2, -1)$.

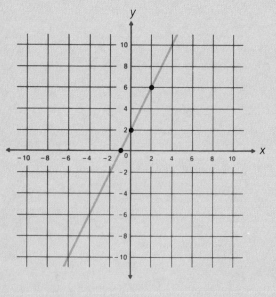

3. All 3 points seemed close, so the students checked.

   Inga: $4(-5) - 2(-7) + 4$
   $= -20 + 14 + 4 = -2$
   Gareth: $4(2) - 2(5) + 4$
   $= 8 - 10 + 4 = 2$
   Ariel: $4(-2) - 2(-1) + 4$
   $= -8 + 2 + 4 = -2$

The 3 numbers are equally close to 0, so it is a 3-way tie. If you don't mark the points on the graph, you can use the same line several times.

You learned several ways to solve equations in chapter 2. Graphs can be used to help estimate solutions to equations. For example, to solve the equation $830 = 80x + 130$, graph $y = 80x + 130$ and see what value of x makes $y = 830$.

x	0	5	10
y	130	530	930

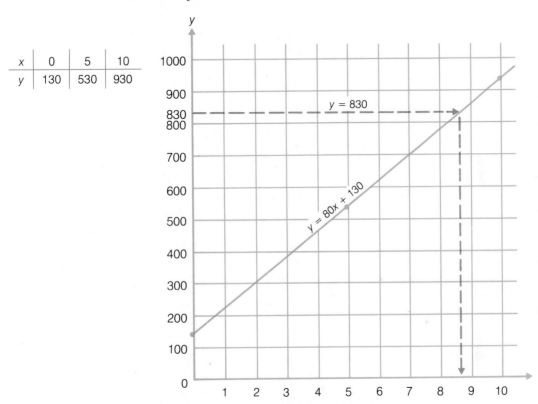

From the graph, it appears that $y = 830$ when x is between 8 and 9 and is somewhat closer to 9.

Use the graph to answer these questions.

1. About what value of x would make $y = 700$?
2. About what value of x would make $y = 500$?
3. About what value of x would make $y = 1000$?
4. About what value of x would make $y = 400$?
5. About what value of x would make $y = 200$?

Graphing: Applications

Solve these problems.

1. Rick walks at a rate of about 5 kilometers per hour. So, the number of kilometers (d) he walks in t hours is approximately $d = 5t$. Make a graph showing how far Rick walks in t hours. Use the horizontal axis to show time up to 10 hours and the vertical axis to show distance in kilometers. (Think about how many kilometers Rick could walk in 10 hours). Be sure to label your graph.

2. Use the graph from problem 1 to estimate about how many kilometers Rick would walk in

    a. 3 hours   **b.** $7\frac{1}{2}$ hours   **c.** $9\frac{1}{2}$ hours

3. Use your graph to estimate about how long it would take Rick to walk

    a. 25 kilometers   **b.** 17 kilometers   **c.** 41 kilometers

4. Cindy rides her bicycle at a rate of about 18 kilometers per hour ($d = 18t$). Make a graph that shows how far she rides in t hours.

5. Use the graph from problem 4 to estimate about how many kilometers Cindy would ride in

    a. 3 hours   **b.** $7\frac{1}{2}$ hours   **c.** $9\frac{1}{2}$ hours

6. Use the graph from problem 4 to estimate about how long it would take Cindy to ride

    a. 27 kilometers   **b.** 54 kilometers   **c.** 117 kilometers

7. Ms. Nicoll drives her car at an average rate of about 85 kilometers per hour. Make a graph that shows about how far Ms. Nicoll drives in t hours.

8. Use the graph from problem 7 to estimate about how far Ms. Nicoll would drive in

    a. 3 hours   **b.** $7\frac{1}{2}$ hours   **c.** $9\frac{1}{2}$ hours

9. Use your graph to estimate about how long it would take her to drive

    a. 34 kilometers   **b.** 250 kilometers   **c.** 680 kilometers

The average human baby is 50.4 centimeters tall at birth and
grows 3.4 centimeters per month for the first 3 months.

Work in small groups to do these problems. Assume that
growth continues at that rate until age 20.

1. Calculate what height the average person would be at age 20.

2. Make a graph showing what the height of the average person
   would be at each of the first 20 birthdays. (Use the 2 figures—
   height at birth and height at 20 years—to draw the graph.)

3. Use your graph to determine the height of the average person
   at ages 5, 10, 15, and 20.

4. Compare the heights calculated from the graph with real data
   you can get from the library. Your teacher may be able to help
   you get these data.

5. Do you think the human growth rate is linear from birth until
   20 years?

The following table contains data about the growth rate of average
American boys and girls.

Age	Average Height (cm)		Age	Average Height (cm)		Age	Average Height (cm)	
	Girls	Boys		Girls	Boys		Girls	Boys
Birth	50.0	50.8	2 yr	86.6	87.9	12 yr	151.9	149.6
3 mo	59.7	61.5	3 yr	95.8	96.5	14 yr	160.3	162.8
6 mo	65.8	68.1	4 yr	101.9	102.9	16 yr	162.3	173.2
9 mo	70.9	72.4	5 yr	108.2	110.0	18 yr	163.6	176.8
1 yr	74.7	76.5	6 yr	114.6	116.3	20 yr	163.7	176.9
			8 yr	126.5	126.7			
			10 yr	138.2	137.7			

6. Make a graph of these data. Use pencils of different colors to
   graph the data for boys and for girls. Study and discuss the
   shapes of the lines you have graphed.

Find x in each of the following proportions.

1. $\frac{x}{3} = \frac{12}{6}$

2. $\frac{x}{4} = \frac{10}{5}$

3. $\frac{50}{x} = \frac{10}{2}$

4. $\frac{4}{x} = \frac{1}{9}$

5. $\frac{40}{8} = \frac{x}{5}$

6. $\frac{4}{32} = \frac{x}{16}$

7. $\frac{7}{8} = \frac{x}{16}$

8. $\frac{22}{11} = \frac{x}{4}$

9. $\frac{1}{3} = \frac{3}{x}$

10. $\frac{3}{4} = \frac{9}{x}$

11. $\frac{2}{3} = \frac{8}{x}$

12. $\frac{5}{4} = \frac{25}{x}$

13. $\frac{3}{x} = \frac{12}{4}$

14. $\frac{30}{x} = \frac{120}{40}$

15. $\frac{x}{9} = \frac{9}{81}$

16. $\frac{x}{8} = \frac{3}{24}$

17. $\frac{3}{15} = \frac{x}{10}$

18. $\frac{3}{2} = \frac{x}{15}$

19. $\frac{21}{14} = \frac{x}{15}$

20. $\frac{3}{8} = \frac{6}{x}$

21. $\frac{3}{8} = \frac{9}{x}$

22. $\frac{3}{9} = \frac{8}{x}$

23. $\frac{x}{22} = \frac{33}{11}$

24. $\frac{x}{7} = \frac{35}{5}$

25. $\frac{24}{6} = \frac{12}{x}$

26. $\frac{6}{x} = \frac{24}{12}$

27. $\frac{6}{24} = \frac{x}{12}$

28. $\frac{x}{6} = \frac{12}{24}$

29. $\frac{x}{24} = \frac{6}{12}$

30. $\frac{x}{6} = \frac{24}{12}$

Rolling a Ball

Leo found a long ramp that had meters marked on it. He decided to roll a ball down the ramp. He decided to time the ball the second time he rolled it down the ramp.

He got friends to help him see how far it rolled each second. They decided the ball rolled just about 1 meter in the first second, 4 meters in the first 2 seconds, 9 meters in the first 3 seconds, 16 meters in the first 4 seconds, 25 meters in the first 5 seconds, and 36 meters in the first 6 seconds. Then the ball reached the bottom of the ramp.

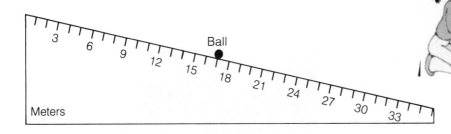

1. If the ramp were longer, about how far do you think it would have rolled by the end of

   a. 7 seconds?   **c.** 9 seconds?
   b. 8 seconds?   **d.** 10 seconds?

2. Complete this table showing how many meters (d) the ball had rolled at the end of t seconds.

t	0	1	2	3	4	5	6
d	0	1					

3. Make a graph of this information. Put t, the number of seconds, on the horizontal axis. Put d, the number of meters the ball had rolled, on the vertical axis. Does the graph appear to be a straight line?

4. Which of the following equations best shows how many meters (d) the ball travels in t seconds?

   a. $d = t$ **c.** $d = 2t$ **e.** $d = 6t - 5$
   b. $d = 3t - 2$ **d.** $d = t^2$ **f.** $d = 4t - 3$

Falling Bodies

If you drop something from the top of a tower, the distance it travels in t seconds is about $d = 4.9t^2$ meters, or $d = 16.1t^2$ feet. A feather or a piece of paper will fall more slowly than shown by this equation because of air resistance. But in a vacuum (with no air), a feather and an iron ball would fall at the same rate.

Vacuum   Air

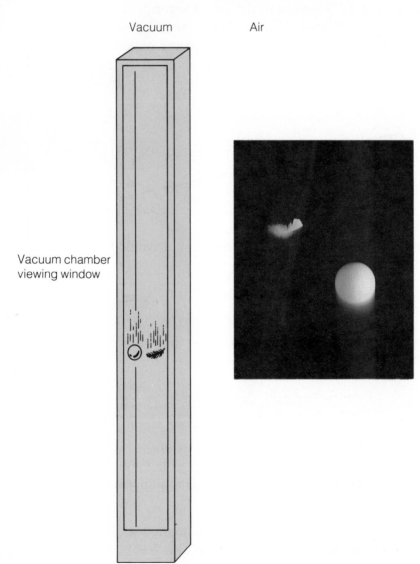

Vacuum chamber
viewing window

1. If a steel ball is dropped from the top of the Sears Tower in Chicago (height approximately 443 meters), it will fall 4.9 meters in the first second. It will have fallen $4.9 \times (2^2) = 19.6$ meters after 2 seconds, and so on. Make a table that shows how far (d) in meters the ball will have fallen after t seconds. The first 3 entries have been done for you.

t	0	1	2	3	4	5	6
d	0	4.9	19.6				

2. Make a table as in problem 1 but assuming that the ball is dropped from the CN Tower in Toronto (height approximately 555 meters).

   a. For which values of t are the 2 tables different?
   b. Why?

3. Make a graph of the information in your table for problem 2.

4. Use your graph to estimate about how far the ball will have fallen after $5\frac{1}{2}$ seconds. Calculate the answer from the formula and compare the calculated answer with the estimate from the graph.

5. Use your graph to estimate how long it would take the ball to hit the ground if it were dropped from

   a. the Sears Tower   b. the CN Tower

6. Use the formula $t = \sqrt{\frac{d}{4.9}}$ to calculate the answers to problem 5. Compare the estimates and calculated answers.

If you could throw a ball in space without any effects of gravity, the distance it would travel would be given by the following formula:

$$d = rt$$

where d = distance in meters, r = speed in meters per second, and t = time in seconds. So, if you threw the ball at a speed of 20 meters per second, it would go 20 meters in 1 second, 40 meters in 2 seconds, 100 meters in 5 seconds, and so on.

Both gravity and air affect a ball thrown straight up from the earth. In the discussion we will ignore the effects of air, because they are small compared to those of gravity.

When you throw a ball straight up at a speed of r meters per second, gravity will pull it *down* according to the formula $d = 4.9t^2$. So, the distance, d, in meters, above you that the ball will be at any time, t, will be expressed by $d = rt - 4.9t^2$.

1. Suppose Al throws a ball straight up at a speed of 20 meters per second. The distance the ball will be above Al at time t is $20t - 4.9t^2$. Copy and complete this table showing how far (d) the ball is above Sam (in meters) at any time t (in seconds) after he throws it up at 20 meters per second.

t	0	1	2	3	4	5
d						

2. You calculated a negative number for d when $t = 5$ in problem 1.
   a. What does this mean?
   b. Is this possible?
   c. Is it likely under ordinary conditions?

3. When Al threw the ball up, he released it above his head. Assume he released it 2 meters above the ground.
   a. Is a distance above the release point of -2 meters reasonable?
   b. Where is that?
   c. If the ball hasn't fallen down a well or over a cliff, is a distance of -22.5 meters reasonable?

4. Graph the information from problem 1 with d on the vertical axis and t on the horizontal axis.
   a. When do you think the ball was at its highest point?
   b. Approximately how high (above the release point) do you think the ball went?

5. Suppose Flo throws a ball straight up at a speed of 10 meters per second.
   a. About how high will it go?
   b. About how long will it take to hit the ground? (Assume Flo releases it from a point 2 meters above the ground.)

6. Suppose Helga throws a ball straight up at a speed of 30 meters per second.
   a. About how high will it go?
   b. About how long will it take to hit the ground? (Assume Helga releases it from a point 2 meters above the ground.)

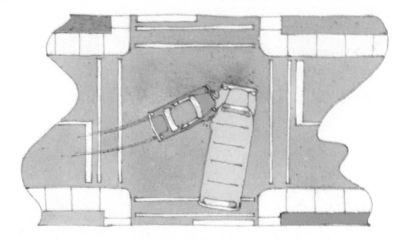

A car and a bus collided at an intersection. A headlight on each was broken. The glass from the bus headlight landed 15 feet from the front of the bus. The bus headlight was 3 feet above the ground. The police officers want to know about how fast the bus was going.

Let's try to find the answer to this question.

After the collision, the glass continues to move forward at about the speed the bus was traveling just before the collision. The glass is also falling at the same time.

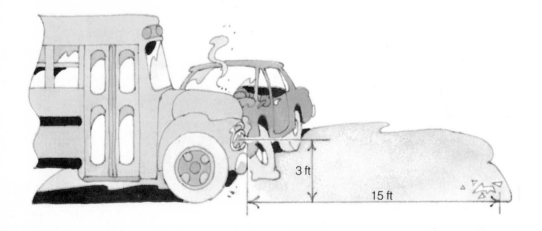

3 ft

15 ft

1. A formula that tells about how far, d, something falls (in feet) in t seconds is $d = 16.1t^2$. About how long did it take the glass to fall 3 feet?

2. The speed of the glass in feet per second is given by the formula $r = \frac{d}{t}$, where d is the number of feet it traveled and t is the number of seconds it took. Since the glass traveled about 15 feet in the time it took to fall, about how fast was it traveling?

3. To convert feet per second to miles per hour, multiply by $\frac{5280}{3600}$ (or $\frac{22}{15}$). In miles per hour, about how fast was the glass traveling?

4. It is safe to assume that the bus must have been going 3 or 4 miles per hour faster than the speed calculated for the glass. About how fast was the bus traveling just before the collision?

Figure out how to solve these additional problems.

5. Assume that the broken glass from the bus headlight landed 20 feet from the front of the bus. About how fast was the bus traveling before the collision?

6. Assume that the broken glass from the bus landed 15 feet from the bus but came from a light that was 4 feet from the ground. About how fast was the bus traveling?

Square Roots

In chapter 5 and again in this chapter you have had to find square roots of numbers. You probably used the square root key on a calculator to do so. If you don't have a calculator with a square root key, this graph may help you to estimate a square root.

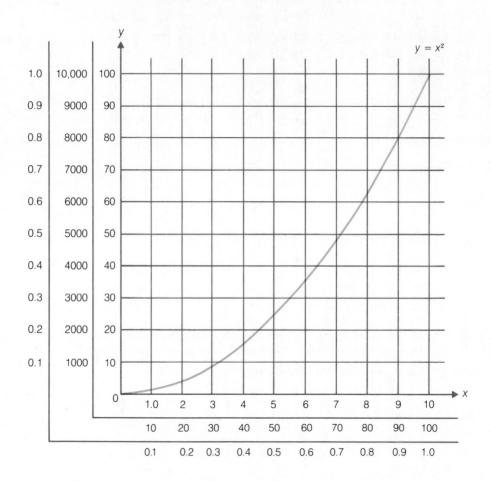

Suppose you want to estimate $\sqrt{30}$. Look for 30 on the y-axis, go across to the graph of $y = x^2$, then down to the x-axis. The answer appears to be just slightly less than 5.5. By a similar process, $\sqrt{74}$ is just about 8.6.

The graph looks exactly the same with numbers from 0 to 100 on the x-axis and numbers from 0 to 10,000 on the y-axis or with numbers from 0 to 1.0 on the x-axis and 0 to 1.0 on the y-axis. It looks the same because when you multiply x by 10, you multiply y by 100. So you can use the other scales on the graph to estimate $\sqrt{3000}$ to be about 55 and $\sqrt{0.3}$ to be about 0.55. In the same way, $\sqrt{7400}$ is about 86 and $\sqrt{0.74}$ is about 0.86.

1. Use the graph on page 246 to estimate the following square roots to 2 digits. Check each answer by squaring it. Then check by squaring the next possible higher or lower estimate. For example, if you estimate that $\sqrt{0.74}$ is 0.86, check your estimate: $(0.86)^2 = 0.7396$. Because 0.7396 is less than 0.74, try 0.87. $(0.87)^2 = 0.7569$. Since 0.7396 is much closer, 0.86 is the better estimate.

a. $\sqrt{10}$ b. $\sqrt{19}$ c. $\sqrt{35}$ d. $\sqrt{56}$ e. $\sqrt{85}$

f. $\sqrt{1000}$ g. $\sqrt{1900}$ h. $\sqrt{3500}$ i. $\sqrt{5600}$ j. $\sqrt{8500}$

k. $\sqrt{0.1}$ l. $\sqrt{0.19}$ m. $\sqrt{0.35}$ n. $\sqrt{0.56}$ o. $\sqrt{0.85}$

2. Draw a graph of $y = x^3$. Choose values of x from 0 to 10 in half-unit steps (0, 0.5, 1, 1.5, . . ., 9.5, 10).

   a. What will be the smallest value of y?
   b. What will be the largest value of y?

   Choose the size of the unit on the y-axis so that you can fit numbers from 0 to 1000 on it.

3. Use your graph for problem 2 to estimate the following cube roots to 2 digits. Check each answer by cubing your estimate and also the next closer possible estimate. For example, if you estimate $\sqrt[3]{55}$ to be 3.9, check: $(3.9)^3 = 59.319$, and $(3.8)^3 = 54.872$. 3.8 is closer.

a. $\sqrt[3]{10}$ b. $\sqrt[3]{50}$ c. $\sqrt[3]{64}$ d. $\sqrt[3]{100}$ e. $\sqrt[3]{200}$

f. $\sqrt[3]{.01}$ g. $\sqrt[3]{.05}$ h. $\sqrt[3]{.1}$ i. $\sqrt[3]{.2}$ j. $\sqrt[3]{10,000}$

Chapter Review

1. Graph the 5 points indicated by the numbers in this table. (Be sure to choose your axes so that you can get all the points on your graph.)

x	3	−4	−1	2	4
y	5	2	−3	−5	0

2. Look at this graph.

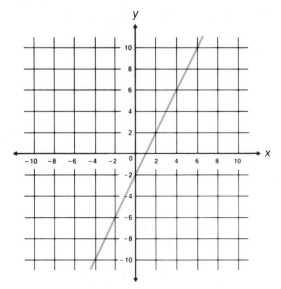

a. What value of x will make $y = 0$?

b. What value of x will make $y = 6$?

c. Copy and complete the table below. Use your answers to parts a and b to help with the first 2 spaces.

x						2	−2
y	0	6	5	−2	−7		

3. Graph this equation and this inequality on the same set of axes.

   a. $3x − 2y − 6 = 0$ b. $3x − 2y − 6 > 0$

4. A baseball player throws a ball straight up at a speed of 120 feet per second. The height of the ball above the ground in feet is given by the formula $d = 7 + 120t − 16.1t^2$.

a. Make a graph to show how high the ball is from t seconds after it is released until it hits the ground.

b. About what is the height of the ball at 3 seconds?

c. About what is the height of the ball at 4 seconds?

d. To the nearest tenth of a second, when does the ball reach its highest point?

e. What (to the nearest foot) is the highest distance the ball reaches?

f. When (to the nearest tenth of a second) does the ball hit the ground?

g. What is the height of the ball above the ground when $t = 0$?

h. In the formula $d = 7 + 120t - 16.1t^2$, what does the 7 stand for?

Chapter Test

1. Graph the 5 points indicated by the numbers in this table. (Be sure to choose your axes so that you can get all the points on your graph.)

x	0	−2	2	8	−6
y	1	0	2	4	−2

2. Look at this graph.

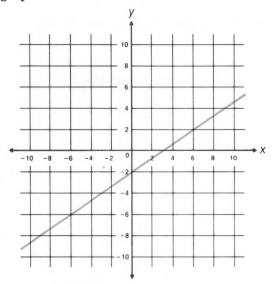

a. What value of x will make $y = 0$?

b. What value of x will make $y = 2$?

c. Copy and complete the table below. Use your answers to parts a and b to help with the first 2 spaces.

x						−8	−2
y	0	2	4	−4	−6		

3. Graph this equation and this inequality on the same set of axes.

   a. $3x − y + 1 = 0$ b. $3x − y + 1 > 0$

4. A football player throws a ball straight up at a speed of 80 feet per second. The height of the ball above the ground in feet is given by the formula $d = 8 + 80t − 16.1t^2$.

a. Make a graph to show how high the ball is from t seconds after it is released until it hits the ground.
b. About what is the height of the ball at 2 seconds?
c. About what is the height of the ball at 3 seconds?
d. To the nearest tenth of a second, when does the ball reach its highest point?
e. What (to the nearest foot) is the highest distance the ball reaches?
f. When (to the nearest tenth of a second) does the ball hit the ground?
g. What is the height of the ball above the ground when $t = 0$?
h. In the formula $d = 8 + 80t - 16.1t^2$, what does the 8 stand for?

You may need to use a calculator or a computer to help you do parts of this problem.

The number 2025 has a special property. If you separate it into two 2-digit numbers, 20 and 25, and add the numbers, you get the square root of 2025 ($20 + 25 = 45$; $45^2 = 2025$).

1. Find the one 2-digit number that has this property.
2. Find all the 4-digit numbers that have this property.
3. Find the one 6-digit number that has this property.

Enrichment: ISBNs

Have you ever wondered how librarians keep track of all their books?

Something that helps librarians do this is a system known as the International Standard Book Number system. People in publishing call these numbers ISBNs.

ISBNs are printed on books, sometimes on the backs. Look at the back of this book. The number 0-89688-806-1 in the lower right corner is the ISBN for this book. You'll also find it on the copyright page—the page right after the full title page. The copyright page in this book is the fourth page from the front. Look for the ISBN there.

ISBNs are in the form A-BCDEF-GHI-J. All ISBNs have a special characteristic that makes it possible to check that all the digits are correct. See if you can figure out what that characteristic is by looking at the ISBNs on several books. (Hint: Calculate the following numbers: $10a + 9b + 8c + \ldots + 1j$. Is this number always divisible by some small number?)

CHAPTER 8
GEOMETRY

Doris wants to estimate the area of the blob shown here.

[1] How might she proceed?

[2] How good an estimate could she get?

A method sometimes used to estimate the area inside a figure is first to draw the figure inside a figure of known area (or to draw a figure of known area outside the figure). The next step is to choose points at random inside the larger figure. If enough random points are chosen, the ratio of the smaller area to the larger area should be about equal to the ratio of the number of points inside the smaller figure to the number of points inside the larger figure.

Because this procedure uses randomly chosen points, it is called the *Monte Carlo* method. (Monte Carlo is a town in the European principality of Monaco where people go to gamble.)

To find the area of the figure, Doris copied the figure of the blob inside a square that was 8 centimeters on a side. She put it on a dart board, stood about 4 meters away, and, rather than aiming at the center of the figures, closed her eyes and threw darts in the direction of the square. That way, she thought, she would scatter the darts randomly. Lots of the darts missed. She counted only darts that landed inside the square.

By the time she had thrown 100 darts that landed in the square, she had counted only 36 that landed in the blob.

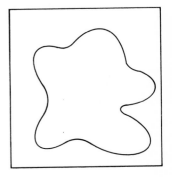

She let b equal the number of square centimeters in the blob. Then she wrote the 2 ratios and said that they were about equal:

$$\frac{b}{64} \approx \frac{36}{100}, \text{ so } b \approx \frac{36(64)}{100}$$
$$\text{and } b \approx 23.04$$

Remember: $\approx$ means "is about equal to."

Doris decided that the area of the blob is about 23 square centimeters.

Do these problems.

1. Doris threw 500 darts that landed in the square. 193 of the 500 landed in the blob. Now estimate the area of the blob.
2. After 100 darts had landed in the square, 379 had landed in the blob. Make a new estimate of the area of the blob.
3. What are some of the disadvantages of finding areas by throwing darts?

Instead of throwing darts, you could draw the blob on a computer screen and put it inside a figure of known area. Then you could have the computer choose random points inside the figure and keep track of the number of points that fall inside the blob and the total number of points. This method is safer and quicker than using darts. It is also likely to be more accurate. If the dart thrower is too skillful, too large a share of the darts may land inside the blob.

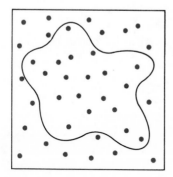

4. Doris drew the blob on a computer screen and put it inside a 20-character by 20-character square. The square is 10 centimeters on a side. Then Doris had the computer pick various numbers of points with x coordinates between 0 and 20 and y coordinates between 0 and 20. She programmed the computer to generate pairs of random numbers with 4 digits each, such as (17.08, 02.95). She had the computer repeat this procedure several times. Each time more points were chosen.

Estimate the area of the blob on the basis of each of the results shown in this output.

	POINTS IN BLOB	TOTAL RANDOM POINTS
a.	38	100
b.	372	1000
c.	3746	10,000
d.	37,509	100,000
e.	375,034	1,000,000
f.	3,750,107	10,000,000

5. How many points are there inside a 20-character by 20-character square if their coordinates are generated as described in problem 4? Points such as (0, 0), (0, 62.95), (34.24, 80) are not *inside* the square and should not be counted.

6. If 5-digit coordinates such as (24.763, 79.059) could be used, how many points would there be?

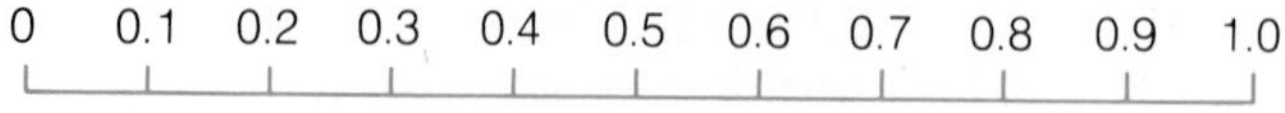

0 0.1 0.2 0.3 0.4 0.5 0.6 0.7 0.8 0.9 1.0

On the line segment shown here, the end points are labeled 0 and 1.0.

1. Points in between that can be labeled by decimals with only 1 digit to the right of the decimal point have been labeled that way.

   a. How many points on the line segment (including the end points) are labeled?

   b. What is the probability that 1 of the labeled points, chosen at random, will be the point 0.7?

2. Suppose all the decimals with 2 digits to the right of the point are used to label points on the line segment between 0 and 1.

   a. How many points (including the end points) will be labeled?

   b. What is the probability that 1 of the labeled points, chosen at random, will be 0.74?

   c. What is the probability that 1 of these points, chosen at random, will be in the range 0.70 through 0.80 inclusive?

3. Suppose all the decimals with 3 digits to the right of the point are used to label points between 0 and 1.

   a. How many points including 0 and 1 will be labeled?

   b. What is the probability that 1 of the labeled points, chosen at random, will be 0.702?

   c. What is the probability that one of these points, chosen at random, will be in the range 0.70 through 0.80 inclusive?

4. Suppose all the decimals with 4 digits to the right of the point are used to label points between 0 and 1.

   a. How many points including 0 and 1 will be labeled?
   b. What is the probability that 1 of the labeled points, chosen at random, will be 0.7003?
   c. What is the probability that 1 of these points, chosen at random, will be in the range 0.70 through 0.80 inclusive?

5. Suppose all the decimals with 10 digits to the right of the point are used to label points between 0 and 1.

   a. How many points including 0 and 1 will be labeled? It will be easier to use exponential notation. For example, 10001 can be written $10^4 + 1$.
   b. What is the probability that 1 of the labeled points, chosen at random, will be 0.7000003000?
   c. What is the probability that 1 of these points, chosen at random, will be in the range 0.70 through 0.80 inclusive?

6. Suppose all the decimals with 100 digits to the right of the point are used to label points between 0 and 1.

   a. How many points including 0 and 1 will be labeled?
   b. What is the probability that 1 of the labeled points, chosen at random, will be 0.700010 with 94 more zeros?
   c. What is the probability that 1 of these points, chosen at random, will be in the range 0.70 through 0.80 inclusive?

7. Suppose all the decimals with 1000 digits to the right of the point are used to label points between 0 and 1.

   a. How many points including 0 and 1 will be labeled?
   b. What is the probability that 1 of the labeled points, chosen at random, will be 0.7000030000 with 990 more zeros?
   c. What is the probability that 1 of these points, chosen at random, will be in the range 0.70 through 0.80 inclusive?

8. How many digits can you imagine having to the right of the decimal point?

9. What happens to the probability of randomly choosing 1 labeled point on a line as the number of labeled points increases and becomes very large?

10. What nonnegative number is less than every positive number?

11. Suppose all the real numbers from 0 through 1 inclusive are used to label points on the line segment between 0 and 1.

   a. How many points including 0 and 1 will be labeled?
   b. What is the probability that one of the labeled points, chosen at random, will be 0.70000 . . . ?
   c. What is the probability that the point will be 0.77777 . . . ?
   d. What is the probability the point will be $\sqrt{0.5}$?
   e. What is the probability that 1 of these points, chosen at random, will be in the range 0.70 through 0.80 inclusive?

12. Suppose that you can choose prints randomly on a number line that is labeled with all the real numbers from 0 through 1.

   a. Is it possible that the point 0.70000 . . . would be chosen?
   b. Is it possible that the point 0.777 . . . would be chosen?
   c. Is it possible that the point $\sqrt{0.5}$ would be chosen?
   d. Is it true that, in fact, *some* point must be chosen?
   e. Before you choose, is the probability of picking that point 0?

13. You know that if an event cannot occur, its probability of occurring is 0.

   a. If the probability that an event does occur is 0, is it impossible for the event to occur?
   b. How many possible events must there be for the probability of a possible event to be 0?

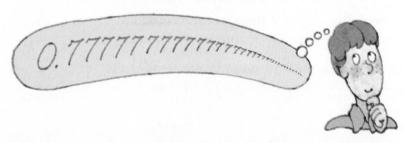

Do these problems.

1. 5% of $2200
2. 10% of $2200
3. 15% of $2200
4. 20% of $2200
5. 50% of $2200

6. 5% of 220
7. 5% of 440
8. 5% of 660
9. 5% of 1100
10. 25% of $44,000

11. 25% of $4400
12. 25% of $440
13. 25% of $44
14. 1% of $27.68
15. 2% of $27.68

16. 5% of $27.68
17. 10% of $27.68
18. 50% of $27.68
19. 50% of 33,688
20. 25% of 33,688

21. 12.5% of 33,688
22. 6.25% of 33,688
23. 3% of 800
24. 3% of 880
25. 3% of 888

26. 4% of 1600
27. 4% of 1616
28. 4% of 3232
29. 4% of 6464
30. 4% of 12,928

31. 10% of 72,000
32. 11% of 72,000
33. 12% of 72,000
34. 22% of 72,000
35. 20% of 6000

36. 21% of 6000
37. 19% of 6000
38. 50% of 6000
39. 0.5% of $200
40. 0.5% of $110

41. 0.5% of $400
42. 1% of $1000
43. 1% of $1100
44. 1.5% of $1000
45. 1.5% of $1100

46. $66\frac{2}{3}$% of $900
47. 30% of $900
48. $33\frac{1}{3}$% of $900
49. 75% of $900
50. 50% of $5000

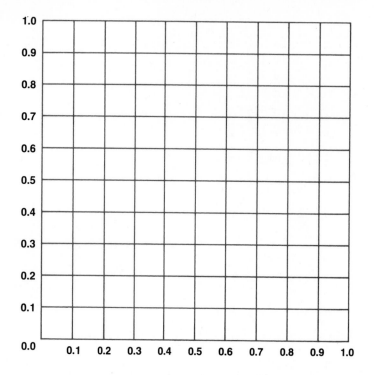

To pick a point randomly in a square whose side is 1 unit long, you would first pick a number between 0 and 1 for the *x*-coordinate, and then a number between 0 and 1 for the *y*-coordinate. You could use any real number between 0 and 1 for either coordinate.

Do these problems.

1. Suppose you choose a point at random in the square. What is the probability

   a. that its x-coordinate will be 0.5?
   b. that its y-coordinate will be 0.5?
   c. that its coordinates will be (0.5, 0.5)?
   d. that its coordinates will be $\left(\pi - 3, \frac{\sqrt{3}}{3}\right)$?
   e. that it will be any particular prechosen point?

2. Think about the probability that a point chosen at random will be on a particular line. For example, what is the probability that a point will be on the line

   a. $x = 0.5$?
   b. $y = 0.5$?
   c. $x + y = 1$?

3. Suppose you threw 3 pennies on the ground.

   a. What is the probability that the centers of all 3 would be on a single straight line?
   b. What is the probability that the centers of any 2 of them would be on a single straight line?

4. Try the experiment proposed in problem 3. For the center points of the pennies to be on a single straight line, a straightedge would have to just touch the edges of all the pennies at the same time.

These pennies are not all on the same straight line.

These pennies are on the same straight line.

Points that are on the same line are said to be *collinear*.

5. Draw any 2 lines. Choose any 3 points on 1 line and label them *A, B,* and *C*. Choose any 3 points on the other line and label them *A', B',* and *C'*.

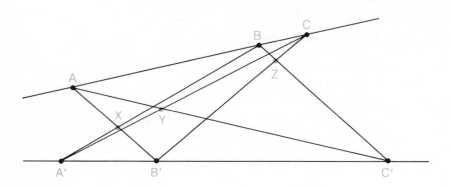

Now very carefully draw *AB'* and *A'B* and circle their intersection. Call it *X*. Draw *AC'* and *A'C* and circle their intersection. Call it *Y*. Draw *BC'* and *B'C* and circle their intersection. Call it *Z*.

[1] What seems to be true of the 3 circled points, X, Y, and Z?

[2] What is the probability that this outcome occurred by chance?

[3] Compare your results with other people's results.

6. Through 1 point, *O*, draw 3 lines, *OP*, *OQ*, and *OR*. Choose
points *A* and *A'* on *OP*, *B* and *B'* on *OQ*, and *C* and *C'* on
OR. (Try to choose the points so that *AB* and *A'B'*, *AC* and
A'C', and *BC* and *B'C'* will meet on your paper.) Draw *AB* and
A'B' until they meet. Label the point where they meet *Z*. Draw
AC and *A'C'* until they meet. Label that point *Y*. Draw *BC* and
B'C' until they meet. Label that point *X*.

[4] **What seems to be true of points *X*, *Y*, and *Z*?**

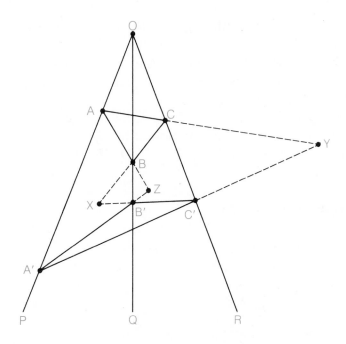

7. In doing problems 5 and 6, suppose you did choose the points
in such a way that 2 lines that were supposed to meet are
parallel. Would the 2 lines seem also to be parallel to the line
through the other 2 intersection points? For example, if *AC* and
A'C' are parallel, are they also parallel to *XY*?

8. Can you draw a figure in which 2 out of the 3 pairs of lines that produce points X, Y, and Z are parallel?

To produce the *dual* of a geometry statement:

A. replace lines with points, and

B. replace points with lines.

---

9. Draw the dual of problem 5. (This problem will require considerable concentration.)

Here's the way to do it. Start with any 2 *points*. Draw 3 lines (call them a, b, and c) through one point and 3 lines (a', b', and c') through the other. (Choose these lines so that a intersects b' and c' on your paper, b intersects a' and c' on your paper, and c intersects a' and b' on your paper.)

Now use a pen or pencil of a different color. Draw a line, x, through BC' (the point that is the intersection of lines b and c') and $B'C$. Draw a line, y, through AC' and $A'C$. Draw a line, z, through AB' and $A'B$.

[5] What is true about lines x, y, and z?

10. Draw the dual of problem 6.

Pappus and Desargues

Here is some historical background. When you did problem 5 on page 266, you discovered that points X, Y, and Z lie on the same straight line under the given conditions. This statement is known as Pappus's Theorem. When you did problem 6 on page 267, you discovered that points X, Y, and Z lie on the same straight line under another set of conditions. This statement is known as Desargues's Theorem.

Pappus (about A.D. 320) was the last of the great Greek scholars of geometry. He wrote about his own work and the work of other, earlier, Greeks in his *Collection*. Mathematicians today know much about Euclid's work through reading what Pappus wrote.

One of the subjects that interested him was the geometry of the honeycomb. He was fascinated by the fact that bees build hexagonal cells in their honeycombs, because he knew that square or triangular cells would hold as much honey but that hexagonal cells require the least wax to build.

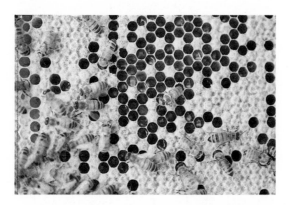

Desargues (1593–1661) was a French architect and engineer. He hoped to help artists produce more realistic art by combining the mathematical ideas on perspective into simple, easy-to-understand rules. Desargues discovered many ideas that are the foundation of modern projective geometry, but his work was not accepted by the mathematicians of his time.

In fact, every printed copy of his book was lost, and his ideas were forgotten. The discoveries he had made were remade by mathematicians in the 1800s. In the 1800s, too, a handwritten copy of his book was found, which is why we know of his work today.

PAP-PUS-POE

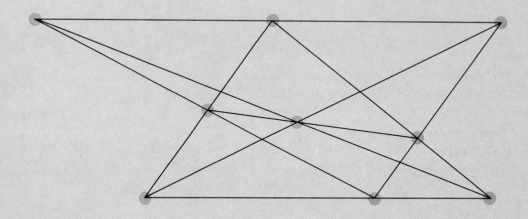

Notice that every circle is situated in exactly 3 rows of circles.

Players: 2
Materials: 5 each of 2 different colored markers (play dimes and play pennies, for example)
Object: To get 3 markers of your color in a row

Rules

1. Take turns placing 1 marker on a circle.
2. The first player to complete a row wins. The loser should play first in the next game.

Another Way to Play This Game

Continue playing until all 9 circles have markers in them.
The player who has more rows is the winner.

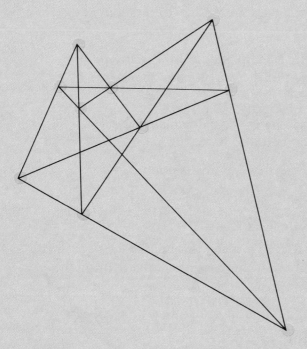

Notice that each of the 10 circles is situated in exactly 3 rows of circles.

Players: 2
Materials: 5 each of 2 different colored markers (play dimes and play pennies, for example)
Object: To get 3 markers of your color in a row

Rules

1. Take turns placing 1 marker on a circle.
2. The first player to complete a row wins. The loser should play first in the next game.

Another Way to Play This Game

Continue playing until all 10 circles have markers in them.
The player who has more rows wins.

Points and Planes

Do these problems. For each, draw a picture or give an example that will convince other people you are right. Think about and look at the walls, lines, and points in your classroom.

1. If 2 lines are drawn in the same plane, in how many points will they meet? Think carefully. Discuss your answer.

2. **a.** How many lines are there through 2 points?
   b. Do the 2 points have to be in the same plane?
   c. Is it possible for 2 points not to be in the same plane?

3. How many planes are there through any 2 points?

4. How many planes are there through any 3 points?

5. Pick at random 4 points in space.

   a. Is it always possible to find a plane through all 4?
   b. What is the probability that there will be a plane through all 4 points?

6. If 2 lines do not intersect in a point, must they be parallel?

7. **a.** Can 2 planes be parallel?
   b. If 2 planes are not parallel, what does their intersection look like?

8. Is it possible for a line and a plane to be parallel? Give an example.

9. Is it possible for a line and a plane to have exactly 1 point in common? Give an example.

10. **a.** Is it possible for a line and a plane to have exactly 2 points in common?
    b. Is it possible for a line and a plane to have at least 2 points in common?
    c. If they do, how would you describe the relationship of the line and plane?

11. Pick 3 points in space. Be sure they are not on the same straight line.

 a. How many lines are there that go through all 3 points?
 b. How many lines are there that go through exactly 2 points?
 c. How many lines are there that go through exactly 1 point?

12. If 3 lines are in the same plane, how many points of intersection (points that are on 2 or more lines) might there be? Be sure you've considered all possibilities.

13. Consider any 3 planes in space. How many lines of intersection (lines that are in 2 or more planes) might there be?

Solve for n.

1. $24.24 \div 2.02 = n$
2. $24.24 \times 2.02 = n$
3. $24.24 + 2.02 = n$
4. $24.24 - 2.02 = n$
5. $2.424 \div 0.202 = n$

6. $242.4 \div 0.202 = n$
7. $2.424 \div 20.2 = n$
8. $242.4 \times 20.2 = n$
9. $24.24 - 0.202 = n$
10. $242.4 + 202 = n$

11. $888.8 \times 1.111 = n$
12. $888.8 \times 11.11 = n$
13. $88.88 \times 11.11 = n$
14. $8.888 \div 111.1 = n$
15. $0.8888 + 0.1111 = n$

16. $0.8888 + 1.111 = n$
17. $888.8 - 11.11 = n$
18. $88.88 \div 11.11 = n$
19. $0.08888 \div 0.01111 = n$
20. $8.888 - 0.01111 = n$

21. $4.705 \div 0.606 = n$
22. $4.705 \div 0.0606 = n$
23. $0.4705 \div 0.606 = n$
24. $4705 + 0.606 = n$
25. $47.05 \times 606 = n$

26. $470.5 - 60.6 = n$
27. $470.5 \times 0.606 = n$
28. $47.05 + 606 = n$
29. $47.05 - 6.06 = n$
30. $4.705 + 606 = n$

31. $9.449 + 855 = n$
32. $94.49 \div 8.55 = n$
33. $944.9 \times 8.55 = n$
34. $94.49 \times 0.855 = n$
35. $9.449 \times 85.5 = n$

36. $9449 - 855 = n$
37. $9449 + 855 = n$
38. $9.449 - 0.855 = n$
39. $94.49 + 85.5 = n$
40. $0.9449 \div 0.855 = n$

Projection in Art

During the 15th century, artists tried to find a better way of showing a 3-dimensional scene on a 2-dimensional canvas. A method that artists used was to pretend they were looking at the scene with 1 eye, so that a light ray from each point of the scene came directly to the eye. They would imagine (or actually place) a glass screen between the scene and the eye. Then they painted what was on the screen.

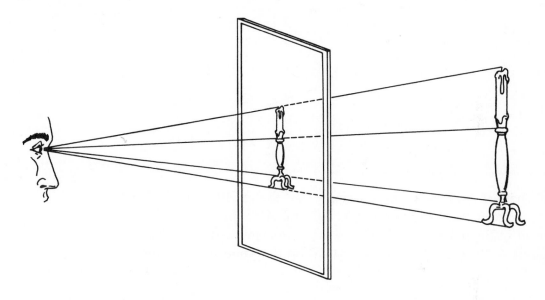

Many interesting questions about the relationship of such projections to the original scene and to each other can be asked. Gérard Desargues was a mathematician who asked and answered many questions about such projections. You learned about one of his theorems on page 269. The theorem we are going to look at now is related to that theorem but applies to lines and planes.

In the drawing below, assume that triangle ABC is projected onto a glass screen. The projection is triangle $A'B'C'$. Notice that there are 5 planes: $OA'B'AB$, $OB'C'BC$, $OC'A'CA$, $A'B'C'$, and ABC. Since AB and $A'B'$ are in the same plane, they can be extended to meet at a point. This statement is true of $B'C'$ and BC and of $A'C'$ and AC.

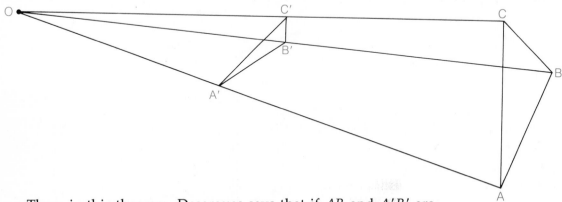

Then, in this theorem, Desargues says that if AB and $A'B'$ are extended to meet in the point X, AC and $A'C'$ are extended to meet in the point Y, and BC and $B'C'$ are extended to meet in the point Z, then X, Y, and Z will all be on the same straight line.

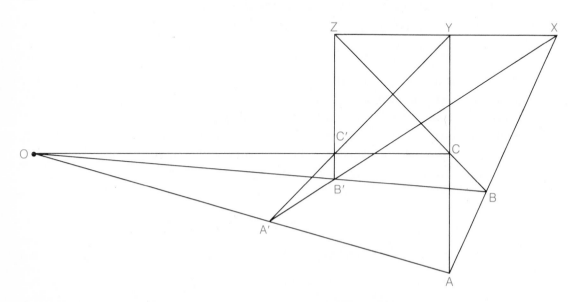

You can prove this theorem easily using your answers to the problems on pages 272 and 273.

1. How many planes are there that contain points A, B, and C?
2. Does the plane containing A, B, and C contain the whole of lines AB, AC, and BC?
3. a. Is there 1 plane that contains A', B', and C'?
   b. Does it contain the whole of lines $A'B'$, $A'C'$, and $B'C'$?
4. If the 2 planes $A'B'C'$ and ABC meet, what is their intersection?
5. Are the points X, Y, and Z in both planes and therefore in their intersection?

Since the intersection of the 2 planes is a straight line, X, Y, and Z are on a straight line.

The theorem you discovered in doing problem 6 on page 267 has both triangles in the same plane and is harder to prove. Desargues proved that theorem, which deals only with lines and points, by using this (3-dimensional) theorem, which deals with planes and lines.

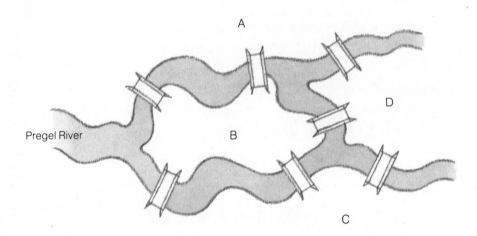

There is a famous problem known as the "7 Bridges of Königsberg" problem. The East Prussian town of Königsberg is now in the Soviet Union and is called Kaliningrad.

Königsberg was built partially on an island where the 2 branches of the Pregel River meet. Parts of the town were built also on both sides of the river and between the 2 branches. (See areas A, B, C, and D on the map above.) There were 7 bridges connecting the various parts of Königsberg. The following 3 questions form the "7 Bridges of Königsberg" problem.

Question 1: Is it possible to plan a walking trip so that you will cross each bridge exactly once and end where you started?

Question 2: Is the trip for question 1 possible if you can end somewhere other than your starting point?

Question 3: Can you state a general theorem that will allow you to solve such problems when there are different numbers of land areas and different numbers of bridges?

Swiss mathematician Leonhard Euler (pronounced "oiler") (1707–1783) solved the Königsberg Bridge problem in 1735. The solution to this problem and the formula relating edges, vertices, and faces of a simply polyhedron ($V + F = 2 + E$) that you discovered in chapter 5 are early contributions by Euler to the subject of topology. Topology can be described as geometry without measurements. In topology we study those geometric properties that don't change when size and shape are changed by squeezing, stretching, bending, twisting, or otherwise distorting an object.

In the bridge problem, the distances between the bridges, the lengths of the bridges, and so on, are of no importance to the problem. In the formula $V + F = 2 + E$, the size of the polyhedron is of no importance.

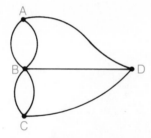

Since length and size aren't of importance in our discussion, this figure shows the important information contained in the bridge problem.

First look just at *A* and its bridges.

[1] How many bridges are there connecting *A* with other sections of town?

[2] If you start at *A* and cross each of these bridges once, will you end up at *A* or somewhere else?

[3] If you start somewhere other than at *A* and cross each of these bridges once, will you end up at *A* or somewhere else?

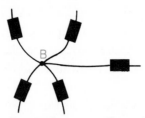

[4] How would you answer discussion questions 1, 2, and 3 for point *B*?

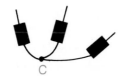

[5] How would you answer discussion questions 1, 2, and 3 for point *C*?

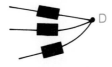

[6] How would you answer discussion questions 1, 2, and 3 for point *D*?

[7] What is a rule that tells when walking trips such as those described in questions 1 and 2 on page 278 are possible?

We will say that a walk is a Königsberg walk if it crosses every bridge on a map exactly once and that it is a complete Königsberg walk if it ends at the same place it started.

For each of the following maps (problems 1–10), find answers to parts a–c.

a. Is it possible to plan a Königsberg walk?

b. It is possible to plan a complete Königsberg walk?

c. What are all the possible starting and ending places? If they are different, list the starting place first.

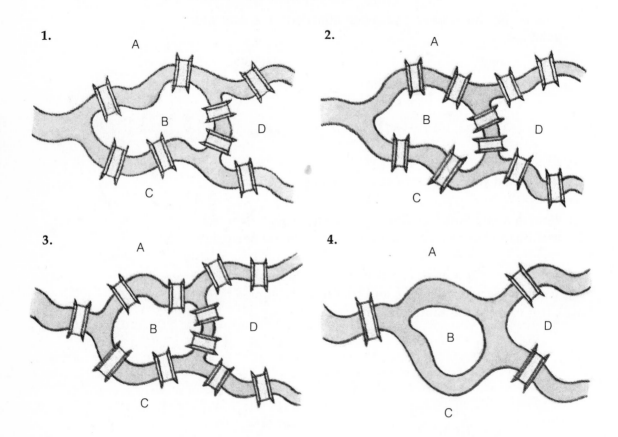

1.

2.

3.

4.

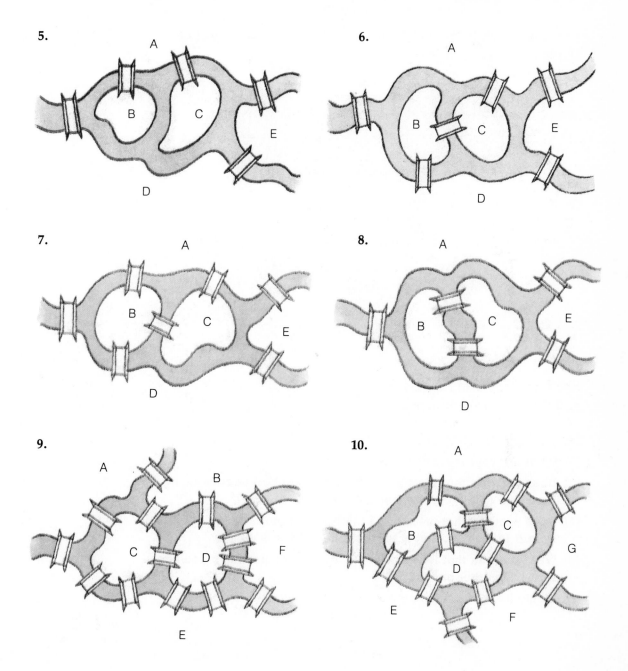

5.

A

B

C

E

D

6.

A

B

C

E

D

7.

A

B

C

E

D

8.

A

B

C

E

D

9.

A

B

C

D

F

E

10.

A

B

C

D

G

E

F

Thomasine was trying to find the ends of a long, tangled hose.
The hose looked like this:

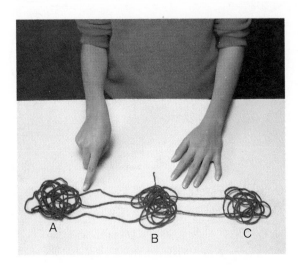

She found one end in mess B. She knows there is only one other
end (the hose is continuous).

[1] Where is the other end?

[2] What are your reasons?

**[3] Does knowing that there are 2 (an even number) strands going
from *B* to *C* tell you whether the other end is in *C*?**

**[4] Does knowing that there are 3 (an odd number) strands going
from *B* to *A* tell you whether the other end is in *A*?**

**[5] What is a rule that tells where one end of the hose is if you know
where the other end is?**

[6] Would the same rule apply to thread as well as to a hose?

A *closed curve* has no ends, so it does have an inside
and an outside.

A *simple curve* does not cross itself.

A *simple closed curve* has 1 clearly defined inside.

How can you tell whether a point is inside or outside a simple
closed curve?

Curve 1

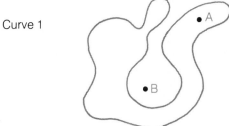

With a curve like curve 1, it is easy. *A* is obviously inside, and *B*
is outside.

**[7] Would you cross the curve an even, or an odd, number of times
to get from *A* to *B*?**

Curve 2

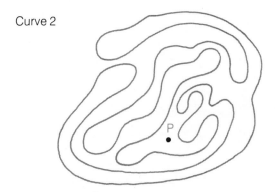

**[8] Is it harder to tell whether a point (*P*) is inside or outside a curve
like curve 2?**

**[9] Do you cross the curve an even or an odd number of times to get
to a point that is obviously outside the curve?**

For each of the following situations, there is 1 continuous piece of yarn. Determine where the missing end is.

1.

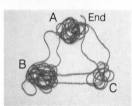

2.

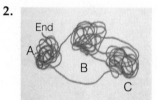

3.

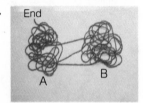

4.

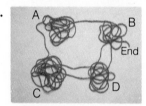

5.

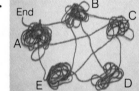

6.

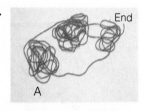

State the smallest number of pieces of hose or thread that might be present. Explain your answer.

7.

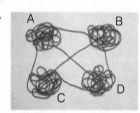

8.

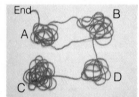

9.

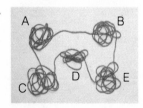

Tell whether the labeled points are inside or outside the closed simple curves.

10.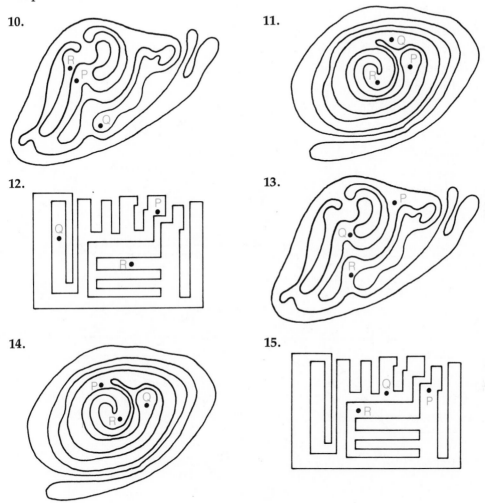

11.

12.

13.

14.

15.

16. Give a rule that tells how you found the answers to problems 10–15.

If you were programming a computer to find area using the Monte Carlo procedure, you might want to include this simple method to help the computer decide whether a point is inside or outside the simple closed curve.

Area

You know that there are many figures for which area can be computed by means of simple formulas. The basis for those formulas is the efficient counting of the number of unit squares that would fit inside a figure.

The drawings of the figures below should help you remember the formulas for their areas. Write the formula for each. The first has been done for you.

1.

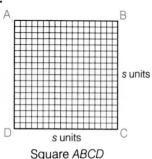

Square *ABCD*

Area = $s \cdot s$ (or s^2) square units

2.

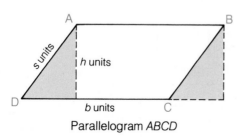

Rectangle *ABCD*

Area = ?

3.

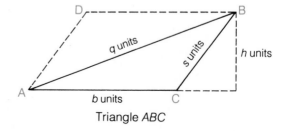

Parallelogram *ABCD*

Area = ?

4.

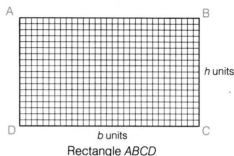

Triangle *ABC*

Area = ?
Hint: In parallelogram *ADBC*, is
△*ABC* congruent to △*BAD*?

5.

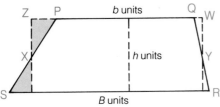

Trapezoid *PQRS*

Area = ?
Hint: Is the length of *XY* equal
to the average of the lengths of
PQ and *SR*?

6.

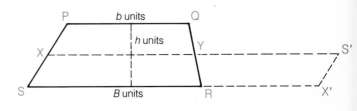

Trapezoid *PQRS*

Area = ?
Hint: Think of *Y* as a hinge,
and swing the top of the
trapezoid to *YS′X′R*, getting
parallelogram *SX′S′X* with
height $\frac{h}{2}$ and base *B* + *b* units.

Are the formulas for problems 5 and 6 the same?

7.

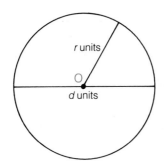

Circumference (or distance around) = ?
Area = ?

Remember
π is an irrational number. Its approximate value is
3.1415926536 . . . . For most purposes, $\pi \approx 3.14$ or $\pi \approx 3\frac{1}{7}$
can be used.

Use the formulas you found on pages 288 and 289 to calculate the areas described in the figures for problems 1–10 below. Assume that plane figures that look like rectangles, squares, circles, and so on *are* rectangles, squares, circles, and so on. Round answers to the nearest hundredth of a square centimeter.

1.

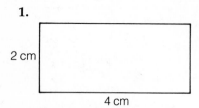

Area of rectangle = ?

2.

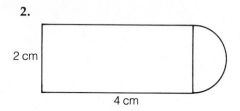

Area of figure = ?

3.

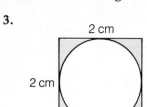

Area of shaded portion = ?

4.

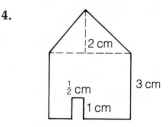

Area of figure = ?

5.

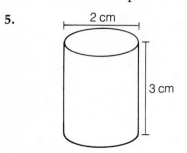

Area of the top and bottom circles plus the lateral (or side) surface of the cylinder = ? Hints: If you cut the lateral surface along a vertical line and flattened it out, what figure would you get? What are the lengths of the base and height of that figure?

6.

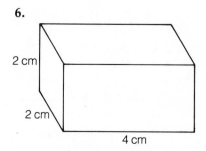

Surface area of box = ? Hint: The box has square ends and rectangular sides, top, and bottom.

7.

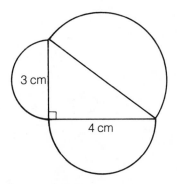

Area of figure = ?
Hint: Remember that the ⌐ symbol indicates a right angle. The Pythagorean Theorem will help you calculate the diameter of the large semicircle.

8.

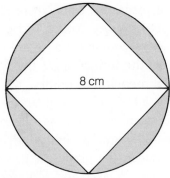

Area of shaded portion = ?
Hint: Use the Pythagorean Theorem if necessary.

9.

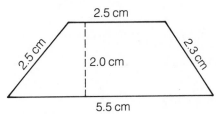

Area of trapezoid = ?

10.

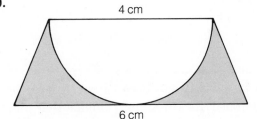

Area of shaded portion = ?

11. Is the area of the semicircle on the hypotenuse of a right triangle always equal to the sum of the areas of the semicircles on the other 2 sides?

12. Use a tape measure to measure the distance around each of several circles (the top of a wastebasket, a large circle you draw, and so on) and the diameter of each circle. Divide the circumference by the diameter in each case. What values of π do you get?

13. Is 3.14 or $3\frac{1}{7}$ closer to π?

Formulas for Volume

There are formulas for calculating the volume of many 3-dimensional figures. You could probably figure out lots of these by yourself. Some are quite surprising. We will give you the formulas for the volume of some common 3-dimensional figures.

A *prism* is a 3-dimensional figure with congruent polygons in parallel planes as its top and bottom. Its sides are parallelograms. Its height is the perpendicular distance between the planes of its top and bottom.

In the figure, *PQRST* and *VWXYZ* are the top and bottom of the polygon and *h* is its height.

The volume of a prism is the product of its height and the area of its base, *B*. (Either the top or the bottom can be the base.)

$$V = hB$$

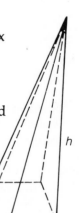

A *pyramid* is a 3-dimensional figure with a polygon as its base. Its sides are triangles that meet at the vertex (or top). Its height is the perpendicular distance between the vertex and the base.

The volume of a pyramid is $\frac{1}{3}$ the volume of the corresponding prism, or $\frac{1}{3}$ the product of the height and the area of the base.

$$V = \frac{1}{3}hB$$

[1] How is a cylinder like a prism?

[2] How is a cone like a pyramid?

The formula for the volume of a cylinder is the same as that for the volume of a prism. The formula for the volume of a cone is the same as that for the volume of a pyramid.

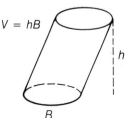

$V = hB$

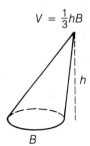

$V = \frac{1}{3}hB$

The volume of a sphere is expressed by the following formula:

$$V = \frac{4}{3}\pi r^3.$$

The area of a sphere is expressed by the following formula:

$$A = 4\pi r^2 \text{ or } \pi d^2.$$

Use the formulas you know for volume and area to do problems 1 and 2. (*Derive* means "to work out from something you know.")

1. Derive a formula for the volume of a cube in terms of the length of a side.

2. Derive a formula for the volume of a rectangular box in terms of the lengths of its length, width, and height (*l, w,* and *h*). (Another name for a rectangular box is *rectangular parallelepiped*.)

[3] Could a computer be programmed to find volume using the Monte Carlo procedure?

[4] How would random points be chosen?

[5] How might you have the computer decide whether a point is inside a simple closed surface?

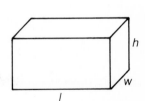

Find the volume of each figure. Round answers to the nearest tenth of a cubic centimeter.

1.

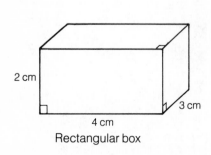

Rectangular box

2. 2 cm

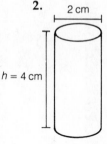

$h = 4$ cm

Right circular cylinder

3. 2 cm

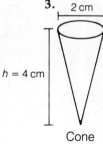

$h = 4$ cm

Cone

4.

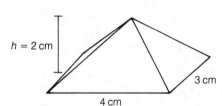

$h = 2$ cm

4 cm

3 cm

Pyramid with rectangular base

5.

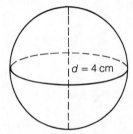

$d = 4$ cm

Sphere, diameter = 4 cm

6. 3 balls are stored in a cylinder. The balls just touch the sides of the cylinder. The top ball and bottom ball just touch the top and bottom of the cylinder. The diameter of each ball is 8 centimeters. How much air space is there in the cylinder when the 3 balls are in it?

7. The diameter of the earth at the equator is about 7926.41 miles.

   a. If you could build a railroad around the earth on the equator, at sea level, how many miles long would it be?

   b. If you built an elevated railroad around the equator that was 528 feet $\left(\frac{1}{10}\text{ of a mile}\right)$ above sea level, how much longer would it be than the railroad at sea level?

8. When the tires on Ms. Ohashi's car are new and properly inflated, their radius is 312 millimeters.

   a. How far does the car go each time a tire turns 1 complete revolution?

   b. If, through wear and underinflation, the tires have a radius of only 300 millimeters, how far will the car go each time a tire turns completely?

   c. Ms. Ohashi's odometer recorded the trip from her home to Chicago as being 2000 kilometers when her tires were new and properly inflated. How long will the odometer say the trip is when the tires have a radius of 300 millimeters? (The odometer counts revolutions and converts to distance.)

9. How would you measure $\frac{1}{7}$ of a foot using an ordinary foot ruler? Be sure that your method can actually be carried out and that it will be accurate to within $\frac{1}{16}$ of an inch.

10. In parallelogram *ABCD*, the length of *AD* is 4 centimeters and the length of *CD* is 3 centimeters. The perpendicular distance from *A* to *DC* is 3 centimeters.

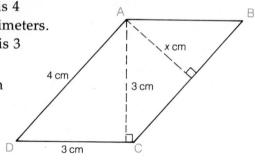

   a. What is the perpendicular distance from *A* to *BC*?
   b. Explain your answer.

11. In right triangle *ABC*, *AB* = 3 centimeters and *BC* = 4 centimeters.

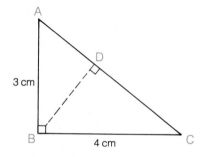

   a. How long is *BD* (the perpendicular from *B* to *AC*)?
   b. How long is *AD*?
   c. How long is *CD*?

12. The 9 dots are arranged in 3 rows and 3 columns, 1 centimeter apart. Copy the figure. Draw 4 connected straight lines through all 9 dots. Don't lift your pencil or retrace any lines. You'll make only 3 turns.

  • • •

  • • •

  • • •

13. With 3 sticks of the same size you can make 1 equilateral triangle. With 4 sticks of the same size you can still make only 1 equilateral triangle. With 5 sticks of the same size you can make 2 equilateral triangles. How many equilateral triangles can you make with 6 sticks?

Mr. Cepeda drives about 10,000 kilometers each year. He uses about 6 liters of gasoline per 100 kilometers. He does most of the driving in town, and he has been purchasing gasoline from the Good Service gas station for about 5 years. He is happy with the service he gets.

1. A new gas station opens and charges 1¢ per liter less than the Good Service station. Should Mr. Cepeda change gas stations?

2. For each of the following situations, how much of a price difference must there be before you would switch stations if you were in Mr. Cepeda's situation?

   a. The service is the same at each station.
   b. The service is better at the Good Service station.
   c. The service is better at the new service station.
   d. There is a plentiful supply of gasoline.
   e. There is a shortage of gasoline.

1. Assume that every point *inside* the unit square that can be labeled using 2-decimal-place coordinates has been labeled. Points such as (0.01, 0.01), (0.78, 0.01), (0.01, 0.99), and (0.99, 0.99) are included, but points on the border such as (0, 0), (0, 0.35), (0.71, 0), and (1, 1) are not.

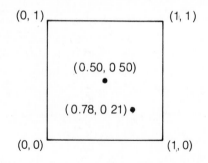

a. How many points inside the square have been labeled?

b. Suppose you picked 100 points inside the square at random, and 25 were inside a simple closed curve and the other 75 were outside the curve. What would you estimate the area inside the curve to be (in square units)?

c. Suppose you repeated the experiment with 1000 points, and 270 were inside. What would you estimate the area inside the curve to be?

d. If you pick 1 point at random, what is the probability that it is the point (0.78, 0.21)?

2. Is it possible for a line and a plane to have no points in common? If so, how would you describe their relationship?

3. Is it possible for a line and a plane to have exactly 1 point in common? If so, how would you describe their relationship?

4. Is it possible for a line and a plane to have exactly 2 points in common? If so, how would you describe their relationship?

5. Is it possible for a line and a plane to have at least 2 points in common? If so, how would you describe their relationship?

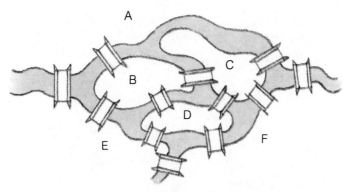

6. a. For the map above, is it possible to plan a Königsberg walk —a walk that crosses every bridge exactly once?

b. Is it possible to plan a complete Königsberg walk—a walk that crosses every bridge exactly once and ends at the starting point?

c. What are the possible starting points for Königsberg walks?

d. For each starting point, what are the possible ending points?

7. In each figure, a continuous piece of string is shown and one end is identified. In which tangle is the other end?

a.

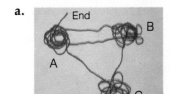

b.

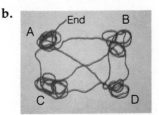

8. Tell whether each labeled point (*P, Q, R*) is inside or outside the simple closed curve.

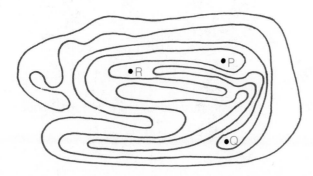

9. Calculate the area of each of the following figures to the nearest tenth of a square centimeter.

a.

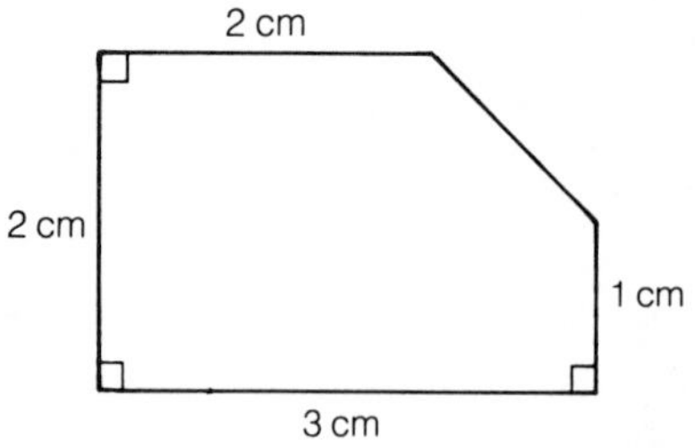

2 cm

2 cm

3 cm

1 cm

b.

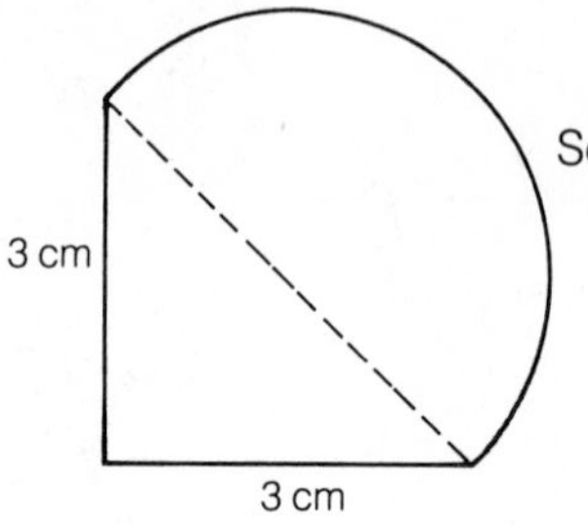

Semicircle

3 cm

3 cm

c.

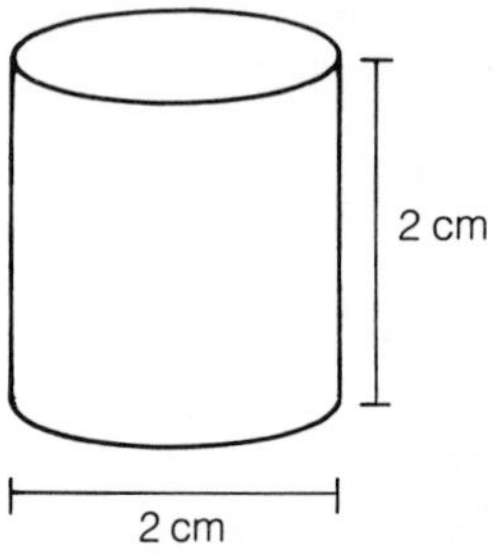

2 cm

2 cm

All surface area of the right circular cylinder

d.

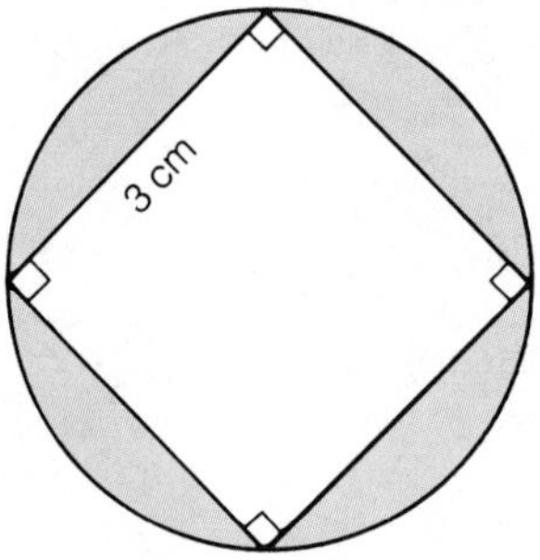

3 cm

Area of shaded region if square has sides 3 cm long

10. Calculate the volume of each of the following figures to the nearest tenth of a cubic centimeter.

a.

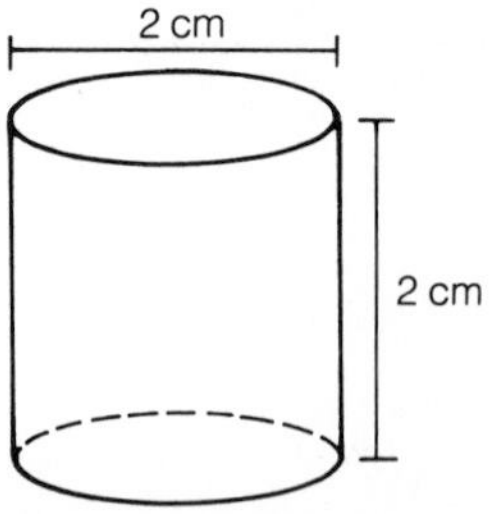

2 cm

2 cm

Right circular cylinder

b.

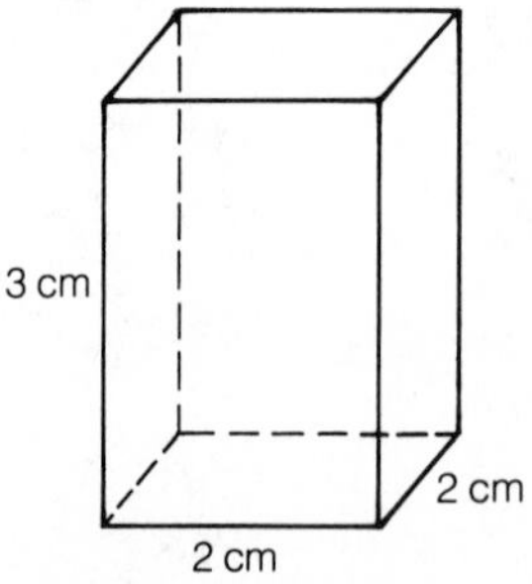

3 cm

2 cm

2 cm

Rectangular box

c.

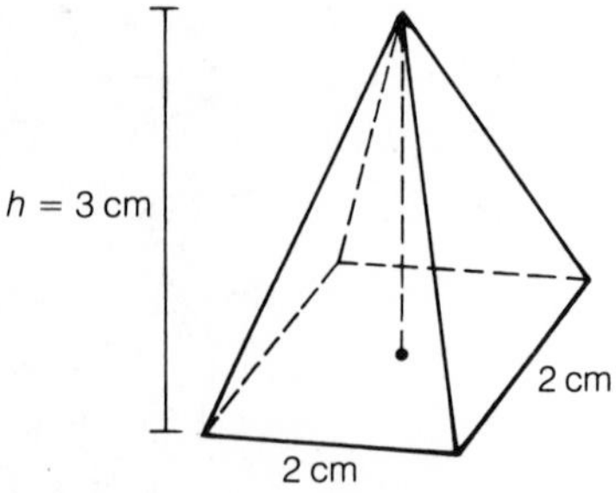

$h = 3$ cm

2 cm

2 cm

Square pyramid

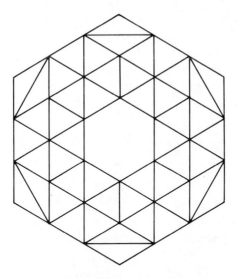

1. How many triangles are there in this figure?
2. How many hexagons are there in this figure?

Make up puzzles like this to share with your family and friends.
Try using other geometric shapes.

1. Assume that every point *inside* the 10-unit by 10-unit square that can be labeled using 1-decimal-place coordinates has been labeled. Points such as (0.1, 0.1), (7.8, 0.1), (0.1, 9.9), and (9.9, 9.9) are included, but points on the border such as (0, 0), (0, 3.5), (7.1, 0) and (10, 10) are not.

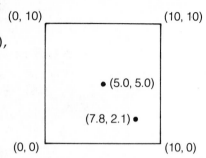

   a. How many points inside the square have been labeled?
   b. Suppose you picked 100 points inside the square at random, and 25 were inside a simple closed curve and the other 75 were outside the curve. What would you estimate the area inside the curve to be (in square units)?
   c. Suppose you repeated the experiment with 1000 points, and 270 were inside. What would you estimate the area inside the curve to be?
   d. If you pick 1 point at random, what is the probability that it is the point (7.8, 2.1)?

2. Is it possible for a line and a plane to have no points in common? If so, how would you describe their relationship?

3. Is it possible for a line and a plane to have exactly 1 point in common? If so, how would you describe their relationship?

4. Is it possible for a line and a plane to have exactly 2 points in common? If so, how would you describe their relationship?

5. Is it possible for a line and a plane to have at least 2 points in common? If so, how would you describe their relationship?

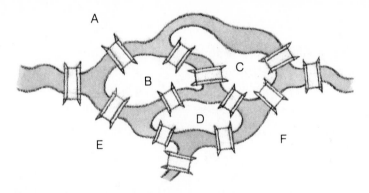

6. **a.** For the map above, is it possible to plan a Königsberg walk
—a walk that crosses every bridge exactly once?
 b. Is it possible to plan a complete Königsberg walk—a walk
that crosses every bridge exactly once and ends at the
starting point?
 c. What are the possible starting points for Königsberg walks?
 d. For each starting point, what are the possible ending points?

7. In each figure, a continuous piece of string is shown and one
end is identified. In which tangle is the other end?

a. 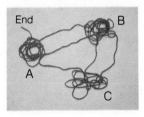   **b.**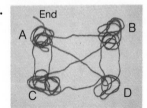

8. Tell whether each labeled point (*P*, *Q*, *R*) is inside or outside
the simple closed curve.

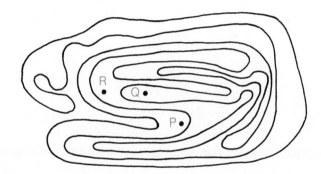

9. Calculate the area of each of the following figures to the nearest tenth of a square centimeter.

a.

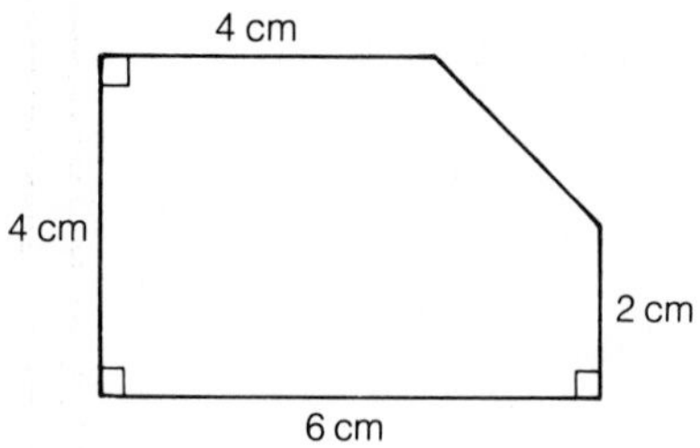

4 cm

4 cm

2 cm

6 cm

b.

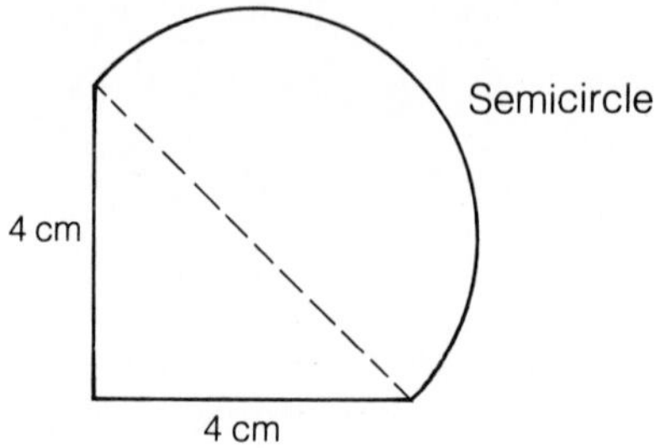

4 cm

Semicircle

4 cm

c.

4 cm

4 cm

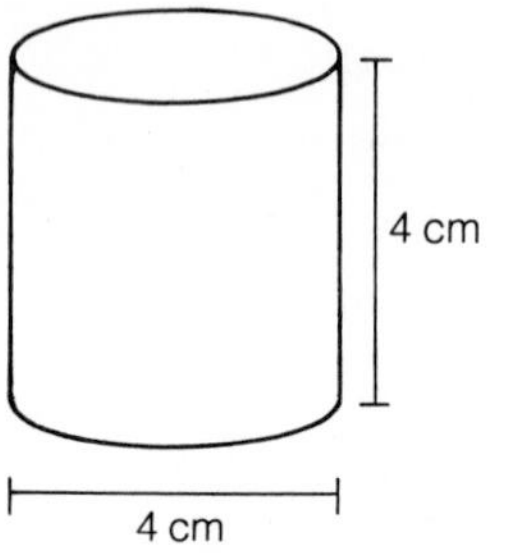

All surface area of the right circular cylinder

d.

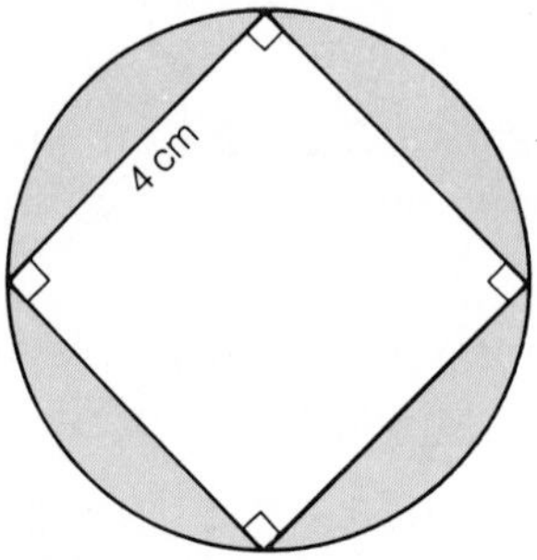

4 cm

Area of shaded region if square has sides 4 cm long

10. Calculate the volume of each of the following figures to the nearest tenth of a cubic centimeter.

a.

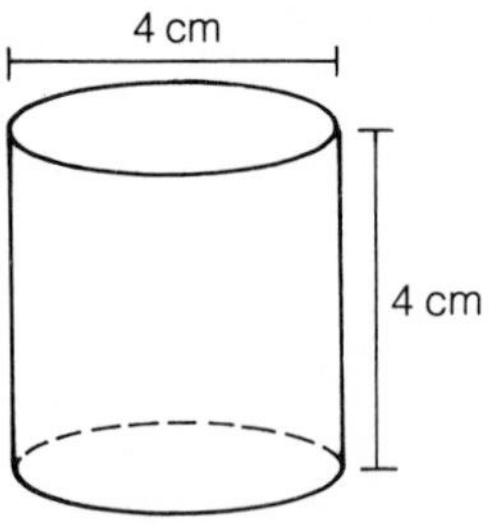

4 cm

4 cm

Right circular cylinder

b.

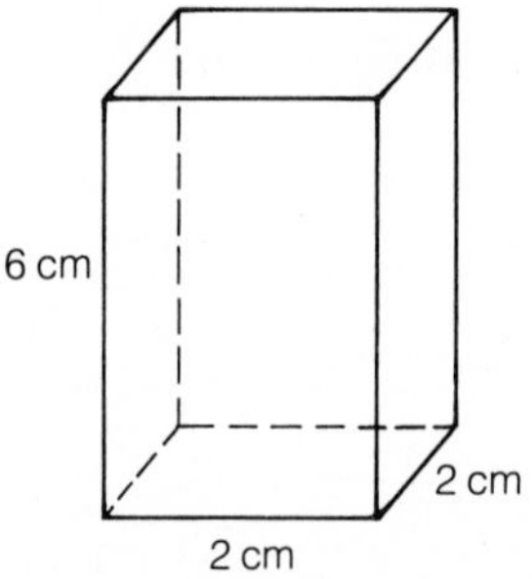

6 cm

$h = 4$ cm

2 cm

2 cm

Rectangular box

c.

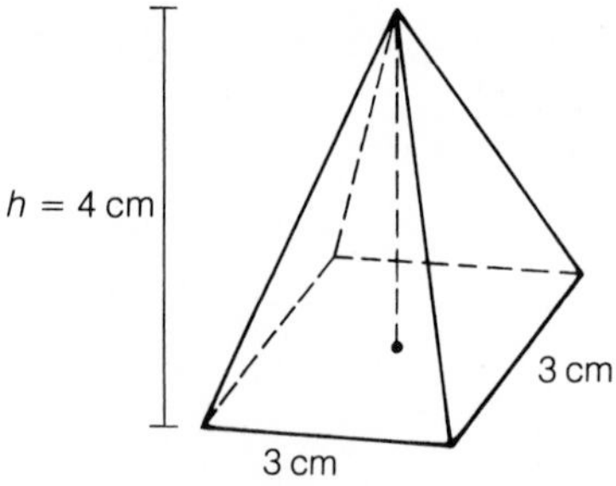

3 cm

3 cm

Square pyramid

1. Draw 3 identical rectangles. Each rectangle should be 5 times as long as it is high.

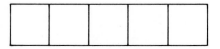

2. Draw 4 lines on each rectangle to divide it into 5 squares.
3. Cut out the rectangles and fold them on the lines.

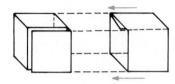

4. Fold one strip as shown and slide another over it to form a cube.

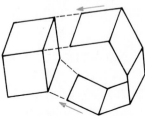

5. Slip one end of the third strip into the slot at the top of the second and slip the other end into the slot at the bottom.

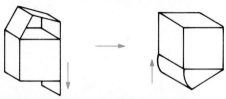

6. Push and pull the third strip through the slot as far as it will go and tuck the end into the nearest slot.

Think of something interesting you can do with a cube like this.

CHAPTER 9
ALGEBRA

9

[1] Do you remember the distributive law?

The distributive law is sometimes called the distributive law of multiplication over addition. What this term means is that the multiplication is *distributed* or "spread out" over the addition.

$$a \cdot (b + c) = a \cdot b + a \cdot c$$

We use the distributive law often in doing arithmetic. Sometimes we are not aware that we are using it, because it is such a natural thing to do.

The distributive law was used by the ancient Egyptians. The Rhind papyrus is a collection of mathematical examples copied by a scribe named Ahmes about 1650 B.C. It is a copy of a much earlier mathematical work and tells us a great deal about how the ancient Egyptians did their mathematics. In one of the problems Ahmes shows how to do this problem:

$$\text{Double } 3\tfrac{21}{64}.$$

The Egyptians wrote $3\tfrac{21}{64}$ as $3 + \tfrac{1}{4} + \tfrac{1}{16} + \tfrac{1}{64}$. So to double $3\tfrac{21}{64}$, they doubled each term: $6 + \tfrac{1}{2} + \tfrac{1}{8} + \tfrac{1}{32}$. Then they added to get $6\tfrac{21}{32}$.

The Greeks also used the distributive law. Euclid showed geometrically that $a(b + c + d) = ab + ac + ad$. He used a rectangle $BCGH$ and cut it with 2 lines DK and EL.

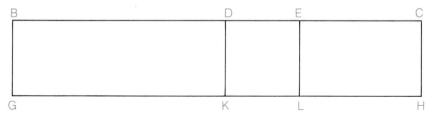

Next he used letters to represent different lengths: $BG = a$, $GK = b$, $KL = c$, and $LH = d$.

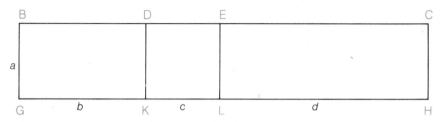

Then he could show the following relationship:

Area $BGHC$ = area $BGKD$ + area $DKLE$ + area $ELHC$, or
$a(b + c + d) = ab + ac + ad$.

[2] What are some ways that you use the distributive law?

Calculations with the Difference of 2 Squares

Andrew was asked to multiply 37 times 43. He thought for a moment and said, "1591."

[1] How did he figure out the answer without a calculator or pencil and paper?

"Easy," said Andrew. "40 squared is 1600 and 3 squared is 9, so 37 × 43 is 1600 − 9, or 1591."

[2] Does any of this make sense?

[3] Did Andrew get the right answer?

You know that the distributive law is sometimes useful in doing arithmetic. Let's use the distributive and commutative laws to consider the following relationship.

$$(x - y)(x + y) = (x - y)x + (x - y)y$$
$$(x - y)(x + y) = x^2 - yx + xy - y^2$$
$$(x - y)(x + y) = x^2 - xy + xy - y^2$$
$$(x - y)(x + y) = x^2 - y^2$$

Remember

$$(x - y)(x + y) = x^2 - y^2$$

[4] Is this true for all values of x and y?

Is 37 equal to 40 − 3? Is 43 equal to 40 + 3?

$$\text{Then } 37 \times 43 = (40 - 3)(40 + 3)$$
$$37 \times 43 = 40^2 - 3^2$$
$$37 \times 43 = 1600 - 9$$
$$37 \times 43 = 1591$$

To compute 36 × 43, we notice that 36 × 43 = 37 × 43 − 43. So 36 × 43 = 1591 − 43 = 1548. (To subtract 43 from 1591, it may help to subtract 41 and then 2 more.)

Rewrite each of the following problems in the form $(x - y)(x + y)$ or $(x + y)(x - y)$. Choose x and y such that you know the values of x^2 and y^2. Then give the answer.

1. 18×22 **4.** 31×29 **7.** 63×57 **10.** 103×97 **13.** 990×1010

2. 17×23 **5.** 34×26 **8.** 68×72 **11.** 197×203 **14.** 80×120

3. 15×25 **6.** 75×83 **9.** 108×92 **12.** 194×206 **15.** 61×39

Rewrite each problem in a form like $(x - y)(x + y) + q$. Choose x and y such that you know the values of x^2 and y^2. Then give the answer. For example: $47 \times 55 = (50 - 3)(50 + 3) + 2(47) = 2500 - 9 + 94 = 2585$. (You may need to use more steps. For example: $47 \times 55 = 47 \times 53 + 2(47) = 2500 - 9 + 94 = 2500 + 85 = 2585$.)

16. 26×35 **19.** 98×103 **22.** 75×64 **25.** 41×38 **28.** 81×120

17. 31×28 **20.** 75×65 **23.** 76×65 **26.** 197×204 **29.** 62×39

18. 98×101 **21.** 75×66 **24.** 74×65 **27.** 991×1010 **30.** 61×38

31. Look back at problems 16–30.

   a. Were there easier ways to do some of the problems?

   b. Which can be done more easily?

32. Consider this problem: 34×87

   a. Can this problem be modified to involve only the difference of 2 squares?

   b. Think of it as $(33 \times 87) + 87$. What would you write in the blanks to make 33×87 the difference of 2 squares? $(\underline{\quad} - \underline{\quad})(\underline{\quad} + \underline{\quad})$

   c. Do you know what 27^2 is?

   d. Do you think it's easier to just multiply 34 times 87 the usual way?

The work in this chapter is designed to help free you from dependence on just one way to do arithmetic. With a little practice you will find that many arithmetic calculations are more easily done using a little algebra. In this chapter you will be shown some ways to use algebra to simplify calculations. Try to work out others on your own.

Patterns in Squares

Look at the following table of squares of whole numbers. See if you can find a pattern that helps you predict the next square.

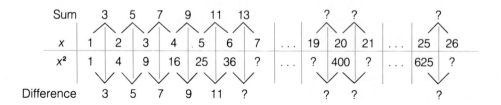

Sum	3	5	7	9	11	13		?	?		?	
x	1	2	3	4	5	6	7	... 19	20	21	... 25	26
x^2	1	4	9	16	25	36	?	... ?	400	?	... 625	?
Difference	3	5	7	9	11	?		?	?		?	

Does it seem that $(x + 1)^2 = x^2 + x + (x + 1)$?

Multiply $(x + 1)(x + 1)$ to see if you can show that for every number x, $(x + 1)^2 = x^2 + x + (x + 1)$.

You can use this formula to help you find the squares of some numbers. For example, what is 21^2? You know $20^2 = 400$, so

$$400 + 20 + 21 = 441.$$

We can also use the formula to go backward:

$$x^2 = (x + 1)^2 = x - (x + 1)$$

For example, what is 19^2? Since $20^2 = 400$,

$$19^2 = 400 - 20 - 19 = 361.$$

If you use the rule twice (one time after another), you can calculate, for example, 42^2:

$$42^2: $$
$$40^2 = 1600$$
$$41^2 = 1600 + 40 + 41 = 1681$$
$$42^2 = 1681 + 41 + 42 = 1681 + 83 = 1764$$

(You may decide that it's easier just to multiply 42 by 42.)

Solve for n. Use any procedure you like.

1. $50^2 = n$	**10.** $70^2 = n$	**19.** $14^2 = n$	**28.** $140^2 = n$
2. $51^2 = n$	**11.** $71^2 = n$	**20.** $15^2 = n$	**29.** $141^2 = n$
3. $52^2 = n$	**12.** $61^2 = n$	**21.** $16^2 = n$	**30.** $150^2 = n$
4. $49^2 = n$	**13.** $39^2 = n$	**22.** $81^2 = n$	**31.** $151^2 = n$
5. $7^2 = n$	**14.** $201^2 = n$	**23.** $79^2 = n$	**32.** $149^2 = n$
6. $7^4 = n$	**15.** $1001^2 = n$	**24.** $110^2 = n*$	**33.** $3^4 = n$
7. $100^2 = n$	**16.** $11^2 = n$	**25.** $111^2 = n$	**34.** $3^8 = n$
8. $101^2 = n$	**17.** $12^2 = n$	**26.** $31^2 = n$	
9. $99^2 = n$	**18.** $13^2 = n$	**27.** $29^2 = n$	

Calculate the area of each figure.

35.   **36.**

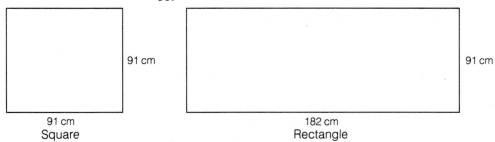

71 cm — 71 cm — Square

142 cm — 71 cm — Rectangle

37.   **38.**

91 cm — 91 cm — Square

182 cm — 91 cm — Rectangle

39.   **40.**

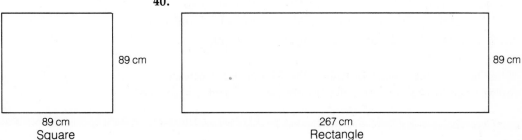

89 cm — 89 cm — Square

267 cm — 89 cm — Rectangle

*Hint: does the answer to problem 16 help?

Algebra **313**

Product of 2 Binomials

Knowing and using the relationship $(x - y)(x + y) = x^2 - y^2$ can be very helpful in doing some calculations, as you have seen. Sometimes using even more complicated algebraic calculations can also be useful.

Consider $(a + b)(c + d) = (a + b)c + (a + b)d = ac + bc + ad + bd$. You can look at $(a + b)(c + d) = ac + bc + ad + bd$ geometrically. Divide a rectangle into 4 parts by drawing 2 perpendicular lines. Label appropriate lengths a, b, c, and d.

The area of the rectangle can be found in 2 ways:

A. Multiply the length by the width: $(a + b)(c + d)$.
B. Add the areas of the 4 parts: $ac + bc + ad + bd$.

Since the area must be the same,

$$(a + b)(c + d) = ac + bc + ad + bd.$$

Now, suppose you let $a = 70$, $b = 4$, $c = 50$, and $d = 8$.

$$(70 + 4)(50 + 8) = (70 \times 50) + (4 \times 50) + (70 \times 8) + (4 \times 8)$$
$$= 3500 + 200 + 560 + 32$$

If you multiplied 74 by 58 in the usual way it would look like the process shown at the right. What you would do is multiply 8×4, getting 32 (notice the 32 above). Then you'd multiply 8×7 (really 8×70), getting 56 tens (notice the 560 above). Usually, we combine the 32 and the 560 as shown to get 592.

$$\begin{array}{r} 74 \\ \times\ 58 \\ \hline 592 \\ 370 \\ \hline \end{array}$$

What is the relationship between the 370 in the ordinary multiplication problem and the numbers 3500 and 200 above?

When you multiply two 2-digit numbers, you multiply each digit in the first factor by each digit in the second, getting 4 partial products. In algebra, we do the same thing. First let's look at some important words.

A *term* is a number or a variable (such as 5, 16, x, y, and so on), or a product of numbers and variables (such as $\frac{x}{2}$, $3x$, $\frac{2}{y}$, and so on).

A *binomial* is an expression with 2 terms separated by the plus or the minus sign (such as $a + b$, $3x - 7y$, $pqr - 37z$, $\frac{x}{2} - \frac{3}{y}$, and so on).

When you multiply 2 binomials, you multiply each term in one factor by each term in the other and add or subtract the resulting terms. Remember that a term like $3x$ means 3 times x. If $x = 6$, $3x = 3 \times 6 = 18$. ($3x$ is not equal to 36 or to $3 + 6$.) Remember too that you can always think about the terms being added if you allow negative numbers. That means that you can think of $y - 3x$ as $y + (-3x)$.

You can find the product of two 2-digit numbers without using a calculator or pencil and paper if you understand base-ten numeration and think of the numbers as binomials.

Here is an example of finding the product of two 2-digit numbers without using a calculator or doing it the long way with pencil and paper.

A. $\begin{array}{r} 74 \\ \times\ 58 \\ \hline 2 \end{array}$ Find the ones digit: $8 \times 4 = 32$. Write the 2. Remember the 3 tens.

B. $\begin{array}{r} 74 \\ \times\ 58 \\ \hline 92 \end{array}$ Find the tens digit: Multiply 8×7 (tens) and add the 3 tens from step A. Then multiply 5 (tens) $\times$ 4 and add it. $8 \times 7 = 56$; $56 + 3 = 59$; $4 \times 5 = 20$; $59 + 20 = 79$. Write the 9 in the tens column and remember the 7 hundreds.

C. $\begin{array}{r} 74 \\ \times\ 58 \\ \hline 4292 \end{array}$ Find the next digits: Multiply 5 (tens) $\times$ 7 (tens) and add the 7 hundreds from step B. $5 \times 7 = 35$; $35 + 7 = 42$. Write 2 in the hundreds column and 4 in the thousands column.

With practice you can do this procedure quickly without mentioning "tens" and "hundreds."

$\begin{array}{r} 74 \\ \times\ 58 \\ \hline 4292 \end{array}$ $8 \times 4 = 32$. Write 2 and remember 3.
$(8 \times 7) + 3 + (5 \times 4) = 79$. Write 9 and remember 7.
$(5 \times 7) + 7 = 42$.

Try to do the following problems in your head. Write just the answers on your paper.

1.   23
   × 34

2.   37
   × 37

3.   14
   × 13

4.   42
   × 32

5.   25
   × 25

6.   104
   × 103

7.   71
   × 54

8.   85
   × 85

9.   107
   × 206

10.   27
   × 52

11.   18
   × 18

12.   207
   × 502

13.   57
   × 46

14.   73
   × 73

15.   2007
   × 5002

More Patterns in Squares

Look at the chart below. Try to find a pattern and use it to predict the other squares on the list.

x	5	15	25	35	45	55	65	75	85	95	105	115
x^2	25	225	625	1225	2025	3025						

Each value of x can be written as $10n + 5$, where n is a whole number. See if the following explanation tells why your pattern will work for all values of n.

If you square a number in the form $10n + 5$, you get

$$(10n + 5)^2 = (10n + 5)(10n + 5)$$
$$= 100n^2 + 50n + 50n + 25$$
$$= 100n^2 + 100n + 25.$$

Using the distributive rule on the first 2 terms, $100n^2 + 100n = 100(n^2 + n)$, so $100n^2 + 100n + 25 = 100(n^2 + n) + 25$. So, to square 85, square 8 (64), add 8 (72), multiply by 100 (7200), and add 25 (7225).

Since $n^2 + n$ is multiplied by 100, 25 will always be added to some number of 100s in this process. So writing 25 after $n^2 + n$ is the same as adding 25 to $100(n^2 + n)$.

You may also think of $n^2 + n$ as $n(n + 1)$ if you prefer. Then $(10n + 5)^2 = 100 \cdot n(n + 1) + 25$. Just multiply $n(n + 1)$ and write 25 after the product.

Example: 85^2

Write 8×9 (72) followed by 25: 7225. Or write $8^2 + 8$ (72) followed by 25: 7225.

You can combine this procedure with others that you know.

Examples: $84 \times 86 = 85^2 - 1 = 7225 - 1 = 7224$

$87 \times 83 = 85^2 - 4 = 7221$

$86^2 = 85^2 + 85 + 86 = 7225 + 171 = 7396$

$84^2 = 85^2 - 85 - 84 = 7225 - 169 = 7056$ (You may subtract 170 and add 1 instead of trying to subtract 169 in the last step.)

When you use these procedures, a good check that will catch many possible errors is to multiply units digits to find out what the units digit is and then to compare it with the units digit in your answer. In the last example, $4 \times 4 = 16$. 6 checks with 6 in the answer.

Calculate the following numbers without pencil and paper or a calculator.

1. 15^2	11. 16^2	21. 14×16	31. 14^2
2. 25^2	12. 26^2	22. 26×24	32. 24^2
3. 75^2	13. 76^2	23. 74×76	33. 77×73
4. 45^2	14. 46^2	24. 46×44	34. 47^2
5. 95^2	15. 96^2	25. 97×93	35. 92×98
6. 35^2	16. 36^2	26. 33×37	36. 39×31
7. 55^2	17. 54^2	27. 52×58	37. 53^2
8. 65^2	18. 64^2	28. 69×61	38. 63^2
9. 105^2	19. 104^2	29. 104×106	39. 103^2
10. 115^2	20. 116^2	30. 116×114	40. 112×118

Solve for n. Don't use pencil and paper or a calculator.

41. $43 \times 37 = n$	46. $10 \times 83 = n$	51. $32^2 = n$
42. $87 \times 54 = n$	47. $205^2 = n$	52. $2^{10} = n$
43. $81^2 = n$	48. $153 \times 147 = n$	53. $27 \times 35 = n$
44. $54 \times 67 = n$	49. $3^8 = n$	54. $28 \times 34 = n$
45. $54 \times 66 = n$	50. $103 \times 107 = n$	55. $33 \times 29 = n$

56. For problems 41–55, write down at least 1 way to do each problem in your head. Compare your procedures with the procedures used by others. Try to decide which procedure would be best if you had to do the problem again.
    For example, here are 2 ways to do problem 50:

    As difference of 2 squares: $103 \times 107 = 105^2 - 2^2 = 11{,}025 - 4 = 11{,}021$.

    As binomials: $3 \times 7 = 21$. $100 \times 7 + 100 \times 3 = 1000$.
    $100 \times 100 = 10{,}000$. Answer is $11{,}021$.

BINOMIAL PRODUCTS GAME

Players: 2 or more
Materials: Two 0–5 cubes, two 5–10 cubes
Object: To get the greatest product

Rules

1. Make a form like this: (___ + ___)(___ + ___)
2. Take turns rolling all 4 cubes. Write each number rolled in 1 of the blanks.
3. The player who makes the greatest product is the winner.

Sample Game

Troy rolled [5] [8] [3] [2]. He wrote $(3 + 5)(8 + 2) = 8 \times 10 = 80$.
Elsbeth rolled [6] [9] [3] [2]. She wrote $(6 + 9)(3 + 2) = 15 \times 5 = 75$.

Troy was the winner. (Could Elsbeth have gotten a higher score with the numbers she rolled?)

Other Ways to Play This Game

1. Try to get the smallest possible product.
2. Play the Trinomial-Binomial Products Game. Use a form like this:
   (___ + ___ + ___)(___ + ___). In step 2, use any of the 4 numbers rolled as your fifth number. For example, if you rolled [5] [8] [3] [2], you could write $(8 + 3 + 2)(8 + 5) = 169$.

BINOMIO

Players: 2 or more
Materials: Two 0–5 cubes, two 5–10 cubes, about 20 markers
Object: To get 5 numbers in a row (vertically, horizontally, or diagonally)

Rules

1. Use this game card.

1	5	9	15
2	6	10	16
3	7	12	18
4	8	14	20

2. Roll 2 cubes. Separate them into a binomial expression. Find the partial products. Here are some examples:

Cubes Rolled	Binomials	Partial Products
5 8	(2 + 3)(5 + 3)	10, 6, 15, 9
3 2	(1 + 2)(1 + 1)	1, 1, 2, 2
4 3	(3 + 1)(3 + 0)	9, 0, 3, 0
8 9	(4 + 4)(6 + 3)	24, 12, 24, 12
7 9	(5 + 2)(9 + 1)	45, 5, 18, 1

3. Put a marker on each of your partial products on the game card. (You may not put a marker on an occupied space.)

4. The first player to get 4 in a row (vertically, horizontally, or diagonally) is the winner.

Other Ways to Play This Game

1. Make your own game cards by drawing them on a sheet of paper. You may put the numbers in different places. You may use other numbers if they have 2 factors that are numbers from 0 through 10. For example, you may use 21 (7 × 3) but not 22 (2 × 11). Mark off squares with a pencil if you don't have any markers.

2. Program a computer to make the game cards and keep score.

Sometimes you can use the relationship $(x^2 - y^2) = (x + y)(x - y)$ to simplify finding the difference of 2 squares.

Examples: $38^2 - 8^2 = ?$

Rather than calculate 38^2 and subtract 8^2, you could rewrite $38^2 - 8^2$ as $(38 + 8)(38 - 8) = 46 \times 30 = 1380$.

$38^2 - 2^2 = ?$

$38^2 - 2^2 = (38 + 2)(38 - 2) = 40 \times 36 = 1440$

Try to compute the answers without pencil and paper or a calculator.

1. $18^2 - 8^2$
2. $17^2 - 7^2$
3. $23^2 - 3^2$
4. $17^2 - 3^2$
5. $18^2 - 2^2$
6. $27^2 - 7^2$
7. $27^2 - 3^2$
8. $23^2 - 7^2$
9. $107^2 - 7^2$
10. $93^2 - 7^2$
11. $94^2 - 6^2$
12. $104^2 - 4^2$

To find the length of a side of a right triangle when we know the lengths of the other 2 sides, we may use the Pythagorean Theorem. Sometimes the procedure on page 322 is useful.

Example: In the right triangle ABC, how long is BC? The Pythagorean Theorem says that $18^2 = 8^2 + x^2$, so $x^2 = 18^2 - 8^2$. But $18^2 - 8^2 = 10 \times 26 = 260$. So $x^2 = 260$, and $x = \sqrt{260}$.

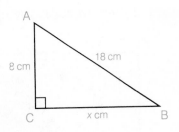

You could leave this answer in radical form ($\sqrt{260}$ centimeters) or you could estimate it. ($16^2 = 256$. $17^2 = 289$. So 16.1 or 16.2 would be a good estimate.)

Estimate the length to the nearest centimeter of the unknown side in each problem. Don't use paper and pencil or a calculator.

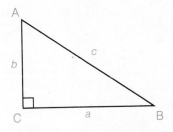

13. $c = 17, b = 7, a = ?$

14. $c = 17, b = 3, a = ?$

15. $c = 22, a = 2, b = ?$

16. $c = 12, b = 2, a = ?$

17. $c = 120, a = 20, b = ?$

18. $c = 16, a = 6, b = ?$

19. $c = 160, a = 40, b = ?$

20. $c = 15, b = 5, a = ?$

Rhoda played a game with her younger sister and brother, Ginny and Todd. Rhoda put a number on each of their foreheads. Then she told them the product of the 2 numbers. Ginny could see only Todd's number and Todd could see only Ginny's number. Rhoda wanted them to guess the numbers on their own foreheads.

[1] In the first game, Rhoda said the product was 56. Todd could see a 7 on Ginny's forehead. What number was on Todd's forehead?

Here are the products and numbers on Ginny's forehead for several games. Decide what number is on Todd's forehead.

	Product	Ginny's Number	Todd's Number
1.	100	5	
2.	24	8	
3.	50	5	
4.	0	5	
5.	0	0	
6.	0	783	
7.	1	0	

[2] **What is wrong with problem 7?**

[3] **When you multiply 0 and any other number, what is the product?**

[4] **If the product of 2 numbers is 0, what do you know about at least 1 of the numbers?**

8. Consider the equation $xy = 0$. 1 pair of numbers that makes this a true statement is $x = 7$, $y = 0$. We write it (7, 0), giving the x-value first.

   a. Write 5 more pairs of numbers that make the equation a true statement.

   b. How many such pairs are there altogether?

Consider the equation $x(x - 3) = 0$.

[1] What value or values of x would make this equation a true statement?

[2] Are there 2 values of x that work?

[3] What value of x makes x − 3 = 0?

[4] Are there any other values of x that make x(x − 3) = 0?

Remember

Numbers that make an equation a true statement are called *solutions* to the equation.

---

[5] How are the equations xy = 0 and x(x − 3) = 0 different?

[6] Why are there only 2 solutions to the equation x(x − 3) = 0 but an infinite number of solutions to the equation xy = 0?

[7] If you know what x is in the equation xy = 0, does that determine what y is?

[8] If you know what x is in the equation x(x − 3) = 0, does that determine what x − 3 is?

To find the solutions to an equation in which the product of several factors equals 0, simply find the numbers that make each factor 0.

Example: $3(x - 7)(x + 4)\left(x + 2\frac{1}{2}\right) = 0$.
There is no way to make $3 = 0$.
$x = 7$ makes $x - 7 = 0$
$x = -4$ makes $x + 4 = 0$
$x = -2\frac{1}{2}$ makes $x + 2\frac{1}{2} = 0$
So the solutions are 7, −4, and $-2\frac{1}{2}$.

To check, let $x = 7$.

$$3(7 - 7)(7 + 4)\left(7 + 2\frac{1}{2}\right) = 3(0)(11)\left(9\frac{1}{2}\right) = 0.$$
-4 and $-2\frac{1}{2}$ can be checked in a similar manner.

Find all solutions to each equation.

1. $(x - 2)(x - 3) = 0$
2. $(x + 1)(x - 1) = 0$
3. $(x + 7)(x - 5) = 0$
4. $(x - 4)(x + 4) = 0$
5. $x^2 - 16 = 0^*$
6. $x(x + 1)(x + 2) = 0$
7. $(x - 1)(x - 2)(x - 3) = 0$
8. $(x + 1)(x + 1)(x + 1) = 0$
9. $(x - 2)(x + 1)(x - 5) = 0$
10. $(2x - 1)(x + 4) = 0$†
11. $(2x + 1)(x - 4) = 0$
12. $(2x - 3)(3x - 4) = 0$

*Compare answers with those for problem 4.
†Be careful.

Suppose you wanted to find the values of x that make $x^2 - 2x - 15$ equal to 0. You could graph the function $y = x^2 - 2x - 15$ and see which values of x make $y = 0$. You could simply try values of x until you found one that worked. (In this case, graphing can be thought of as a well-organized method of guessing.)

A third way to find the values of x that make $x^2 - 2x - 15$ equal 0 is to look for 2 binomial factors of $x^2 - 2x - 15$ and then find the values of x that make either of those equal to 0. You can't always find binomial factors. They are not always there.

Example: Solve $x^2 - 2x - 15 = 0$.

Think: What are factors of 15 whose sum or difference is 2?
5 and 3

Let's try them.
$x^2 - 2x - 15 = (x - 5)(x + 3)$.
To make $x - 5 = 0$, x must be 5.
To make $x + 3 = 0$, x must be -3.
So $x = 5$ or $x = -3$ must be the solution, and we usually write this $x = 5, -3$ to show that both values satisfy the equation.

Check: $(5)^2 - 2(5) - 15 = 25 - 10 - 15 = 0$
$(-3)^2 - 2(-3) - 15 = 9 + 6 - 15 = 0$

Example: Solve $6x^2 - 17x + 12 = 0$.

If you try to do this problem by guessing or by graphing, you will probably find it very difficult. Finding 2 factors is also difficult, but we can make it easier in the following way.

The 2 factors should be in the form $(ax + b)(cx + d)$. Remember that some of the numbers may be negative, so some plus signs may be minus signs.

We multiply and get $acx^2 + (ad + bc)x + bd$. If this expression is to be the same as $6x^2 - 17x + 12$, $ac = 6$, $bd = 12$, and $ad + bc = -17$. First we check to see whether ac, bd, and $ad + bc$ have any common numerical factors. They don't.

We try looking at ac. Since 6 is positive, we know that a and c have the same sign, so we will look at factors of 6 where both are positive.

$(1x +$ ___$)(6x +$ ___$)$
$(2x +$ ___$)(3x +$ ___$)$
$(3x +$ ___$)(2x +$ ___$)$ ⎫   By the commutative law, these 2 lines are
$(6x +$ ___$)(1x +$ ___$)$ ⎭   the same as the top 2 lines, so we need
                               use only the top 2 lines.

In order for bd to be $+12$, b and d must both be the same sign—either both positive or both negative. Since the middle term is negative, they must both be negative. Let's try putting -1 and -12, -2 and -6, and -3 and -4 into the 2 possible combinations we find from looking at ac.

$$(1x - 1)(6x - 12) = 6x^2 - 18x + 12$$
$$(1x - 2)(6x - 6) = 6x^2 - 18x + 12$$
$$(1x - 3)(6x - 4) = 6x^2 - 22x + 12$$
$$(1x - 4)(6x - 3) = 6x^2 - 27x + 12$$
$$(1x - 6)(6x - 2) = 6x^2 - 38x + 12$$
$$(1x - 12)(6x - 1) = 6x^2 - 73x + 12$$

You may write the 1 in $(1x - 2)$ or just write it $(x - 2)$. It is customary to omit the 1.

$$(2x - 1)(3x - 12) = 6x^2 - 27x + 12$$
$$(2x - 2)(3x - 6) = 6x^2 - 18x + 12$$
$$(2x - 3)(3x - 4) = 6x^2 - 17x + 12$$

This is it! We show the others so that you can see all the possibilities.

$$(2x - 4)(3x - 3) = 6x^2 - 18x + 12$$
$$(2x - 6)(3x - 2) = 6x^2 - 22x + 12$$
$$(2x - 12)(3x - 1) = 6x^2 - 38x + 12$$

If you look for patterns and use your imagination, you can usually find the factors without trying all the possibilities.

So, $6x^2 - 17x + 12 = (2x - 3)(3x - 4)$. The values of x that make $6x^2 - 17x + 12$ equal 0 are just those that make either $2x - 3$ equal 0 or $3x - y$ equal 0.

[1] Does $\frac{3}{2}$ make $2x - 3$ equal 0?

[2] What makes $3x - 4$ equal 0?

Then $\frac{3}{2}$ and $\frac{4}{3}$ are the only numbers that make $6x^2 - 17x + 12$ equal 0.

So $x = \frac{3}{2}$ or $\frac{4}{3}$.

Check: $6\left(\frac{3}{2}\right)^2 - 17\left(\frac{3}{2}\right) + 12 = 3\left(\frac{9}{2}\right) - \frac{51}{2} + 12 = \frac{27}{2} - \frac{51}{2} + \frac{24}{2} = 0$

$6\left(\frac{4}{3}\right)^2 - 17\left(\frac{4}{3}\right) + 12 = 6\left(\frac{16}{9}\right) - \frac{68}{3} + 12 = \frac{32}{3} - \frac{68}{3} + \frac{36}{3} = 0$

Solve. Find all values of x that make each equation true. Check your answers. 1 of these problems is impossible to do.

1. $x^2 - 8x + 15 = 0$
2. $x^2 - 8x + 16 = 0$
3. $x^2 - 7x + 12 = 0$
4. $x^2 + 7x + 12 = 0$
5. $x^2 + x - 12 = 0$
6. $2x^2 + 2x - 24 = 0$
7. $x^2 - x - 12 = 0$
8. $x^2 + x + 1 = 0$
9. $x^2 - 4x - 12 = 0$
10. $2x^2 - 11x + 15 = 0$
11. $2x^2 + x - 15 = 0$
12. $4x^2 + 2x - 30 = 0$

List all pairs of whole-number factors of each number. Don't repeat pairs with the same numbers. The first problem has been done for you.

1. 20 $1 \times 20, 2 \times 10, 4 \times 5$
2. 2
3. 4
4. 6
5. 8
6. 12
7. 15
8. 18
9. 21
10. 24
11. 28
12. 32
13. 36
14. 40
15. 42
16. 45
17. 51
18. 3
19. 9
20. 10

21. 1
22. 14
23. 16
24. 19
25. 22
26. 25
27. 27
28. 30
29. 34
30. 38
31. 44
32. 48
33. 50
34. 54
35. 56
36. 60
37. 72
38. 80
39. 100
40. 120

$$Ax^2 + Bx + C = 0$$

An equation of this form is called a *quadratic equation*.

$$y = Ax^2 + Bx + C$$

A function with a rule of this form is a *quadratic function*. As you have seen in earlier chapters of this book, such functions can be used to describe the behavior of falling bodies and other physical events.

A is called the coefficient of x^2 and B is called the coefficient of x. In the expression $3x$, 3 is the coefficient of x.

The ancient Greeks solved quadratic equations using geometry as early as 540 B.C., and Hindus and Arabs solved quadratic equations by algebraic procedures between A.D. 500 and A.D. 1100.

Factor each expression.

1. $x^2 - 5x + 6$
2. $x^2 - x - 6$
3. $x^2 + x - 6$
4. $x^2 + 5x + 6$
5. $4x^2 - 8x + 3$
6. $4x^2 - 13x + 3$

7. $4x^2 - 7x + 3$
8. $4x^2 - x - 3$
9. $4x^2 + x - 3$
10. $4x^2 + 4x - 3$
11. $4x^2 - 4x - 3$
12. $2x^2 - 11x + 15$

13. $2x^2 + 7x - 15$
14. $2x^2 - x - 15$
15. $2x^2 + x - 15$
16. $12x^2 + 8x - 15$
17. $12x^2 + 179x - 15$
18. $12x^2 - 3x - 15$

Solve. Some of your results for problems 1–18 may help.

19. $x^2 - 5x + 6 = 0$
20. $x^2 + 5x + 6 = 0$
21. $4x^2 - 13x + 3 = 0$
22. $4x^2 - x - 3 = 0$
23. $4x^2 + x - 3 = 0$
24. $4x^2 + 4x - 3 = 0$

25. $4x^2 - 4x - 3 = 0$
26. $2x^2 + x - 15 = 0$
27. $2x^2 - x - 15 = 0$
28. $12x^2 + 8x - 15 = 0$
29. $12x^2 + 179x - 15 = 0$
30. $12x^2 - 3x - 15 = 0$

MIDDLE-TERM GAME

Players: 2 or more
Materials: Two 0–5 cubes, two 5–10 cubes
Object: To produce the trinomial whose middle term has the largest coefficient of x

Rules

1. Make a game form like this: (___x + ___)(___x + ___)
2. Take turns rolling all 4 cubes. Put each number you roll into 1 of the blanks on the game form.
3. Multiply the 2 binomials to get a trinomial.
4. The player who has the largest coefficient of x is the winner.

Sample Game

Player	Cubes Rolled	Binomials	Trinomial
Melanie	3 5 7 8	$(3x + 5)(7x + 8)$	$21x^2 + 59x + 40$
Melissa	0 4 8 10	$(10x + 0)(4x + 8)$	$40x^2 + 80x + 0$
Evan	3 5 7 8	$(8x + 5)(3x + 7)$	$24x^2 + 71x + 35$

Melissa was the winner, because 80 is greater than 71 or 59.

Other Ways to Play This Game

1. Use this game form: (___x + ___)(___x − ___). The player with the middle term that has the smallest nonnegative coefficient of x is the winner.
2. Change the objective for each game. For example, use the form (___x + ___)(___x + ___) and try to get the smallest middle term, or use the form (___x + ___)(___x − ___) and try to get the largest middle term.

When factoring algebraic expressions, reducing fractions, and doing other sorts of computations, being able to factor whole numbers easily is often useful. To factor a number completely means to write it as the product of all its prime factors.

You know several rules for finding factors of whole numbers. Some of the rules below may be new to you.

A. Numbers ending in 0, 2, 4, 6, or 8 have a factor of 2 (are even).

B. Numbers ending in 0 or 5 have a factor of 5.

C. If the sum of the digits of a number is divisible by 3, the number is divisible by 3.

D. If the sum of the odd-numbered digits of a number equals the sum of the even-numbered digits, or if the difference between the 2 sums is a multiple of 11, the number is divisible by 11. To do this test, you number the digits starting at the right. In 962345, 5, 3, and 6 are the odd-numbered digits and 4, 2, and 9 are the even-numbered digits.

E. To check for divisibility by a *composite number* (a number divisible by other whole numbers greater than 1), check for divisibility by all of the factors of the composite number.

F. To check for divisibility by a *prime number* (a number not divisible by any other whole number greater than 1), if you don't know a simple rule, just divide to check.

Example: Factor 38,808 completely.

38,808 is even. Divide by 2 repeatedly until it is no longer possible to do so.

$$\begin{array}{r} 19404 \\ 2\overline{)38808} \end{array}$$

$$\begin{array}{r} 9702 \\ 2\overline{)19404} \end{array}$$

$$\begin{array}{r} 4851 \\ 2\overline{)9702} \end{array}$$

The sum of the digits of 4851 is 18, so it's divisible by 3 (and by 9). Divide by 9 or by 3 twice.

$$\begin{array}{r} 1617 \\ 3\overline{)\,4851} \end{array}$$

$$\downarrow$$

$$\begin{array}{r} 539 \\ 3\overline{)\,1617} \end{array}$$

The sum of the odd-numbered digits (5 and 9) is 11 more than the sum of the even-numbered digits (3), so 539 is divisible by 11.

$$\begin{array}{r} 49 \\ 11\overline{)\,539} \end{array}$$

$$\downarrow$$

We know that $7 \times 7 = 49$.

$$\begin{array}{r} 7 \\ 7\overline{)\,49} \end{array}$$

So $38{,}808 = 2 \times 2 \times 2 \times 3 \times 3 \times 11 \times 7 \times 7 = 2^3 \times 3^2 \times 7^2 \times 11$.

Factor each number completely. If a number is prime it is already completely factored. To completely factor 37, for example, you write 37.

1. 25	11. 78
2. 63	12. 123
3. 37	13. 105
4. 64	14. 217
5. 125	15. 187
6. 126	16. 143
7. 83	17. 209
8. 91	18. 253
9. 46	19. 319
10. 320	20. 1001

Suppose you want to factor 277 completely. You test for
divisibility by 2, 3, 5, and 11. You try dividing by 7 and then by
13. None of these measures works.

[1] What should you do next?

[2] Why wouldn't you check for divisibility by 4? By 6? By 12?

[3] Would you check for divisibility by 14? By 15? By 16?

**[4] If 277 is divisible by 17, is the other factor greater than 17 or
smaller than 17? (Note that $\sqrt{277} \approx 16.65$.)**

**[5] If there are no factors of 277 that are smaller than $\sqrt{277}$ other
than 1, can there be any factors of 277 greater than $\sqrt{277}$, other
than 277 itself?**

Then 277 must be a prime number.

If n has no factors (other than 1) smaller than or equal to $\sqrt{n}$,
then n is prime.

Factor the following numbers completely. Use a calculator if it
helps.

21. 271	27. 289	33. 189	39. 17,017	45. 1373
22. 270	28. 529	34. 133	40. 19,019	46. 1427
23. 254	29. 4199	35. 143	41. 117	47. 1429
24. 198	30. 899	36. 847	42. 256	48. 1419
25. 119	31. 34,496	37. 1573	43. 1369	49. 2021
26. 169	32. 273	38. 2057	44. 1367	50. 5183

Solve for n.

1. $n = 12 \times 8$
2. $13 \times 7 = n$
3. $13 \times 11 = n$
4. $19 \times 21 = n$
5. $18 \times 22 = n$

6. $n = 23 \times 17$
7. $31 \times 29 = n$
8. $32 \times 28 = n$
9. $n = 27 \times 33$
10. $n = 27 \times 13$

11. $23 \times 37 = n$
12. $n = 48 \times 32$
13. $48 \times 52 = n$
14. $n = 9 \times 13$
15. $109 \times 113 = n$

16. $n = 59 \times 81$
17. $n = 59 \times 61$
18. $41 \times 59 = n$
19. $n = 57 \times 63$
20. $58 \times 62 = n$

21. $n = 67 \times 73$
22. $79 \times 81 = n$
23. $n = 78 \times 82$
24. $n = 75 \times 85$
25. $83 \times 77 = n$

26. $n = 85 \times 75$
27. $n = 91 \times 89$
28. $88 \times 92 = n$
29. $n = 87 \times 93$
30. $85 \times 95 = n$

Prime numbers have interested mathematicians for thousands of years. A famous mathematician who lived in Egypt about 230 B.C. developed a way to identify prime numbers. His name was Eratosthenes, and the method is known as the Sieve of Eratosthenes.

What Eratosthenes did was to write down all the whole numbers from 1 to as far as he wanted to go. First he crossed off every second number after 2 to eliminate numbers divisible by 2. Next he crossed off every third number after 3 (including those already crossed off) to eliminate numbers divisible by 3. Then he crossed off every fifth number after 5, and so on, for other prime numbers. Each time that he crossed off numbers, the smallest number not crossed off would be a prime number. He then crossed off its multiples. When the list was completed, the numbers crossed off were composite numbers (numbers with factors other than themselves and 1) and the numbers not crossed off (except for 1) were prime numbers. (1 is considered to be neither prime nor composite.)

Here is what the Sieve of Eratosthenes would look like for numbers up to 120 with multiples of 2, 3, 5, and 7 crossed off, respectively, with $/$, $\setminus$, $—$, and $|$.

```
  1   2   3   4   5   6   7   8   9  10  11  12
 13  14  15  16  17  18  19  20  21  22  23  24
 25  26  27  28  29  30  31  32  33  34  35  36
 37  38  39  40  41  42  43  44  45  46  47  48
 49  50  51  52  53  54  55  56  57  58  59  60
 61  62  63  64  65  66  67  68  69  70  71  72
 73  74  75  76  77  78  79  80  81  82  83  84
 85  86  87  88  89  90  91  92  93  94  95  96
 97  98  99 100 101 102 103 104 105 106 107 108
109 110 111 112 113 114 115 116 117 118 119 120
```

Notice that the remaining numbers (except 1) are prime, because the first multiple of 11 that is not also a multiple of 2, 3, 5, or 7 is 11^2, or 121.

By writing the numbers in rows of 12, we can arrange for numbers divisible by 2 and 3 to be in easily identified rows and for numbers divisible by 5 and 7 to be in a reasonably convenient pattern (look 1 down and 2 over to find another multiple). Numbers divisible by 11 and 13 are in a diagonal pattern.

Using this method will let you make a list of prime numbers up to any number you want.

In practice, there were undoubtedly many ways by which the sieve was simplified. For example, numbers that were already crossed off were probably not crossed off again, and whole rows were probably crossed off at a time.

Try to find all the primes up to 225, or some other number, using the Sieve of Eratosthenes.

For each problem, show a quick way of calculating the answer that would not require paper and pencil.

Example: Calculate 36×43.

Think: $37 \times 43 = 40^2 - 3^2 = 1600 - 9 = 1591$; so 36×43
$= 1591 - 43 = (1591 - 41) - 2 = 1550 - 2 = 1548.$

Your answers should be like the part that comes after "Think." They should usually be shorter than the answer shown here. You may use the results of other problems on this page.

1. 28×32	**6.** 35^2	**11.** 36×33
2. 37×43	**7.** 36^2	**12.** 41×38
3. 41^2	**8.** 74^2	**13.** 120^2
4. 79^2	**9.** 73×75	**14.** 121^2
5. 85^2	**10.** 33×37	**15.** 122^2

Each triangle below is a right triangle. The lengths of 2 sides are given. Find the length (x) of the third side in centimeters (to the nearest tenth of a centimeter).

16.   **17.**   **18.**

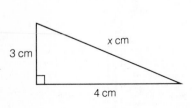

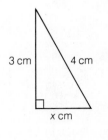

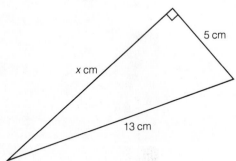

List all solutions for each equation.

19. $x(x - 5) = 0$ **23.** $x^2 - 2x - 8 = 0$
20. $(x - 4)(x + 2) = 0$ **24.** $6x^2 - 5x - 4 = 0$
21. $(2x - 3)(x + 4) = 0$ **25.** $6x^2 + x - 12 = 0$
22. $(2x + 1)(3x - 4) = 0$ **26.** $x^2 - 5x - 36 = 0$

Factor each expression.

27. $x^2 - 5x - 36$ **29.** $6x^2 - 5x - 4$

28. $6x^2 + x - 12$ **30.** $2x^2 - 23x - 12$

Factor completely each number.

31. 24   **33.** 64   **35.** 567   **37.** 209   **39.** 323

32. 100   **34.** 81   **36.** 1001   **38.** 473   **40.** 462

41. What is the greatest prime number less than 400?

42. What is the smallest prime number greater than 400?

For each problem, show a quick way of calculating the answer that would not require paper and pencil.

Example: Calculate 36×43.

Think: $37 \times 43 = 40^2 - 3^2 = 1600 - 9 = 1591$; so 36×43
$= 1591 - 43 = (1591 - 41) - 2 = 1550 - 2 = 1548$.

Your answers should be like the part that comes after "Think." They should usually be shorter than the answer shown here. You may use the results of other problems on this page.

1. 27×33
2. 38×42
3. 39^2
4. 81^2
5. 75^2

6. 45^2
7. 46^2
8. 84^2
9. 83×85
10. 23×27

11. 26×23
12. 31×28
13. 110^2
14. 111^2
15. 112^2

Each triangle below is a right triangle. The lengths of 2 sides are given. Find the length (x) of the third side in centimeters (to the nearest tenth of a centimeter).

16.

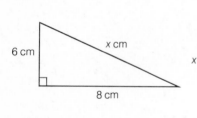

17.

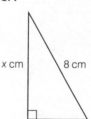

18.

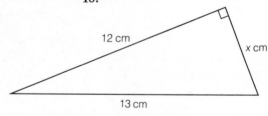

List all solutions for each equation.

19. $x(x - 6) = 0$
20. $(x - 3)(x + 4) = 0$
21. $(2x - 6)(x + 5) = 0$
22. $(2x + 3)(3x - 2) = 0$

23. $x^2 + x - 12 = 0$
24. $6x^2 + 5x - 6 = 0$
25. $2x^2 + 4x - 3 = 0$
26. $x^2 + 4x - 45 = 0$

Factor each expression.

27. $x^2 + 4x - 45$ **29.** $6x^2 + 5x - 6$

28. $2x^2 + 5x - 3$ **30.** $x^2 + x - 12$

Factor completely each number.

31. 36   **33.** 72   **35.** 324   **37.** 340   **39.** 351

32. 120   **34.** 91   **36.** 2520   **38.** 189   **40.** 399

41. What is the greatest prime number less than 300?

42. What is the smallest prime number greater than 300?

Use a calculator, when it will help, to solve the following problems.

1. List the prime numbers between 1 and 100. You should find this task easy even without a calculator. (Hint: The only composite less than 100 that is not obviously composite to somebody who knows the rules on page 334 is 91.)

2. Between 1 and 1000 there are 168 prime numbers. The number of primes in each 100-number interval is shown below:

0-100	100-200	200-300	300-400	400-500	500-600	600-700	700-800	800-900	900-1000
25	21	16	16	17	14	16	14	15	14

a. Does it seem that the number of prime numbers in a given interval gets smaller as the numbers get larger?

b. There are 11 primes between 9000 and 9100 and there are 9 primes between 9900 and 10,000. Does this fact seem to confirm or reject your conclusion for part a?

c. How many prime numbers do you think there are? Can you give a convincing argument that you are right?

3. If you were going to program a computer to list all the prime numbers from 1 to 1000, what steps would you want the computer to take? If you have a computer available, see if you can write a program to make such a list. Check to see how long the computer requires for the job. Can you find a quicker procedure? (Hint: The list you made for problem 1 might help.)

4. a. $2 \times 3 \times 5 \times 7 = 210$. Do you think 211 is divisible by 2, 3, 5, or 7? Why or why not?

b. Do you think 211 is divisible by *any* prime number? How can you decide?

c. Suppose you have a list of all the prime numbers, and you multiply them all together and add 1. Would this new number be divisible by any of the primes on your list? Might the new number be divisible by a prime number bigger than any you had on your list? In any case, could you have a finite list of all the prime numbers? (Go back and think about problem 2c again.)

The *proper divisors* of a number are all the whole-number divisors by which the number can be divided evenly. 1 is a proper divisor of all numbers but has no proper divisors itself. No number is a proper divisor of itself.

Amicable numbers are pairs of numbers in which each number is the sum of the proper divisors of the other. *Perfect numbers* are numbers that are amicable to themselves. A perfect number is the sum of its proper divisors.

Here is an example: $220 = 2^2 \cdot 2 \cdot 11$. So 220 is divisible by 1, 2, 4, 5, 10, 11, 20, 22, 44, 55, and 110. The sum of these divisors is 284. If the sum of the proper divisors of 284 is 220, then 220 and 284 are amicable numbers.

1. Check to see if 220 and 284 are amicable numbers.
2. Check to see if 24 and 36 are amicable numbers.
3. Find 2 perfect numbers less than 30.
4. Try to find another perfect number less than 500. (Hint: There is a perfect number that is almost 500.)

Go to the library and get books that will tell you more about perfect and amicable numbers. See, for example, *Historical Topics for the Mathematics Classroom,* the Thirty-first Yearbook of the National Council of Teachers of Mathematics, 1969, edited by Arthur E. Hallerberg.

CHAPTER 10

RATIONAL AND IRRATIONAL NUMBERS

UNCERTAINTY IN MEASUREMENT

EXPONENTS AND SCIENTIFIC NOTATION

Mr. Mosser was talking with Naomi and Leah. He asked them, "What do you know that's true of all numbers?"

Leah said, "They're all either odd or even."

"What about $\frac{2}{3}$? Is $\frac{2}{3}$ odd or even?" asked Naomi.

Leah replied, "Don't be silly. I didn't mean that kind of number."

[1] **What do *you* know that's true of all numbers? First decide what kind of numbers you mean.**

Let's decide we are talking about whole numbers—the numbers 0, 1, 2, 3, 4, ...

[2] **Think about what happens if you add 2 whole numbers. Do you always get another whole number? Is that true for subtraction?**

[3] **Think about what happens if you multiply 2 whole numbers. Do you always get another whole number? Is that true for division?**

[4] **Does the order in which you add 2 numbers make a difference? For example, does 3 + 5 produce the same answer as 5 + 3?**

[5] **Does the order matter when you subtract? Multiply? Divide?**

[6] **Suppose you have 3 numbers to add: 8, 5, and 2. Is the result when you add 8 and 5 first and then add 2 the same as the result when you add the 5 and 2 first then add that sum to 8? That is, does (8 + 5) + 2 = 8 + (5 + 2)?**

[7] **Suppose you have to subtract. Is (8 − 5) − 2 the same as 8 − (5 − 2)?**

[8] Does order matter for multiplication with 3 numbers? For division with 3 numbers?

_____

Remember

Multiplication is distributive over addition. That is, for any 3 numbers x, y, and z, $x(y + z) = xy + xz$. (For example, $5(8 + 2) = 5(8) + 5(2)$.

_____

[9] Is multiplication distributive over subtraction?

[10] Is addition distributive over multiplication? That is, for any 3 numbers x, y, and z, is it true that x + (yz) = (x + y)(x + z)?

You may remember that in chapter 2 (see page 42) you learned names for the 5 rules we just discussed in questions 1–10. Let's review them.

_____

Remember

A. The commutative law for addition:
   For all pairs of numbers x and y, $x + y = y + x$.

B. The commutative law for multiplication:
   For all pairs of numbers x and y, $xy = yx$.

C. The associative law for addition:
   For all triples of numbers x, y, and z, $(x + y) + z = x + (y + z)$.

D. The associative law for multiplication:
   For all triples of numbers x, y, and z, $(xy)z = x(yz)$.

E. The distributive law for multiplication over addition:
   For all triples of numbers x, y, and z, $x(y + z) = xy + xz$.

_____

There is also a name for the rule stating that whenever you add (or multiply) 2 numbers you get another number. It's called *closure under addition (or multiplication)*. The whole numbers are closed under addition and multiplication (that is, for all pairs of whole numbers x and y, $x + y$ is a whole number and xy is a whole number).

There is 1 whole number with the property that whenever it is added to any number x, the sum is always x.

[11] What is that number?

0 is sometimes called the identity element for addition of whole numbers because for every whole number x, $0 + x = x + 0 = x$.

So, another rule about whole numbers is that there exists an identity element for addition (0) such that, for every number x, $0 + x = x + 0 = x$.

[12] Is there an identity element for multiplication of whole numbers?
[13] What is it?

You know that the identity element for addition of whole numbers is 0.

[14] For any whole number x, can you think of another whole number, y, that you can add to x to get 0?

Instead of considering whole numbers, let's consider the set of all integers (. . . , −4, −3, −2, −1, 0, 1, 2, 3, 4, . . .).

[15] Is it true that for any number x there is always another number, y, such that x + y = 0?

This number y is the additive inverse of x. (For example, −7 is the additive inverse of 7, and 7 is the additive inverse of −7).

The multiplicative inverse of x is the number that can be multiplied by x to give a product of 1.

[16] What is the multiplicative inverse of 2?

[17] Is $\frac{1}{2}$ an integer?

You know that division by 0 is not possible. So 0 does not have a multiplicative inverse. (If $\frac{1}{0} = n$, then $0 \cdot n = 1$, but 0 times any number is 0, so this relationship is not true.)

Now instead of considering only whole numbers, or only integers, let's consider the set of all rational numbers (for example, $1, \frac{1}{3}, \frac{3}{7}, -5, -\frac{8}{3}, 0$, and so on).

[18] Would every number except 0 have a multiplicative inverse?

Do these problems.

1. For the set of rational numbers and the operations of addition and multiplication, there are 2 closure laws, 2 commutative laws, 2 associative laws, 1 distributive law, 2 identity elements, and 2 inverse laws (the multiplicative inverse law has the exception that 0 has no multiplicative inverse). Write out the 11 laws. Use r, s, and t rather than x, y, and z.

2. List both the additive and the multiplicative inverse of each number. If none exists, write *none*.

   a. 3   **c.** $\frac{2}{7}$ **e.** $\frac{73}{859}$ **g.** 0
   b. -8 **d.** $-\frac{5}{3}$ **f.** 1   **h.** -100

3. Consider the operation $x \circledast y$, called exponentiation. $x \circledast y$ is defined to be x^y. For example, $3 \circledast 5 = 3^5 = 243$, and $2 \circledast 3 = 2^3 = 8$.

   a. Which of the laws (closure, commutativity, associativity, existence of identity element, and existence of inverses) are true for the exponentiation operation for the set of whole numbers? Give counterexamples for the laws that aren't true. Identify the identity element if there is one, and show how to find inverses if they exist.

   b. Which of the *valid* laws in part a are true for the set of all integers: . . . $-3, -2, -1, 0, 1, 2, 3, \ . . .$? If 0 is a problem, make it an exception.

A rational number is a number that can be written as the quotient (or ratio) of 2 integers, x and y: $\frac{x}{y}$ (with the restriction that $y \neq 0$). The word *rational* here comes from ratio.

There are many (in fact, an infinite number of) pairs of integers whose quotient is any particular rational number. For example, $\frac{2}{3}$, $\frac{4}{6}$, $\frac{6}{9}$, $\frac{8}{12}$, $\frac{10}{15}$, $\frac{12}{18}$, $\frac{14}{21}$, $\frac{16}{24}$, and so on all stand for the same rational number. The symbols $\frac{2}{3}$, $\frac{4}{6}$, and so on are fractions. They are names for a single rational number.

Since $\frac{-3}{5} = \frac{3}{-5} = -\frac{3}{5}$, and in general $\frac{-a}{b} = \frac{a}{-b} = -\frac{a}{b}$, it is customary to assume always that the denominator is a positive number.

The system of rational numbers is the set of all numbers of the form $\frac{x}{y}$, where x is any integer and y is any integer but 0, for which the operations of addition and multiplication are defined.

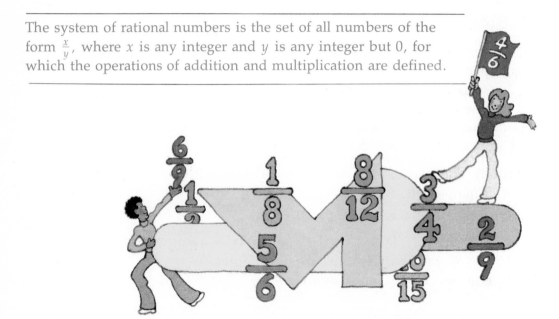

Mathematicians say that a system is a *field* if it has all the properties of the 11 laws you listed to answer problem 1 on page 351. Does the rational number system (or field) seem to be complete enough to do everything you might want to do with numbers?

Can you measure things as precisely as physical limitations allow with rational numbers? Can you add and multiply (and subtract and divide) rational numbers and always get another rational number? What more could we ask of a number system?

The following problems will help you see the powerful nature of the rational number system.

1. **a.** When you add any 2 numbers in the rational number system, do you always get another rational number?
   b. Suppose you add $\frac{a}{b} + \frac{c}{d}$ where a, b, c, and d are integers and $b \neq 0$ and $d \neq 0$. What is the answer?
   c. Is $ad + bc$ an integer?
   d. Is bd an integer?
   e. Could $bd = 0$ if neither b nor d is 0?

2. **a.** When you subtract 1 number from another in the rational number system, do you always get another rational number?
   b. Suppose you do the subtraction $\frac{a}{b} - \frac{c}{d}$, where a, b, c, and d are integers and $b \neq 0$ and $d \neq 0$. What is the answer?
   c. Is $ad - bc$ an integer?
   d. Is bd an integer?
   e. Could $bd = 0$ if neither b nor d is 0?
   f. Is it necessary that $\frac{a}{b}$ be bigger than $\frac{c}{d}$?

3. **a.** What is $\frac{a}{b} \cdot \frac{c}{d}$?
   b. Can you show that this product must be a rational number (if $\frac{a}{b}$ and $\frac{c}{d}$ are rational)?

4. **a.** What is $\frac{a}{b} \div \frac{c}{d}$?
   b. We have assumed that $\frac{a}{b}$ and $\frac{c}{d}$ are rational numbers and that $b \neq 0$ and $d \neq 0$. Is that information adequate to assure us that $\frac{a}{b} \div \frac{c}{d}$ is a rational number?
   c. What more is needed?

So for rational numbers, division—except by 0—is always possible.

5. **a.** Is 3.56 a rational number?
   b. Can you prove that it is? (Write it as the quotient of 2 integers.)

For all of the following problems, we are talking about rational numbers.

1. Suppose you are measuring the length of a book with a metric ruler. You decide that the length is between 23 centimeters and 24 centimeters.

   a. Are there rational numbers between 23 and 24?
   b. Is 23.1 between 23 and 24?
   c. Name 5 more numbers between 23 and 24.

2. Suppose you decide that the length of the book is between 23.4 centimeters and 23.5 centimeters.

   a. Are there numbers between 23.4 and 23.5?
   b. Name 9.

3. Suppose you measure with an instrument that shows that the length of the book is between 23.47 centimeters and 23.48 centimeters.

   a. Are there numbers between 23.47 and 23.48?
   b. Name 5.

4. Name 1 number between each of the following pairs of numbers.

   a. 23.476 and 23.477
   b. 23.4769 and 23.4770
   c. 23.47690 and 23.47691
   d. 23.476903234957680418 and 23.476903234957680419

5. Suppose you are measuring the length of a book with an inch ruler. You decide that the length of the book is between 9 inches and 10 inches.

   a. Are there numbers using fractions between 9 and 10?
   b. Name a rational number (using fractions) between 9 and 10.

6. Name a number (using fractions) between 9 and $9\frac{1}{4}$.

7. Name a number (using fractions) between
   a. $9\frac{1}{8}$ and $9\frac{1}{4}$.
   b. $9\frac{3}{16}$ and $9\frac{1}{4}$.
   c. $9\frac{3}{16}$ and $9\frac{7}{32}$.

8. In the rational number system, will there always be a rational number between any 2 rational numbers no matter how close the 2 rational numbers are together?

9. Choose any 2 words.
   a. Can you always find a word that is alphabetically between any 2 words?
   b. Explain.
   c. Use a dictionary. Find 2 words that have no word between them alphabetically.
   d. If you make up a word that goes between them alphabetically, is it really a word?
   e. Can you always find an integer between 2 other integers?
   f. Explain.

The rational number system can be shown to have all the properties of a field. You've seen that there is always a rational number between any 2 rational numbers. In fact, the rational numbers seem so densely packed on the number line that there is no room for any other numbers.

If you magnify a portion of the number line, there are always more rational numbers, spread quite evenly and densely, between any 2 rational numbers.

For all practical purposes, the rational numbers seem quite sufficient.

Irrational Numbers

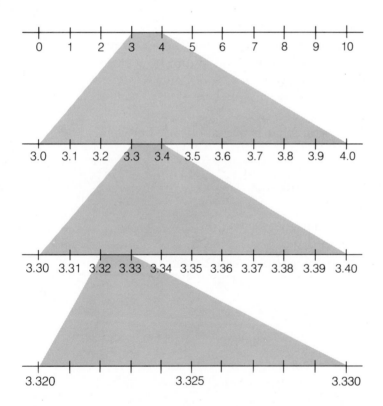

The ancient Pythagoreans, however, discovered a remarkable fact about rational numbers. There are holes in the rational number line. There are lengths that have no rational number to describe them.

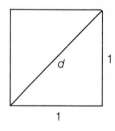

Consider a square 1 unit on a side. How long is the diagonal of the square? According to the Pythagorean Theorem, the square of the length of the diagonal is equal to the sum of the squares of the lengths of the 2 sides.

$$d^2 = 1^2 + 1^2$$
$$= 1 + 1$$
$$= 2$$
$$\text{or } d = \sqrt{2}$$

Let's try to find a rational number $\frac{a}{b}$ that equals $\sqrt{2}$.

$$\frac{a}{b} = \sqrt{2}$$

$$\frac{a^2}{b^2} = 2$$

$$2b^2 = a^2$$

If b has a factor of 2, b^2 has 2 factors of 2. If b has 2 factors of 2, b^2 has 4. If b has 3 factors of 2, b^2 has 6, and so on. So b^2 would have an even number of factors of 2. By the same reasoning, a^2 would also have an even number of factors of 2.

[1] If there were an even number of factors of 2 in b^2, would there be an even or an odd number of factors of 2 in $2b^2$?

[2] Would there be an even or an odd number of factors of 2 in a^2?

But $2b^2$ and a^2 are supposed to be the same number. Our reasoning thus far suggests that the same number has both an odd number of factors of 2 and an even number of factors of 2.

This situation is plainly impossible. So, our original assumption that there is some rational number $\frac{a}{b}$ that equals $\sqrt{2}$ must be false. In fact, $\sqrt{2}$ cannot be a rational number.

Do these problems.

1. Write out an argument (like that on page 357) to show why $\sqrt{3}$ is not a rational number.

2. **a.** Write out an argument to show why $\sqrt{4}$ is not a rational number.
   b. At what step does the argument fail?

3. **a.** For a proof that x is not rational to work, is it necessary that x be a prime number?
   b. If x simply has an odd number of prime-number factors, will the proof work?

4. Write out an argument to show why $\sqrt{6}$ is not a rational number. (Consider factors of 2 or 3.)

5. **a.** Write out an argument to show why $\sqrt{12}$ is not a rational number.
   b. What prime factor occurs an odd number of times in 12?

Following this reasoning, it is possible to see that if a whole number has a rational square root, the square root is a whole number.

Numbers that are not rational numbers are called *irrational* numbers. Neither term refers to the reasonableness of numbers. The word *rational* has to do with being the ratio of 2 whole numbers. So an irrational number is a number that is not the ratio of 2 whole numbers. There are an infinite number of irrational numbers. In fact, in some sense there are more irrationals than rationals.

KEEPING SHARP SOLVING EQUATIONS

Solve. Find all values of x that make each equation true. Check your answers. One of these problems is impossible to do.

1. $x^2 - 10x + 24 = 0$
2. $x^2 - 4x + 4 = 0$
3. $x^2 + 3x + 3 = 0$
4. $x^2 + x - 2 = 0$
5. $x^2 - x - 2 = 0$
6. $x^2 - 3x + 2 = 0$
7. $2x^2 - 11x + 12 = 0$
8. $2x^2 + 11x + 12 = 0$
9. $2x^2 + 2x + 2 = 0$
10. $3x^2 + 10x + 3 = 0$
11. $3x^2 - 10x + 3 = 0$
12. $3x^2 - 8x - 3 = 0$
13. $3x^2 + 8x - 3 = 0$
14. $x^2 - 4x + 3 = 0$
15. $x^2 - 8x + 16 = 0$
16. $x^2 + 8x + 16 = 0$
17. $x^2 - 1 = 0$
18. $x^2 + x - 20 = 0$
19. $x^2 - x - 20 = 0$
20. $x^2 - 10x + 25 = 0$

We have seen that there is no rational number that represents the length of the diagonal of a unit square. That is, there is no number $\frac{a}{b}$, where a and b are integers, whose square is 2.

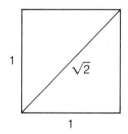

So, we invent numbers, called *irrational numbers,* to represent such lengths. We invent these numbers because it is useful to have numbers to represent all possible lengths. Together, rational and irrational numbers are called *real* numbers.

Any irrational number can be approximated as closely as we like by a rational number, just as we have seen before that any quotient can be approximated as closely as we like by a decimal.

For example, to approximate $\frac{1}{3}$ with a decimal to 20 places, we divide 1 by 3 and get 0.33333333333333333333. Or, to represent $\frac{3}{7}$ to 20 places, we divide 3 by 7 and get 0.42857142857142857143. Although these are not *exact* representations, they are close enough for any ordinary purpose.

We approximate numbers when we use a calculator, since only numbers that can be expressed in the form $\frac{n}{10^7}$, where n is an integer, can be represented exactly on most calculators.

To approximate an irrational number, try to find a decimal or fraction that comes as close as possible to the number.

Example: Approximate $\sqrt{2}$.

Find a decimal, such as 1.414, such that $(1.414)^2$ is very close to 2. $1.414^2 = 1.999396$. That's close, but 1.4142 is closer still. $1.4142^2 \approx 1.9999616$, and so on.

Or, find a fraction: $\left(\frac{239}{169}\right)^2 \approx 1.9999647$

or $\left(\frac{99}{70}\right)^2 \approx 2.000204$.

Find, by whatever means you can, the best approximation for each irrational number. Use a calculator that shows 8 digits.

1. $\frac{1}{3}$
2. $\frac{2}{3}$
3. $\sqrt{2}$
4. $\sqrt{3}$
5. $\frac{2}{7}$
6. $\sqrt{200}$
7. $\sqrt[3]{2}$
8. $\sqrt[3]{3}$
9. $\sqrt[4]{2}$
10. $\sqrt[4]{3}$

For each irrational number, find a fraction with a denominator less than or equal to 200. Try to be within $\frac{1}{1000}$ of the individual number.

Here is a way to do so. Find a decimal approximation. Try multiplying it by whole numbers less than or equal to 200. When the product is very close to an integer, that integer divided by the other factor will be close to the decimal number. Use a calculator (or computer) and experiment.

11. $\sqrt{3}$
12. $\sqrt{5}$
13. 0.1428571
14. 6.24
15. π (3.14159265 . . .)

Suppose you want to find a decimal approximation for $\frac{3}{7}$. You divide 3 by 7. If you are using a long form of division, your steps will look like this. (We've circled the remainder in each step.)

A.
$$\begin{array}{r} .4 \\ 7\overline{)3.000} \\ 28 \\ \hline ② \end{array}$$

B.
$$\begin{array}{r} .42 \\ 7\overline{)3.000} \\ 28 \\ \hline 20 \\ 14 \\ \hline ⑥ \end{array}$$

C.
$$\begin{array}{r} .428 \\ 7\overline{)3.000} \\ 28 \\ \hline 20 \\ 14 \\ \hline 60 \\ 56 \\ \hline ④ \end{array}$$

D.
$$\begin{array}{r} .4285 \\ 7\overline{)3.0000} \\ 28 \\ \hline 20 \\ 14 \\ \hline 60 \\ 56 \\ \hline 40 \\ 35 \\ \hline ⑤ \end{array}$$

[1] The remainders circled so far are 2, 6, 4, and 5. Could the next remainder be greater than 6? Could any remainder be greater than 6?

[2] What, then, are the possible remainders for a division problem in which the divisor is 7?

[3] If 0 is a remainder, what will the quotient look like after the 0 remainder appears?

A decimal representation of a number that is nothing but zeros after some place is called a *terminating decimal*. If $\frac{a}{b}$ is completely reduced, then the decimal representation of $\frac{a}{b}$ will be a terminating decimal if and only if b has no prime factors other than 2 and 5.

The decimal representation of $\frac{3}{7}$ is therefore not terminating, and none of the remainders is 0.

[4] How many possible remainders are there?

When 1 of the remainders is repeated, the division process will be repeated and some numbers in the quotient will be repeated. We can approximate $\frac{3}{7}$ as a decimal in which a sequence of digits is repeated. We call the sequence of digits that is repeated the *repetend*. So we can think of $\frac{3}{7}$ as being represented by an infinitely repeating decimal.

For each of the following fractions, answer questions a–d.

a. Will the decimal representation be repeating or terminating?

b. If your answer to part a is "repeating," what is the maximum possible number of digits in the repetend?

c. What is the repetend? (Divide to find out.)

d. How many digits are there in the repetend?

1. $\frac{3}{7}$	**8.** $\frac{1}{13}$	**15.** $\frac{6}{15}$	**22.** $\frac{1}{20}$	**29.** $\frac{19}{21}$	**36.** $\frac{14}{21}$
2. $\frac{1}{7}$	**9.** $\frac{2}{13}$	**16.** $\frac{3}{17}$	**23.** $\frac{5}{20}$	**30.** $\frac{3}{21}$	**37.** $\frac{2}{21}$
3. $\frac{6}{7}$	**10.** $\frac{5}{13}$	**17.** $\frac{8}{17}$	**24.** $\frac{1}{21}$	**31.** $\frac{6}{21}$	**38.** $\frac{5}{21}$
4. $\frac{1}{2}$	**11.** $\frac{1}{15}$	**18.** $\frac{1}{19}$	**25.** $\frac{4}{21}$	**32.** $\frac{9}{21}$	**39.** $\frac{8}{21}$
5. $\frac{2}{3}$	**12.** $\frac{2}{15}$	**19.** $\frac{3}{19}$	**26.** $\frac{10}{21}$	**33.** $\frac{12}{21}$	**40.** $\frac{4}{21}$
6. $\frac{3}{11}$	**13.** $\frac{3}{15}$	**20.** $\frac{9}{19}$	**27.** $\frac{13}{21}$	**34.** $\frac{15}{21}$	**41.** $\frac{17}{21}$
7. $\frac{8}{11}$	**14.** $\frac{4}{14}$	**21.** $\frac{16}{19}$	**28.** $\frac{16}{21}$	**35.** $\frac{18}{21}$	**42.** $\frac{20}{21}$

(*Note:* If some, but not all, factors of the denominator are 2 or 5, there will be some nonrepeating digits before the repetend begins. These nonrepeating digits are not to be counted in your answer to part d. So for problem 11, the answer to part d should be 1.)

As you are working on the problems, or when you finish, compare your answers for parts b and d to see if you can find some interesting relationship when the denominator is a prime number.

You have seen that every positive rational number (a number that can be written $\frac{a}{b}$, where a and b are whole numbers and $b \neq 0$) can be represented as a repeating decimal or a terminating decimal.

Every terminating decimal or repeating decimal can be shown to represent a rational number. There are 3 cases to consider.

A. Terminating decimals

Example: $N = 0.3875$

$N = 0.3875 = \frac{3875}{10000}$ (It is not necessary to reduce this fraction.)

B. Repeating decimals (with no nonrepeating digits)

Example: $N = 0.438438438438 \ldots$

Multiply each side of the equation by 1000.	$1000N = 438.438438438 \ldots$
Subtract N from each side of the equation.	$1000N - N = 438.438438438 \ldots - 0.438438438 \ldots$
Solve for N.	$999N = 438$
	$N = \frac{438}{999}$ (This fraction may be reduced to $\frac{146}{333}$.)

Can we do this kind of arithmetic with a decimal that goes on forever? If we can, did we do it right? You could reasonably argue that what we did above is hard to justify and should not be allowed. Let's check, however, to see if $\frac{438}{999}$ does have a decimal representation of $0.438438 \ldots$.

```
        .438
999) 438.000000    Since the remainder is 438, the division process
     399 6         will repeat hereafter and produce the repeating
      38 40        decimal 0.438438438 . . . .
      29 97
       8 430
       7 992
         438
```

What if there is a different number of digits that repeat? The number to multiply N by is 10^r, where r is the number of digits in the repetend. So, if $N = 0.387638763876 \ldots$, we multiply N by 10^4, or 10,000.

$$10{,}000N = 3876.38763876 \ldots$$
$$10{,}000N - N = 3876.38763876 \ldots - 0.38763876 \ldots$$
$$9999N = 3876$$
$$N = \frac{3876}{9999}$$

C. Repeating decimals (with some nonrepeating digits). If part of the decimal representation of N is nonrepeating, proceed as in B. But, before determining N, multiply by a power of 10 that will eliminate decimal fractions.

Example

Multiply each side of the equation by 10^2, or 100.

$$N = 0.24371717171 \ldots$$

Subtract N from each side of the equation.

$$100N = 24.371717171 \ldots$$
$$100N - N = 24.371717171 \ldots - 0.243717171$$
$$99N = 24.128$$

There are 3 places to the right of the decimal point, so multiply by 10^3, or 1000, to eliminate the decimal point.

$$99{,}000N = 24128$$

Solve for N.

$$N = \frac{24128}{99000}$$

For each repeating or terminating decimal, find a representation in the form $\frac{a}{b}$ where a and b are whole numbers and $b \neq 0$.

1. 0.333333 . . .

2. 0.09090909 . . .

3. 0.8333333 . . .

4. 0.428571428571 . . .

5. 129292929 . . .

6. 0.514514514 . . .

7. 0.875

8. 0.514

9. 0.428571

10. 0.73561561561

$2 + 2 = 5$ for large enough values of 2.

The sentence above probably seems strange to you. But in a certain sense it is true. Consider the line segments below.

If you measure AB to the nearest centimeter you will record it as being 2 centimeters long. To the nearest centimeter, BC is also 2 centimeters long. However, AC is 5 centimeters long, to the nearest centimeter, and certainly the length of AC equals the sum of the lengths of AB and BC.

Whenever we measure, there is uncertainty in the measurement. The way we record measurements tells how great the uncertainty is. Sometimes we call this uncertainty the *error* in the measurement.

For example, if we see "$AB = 2$ centimeters," we assume that the length of AB is closer to 2 centimeters than to either 1 centimeter or 3 centimeters, that is, that it lies between 1.5 and 2.5 centimeters. If we see "$AB = 2.4$ centimeters," we assume that AB is closer to 2.4 centimeters than to either 2.3 centimeters or 2.5 centimeters, that is, that it lies between 2.3 and 2.5 centimeters. The uncertainty in a measurement is assumed to be no more than $\frac{1}{2}$ the last digit reported. It should be small enough not to cause anyone to question the last digit reported.

When measurements are reported in fractions, uncertainty is assumed to be no more than $\frac{1}{2}$ the unit fraction used. For example, a length recorded as $\frac{3}{8}$ inch is assumed to be off by no more than $\frac{1}{2}$ of $\frac{1}{8}$ inch, or $\frac{1}{16}$ inch, from $\frac{3}{8}$ inch. That is, it is assumed to be between $\frac{5}{16}$ inch and $\frac{7}{16}$ inch.

Sometimes the precision of a measurement is not clear from the recorded value. If we say that it is 2900 miles from New York to Seattle by car, we probably mean that it is between 2850 and 2950 miles, but we might mean that it is between 2899.5 and 2900.5 miles. To avoid confusion of this sort, many people use scientific notation, in which 2900 miles would be written 2.9×10^3 miles if it is correct to the nearest hundred miles, 2.90×10^3 miles if it is correct to the nearest ten miles, and 2.900×10^3 miles if it is correct to the nearest mile. (Remember, $10^3 = 10 \times 10 \times 10$ = 1000, so $2.9 \times 10^3 = 2.9 \times 1000 = 2900$.)

When you add and subtract measurements, you are also adding and subtracting the uncertainty in the measurement. But you can find the smallest and greatest possible values for the sum or difference by taking the uncertainty into consideration. We sometimes call the greatest possible value the upper bound and the smallest possible value the lower bound.

Example: 2.54 centimeters + 7.81 centimeters
(addition)   Smallest possible value: 2.535 + 7.805 = 10.34
        Greatest possible value: 2.545 + 7.815 = 10.36
        Answer: 10.34 centimeters to 10.36 centimeters

(You could also have found the answers by adding 2.54 and 7.81, getting 10.35, then subtracting 2 halves, or 1, to get 10.34 and adding 2 halves, or 1, to get 10.36.)

Example: 7.81 centimeters − 2.54 centimeters
(subtraction)   Smallest possible value: 7.805 − 2.545 = 5.26
        Greatest possible value: 7.815 − 2.535 = 5.28
        Answer: 5.26 centimeters to 5.28 centimeters

Notice that, to produce the smallest possible answer, the minuend (second number) must have the largest possible value and the subtrahend (first number) must have the smallest possible value.

For each problem, list both the smallest and the greatest possible value (assuming that measurements are reported correctly.)

1. 5.1 cm + 8.4 cm
2. 6.4 cm + 2.8 cm
3. 9.7 cm − 4.3 cm
4. 7.1 cm − 5.8 cm
5. 6.2 m + 4.1 m
6. 6.2 m − 4.1 m
7. $7\frac{1}{4}$ in + $2\frac{3}{4}$ in
8. $7\frac{1}{4}$ in − $2\frac{3}{4}$ in
9. 0.54 cm + 0.61 cm
10. 0.78 cm − 0.47 cm

11. 2.9×10^3 mi + 3.7×10^3 mi
12. 3.7×10^3 mi − 2.9×10^3 mi
13. 2.2 cm + 3.5 cm + 6.8 cm + 0.4 cm
14. 1 cm + 2 cm + 3 cm + 4 cm
15. (8.6 cm − 4.3 cm) − 3.0 cm
16. (4 in + 7 in + 3 in) − 8 in
17. (4 yd + 7 yd + 3 yd) − 8 yd
18. 1.32 m + 8.56 m + 4.12 m
19. (8.56 m − 4.12 m) − 1.32 m
20. 4.21×10^3 mi + 8.56×10^3 mi + 1.32×10^3 mi

What is 2×2?

If you think of the 2s as the measures of the sides of a square and assume that the measures have been rounded to the nearest centimeter, each side could be as small as 1.5 centimeters or as large as 2.5 centimeters.

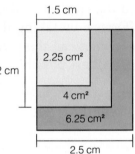

[1] What is the area of a square 1.5 centimeters on a side?

[2] What is the area of a square 2.5 centimeters on a side?

Then 2×2 could be as small as 2.25 "for small enough values of 2" or as large as 6.25 "for large enough values of 2." Since the 2.25 and 6.25 would be reported in square centimeters, and not in centimeters, there is no reason for rounding these to tenths of a square centimeter.

Using the distributive, associative, and commutative laws, you can produce a formula for the maximum error. Let a and b be the 2 measurements and e and f be the maximum respective errors (as positive numbers).

The smallest possible area is

$$(a - e)(b - f) = (a - e)b - (a - e)f = ab - be - af + ef.$$

The greatest possible area is

$$(a + e)(b + f) - (a + e)b + (a + e)f = ab + be + af + ef.$$

So, when both measurements are 2 and the maximum possible errors are both $\frac{1}{2}$,

$$ab - be - af + ef = 2(2) - 2(\tfrac{1}{2}) - 2(\tfrac{1}{2}) + \tfrac{1}{2}(\tfrac{1}{2})$$
$$= 4 - 1 - 1 + \tfrac{1}{4}$$
$$= 2\tfrac{1}{4}, \text{ or } 2.25.$$

$$ab + be + af + ef = 2(2) + 2\left(\tfrac{1}{2}\right) + 2\left(\tfrac{1}{2}\right) + \tfrac{1}{2}\left(\tfrac{1}{2}\right)$$
$$= 4 + 1 + 1 + \tfrac{1}{4}$$
$$= 6\tfrac{1}{4}, \text{ or } 6.25$$

If you have a calculator, you may prefer just to do the calculations with the smallest and largest possible values. But there are 2 interesting facts that the formula helps us to see. In both cases, ab is the "expected" answer. So the positive uncertainty is $be + af + ef$, and the negative uncertainty is $be + af - ef$. (The signs are changed because these values are subtracted from ab.) In both cases, the uncertainty in the answer depends on the size of the original measurements as well as on the size of the original uncertainty. Usually ef is insignificant in comparison with $be + af$ and can be ignored. So an easy rule is that the "expected" answer is ab and the error is $\pm (be + af)$. In the special but important case where the measurements a and b are subject to the same error (for example, in estimating areas), the error further simplifies to $(a + b)e$.

Here is an example: Multiply 3.7×2.3. Our "expected" answer is 8.51, and the error is $\pm(3.7 + 2.3)(0.05)$, or ±0.3.

For division the procedure is even more complicated, and we suggest doing the calculations with largest and smallest possible values of the measurement to find the bounds for the quotient.

Note: The upper bound will be found by dividing the *largest* possible dividend by the *smallest* possible divisor and the lower bound will be found by dividing the *smallest* possible dividend by the *largest* possible divisor.

Determine the upper and lower bounds for each answer. Assume that the original measurements are reported correctly.

1. 6 cm + 3 cm
2. 6 cm − 3 cm
3. 6 cm × 3 cm
4. 6 cm ÷ 3 cm
5. 4 cm + 1 cm
6. 4 cm − 1 cm
7. 4 cm × 1 cm
8. 4 cm ÷ 1 cm

9. 2.1 m × 3.8 m
10. 6.4 m ÷ 1.6 m
11. 2 ft × 4 ft
12. 2 ft ÷ 4 ft
13. 2.8 m + 1.4 m
14. 2.8 m − 1.4 m
15. 2.8 m × 1.4 m
16. 2.8 m ÷ 1.4 m

17. What is the size of the greatest possible error in each *measurement* for problems 1–8?

18. a. What is the size of greatest possible positive error in the answers for problems 1, 2, 5, and 6?
    b. What is the size of the greatest possible negative error in the answers for problems 1, 2, 5, and 6?
    c. Are these numbers easy to predict from the information in problem 17?

19. a. What is the size of greatest possible positive error in the answers for problems 3, 4, 7, and 8?
    b. What is the size of the greatest possible negative error in the answers for problems 3, 4, 7, and 8?
    c. Are these numbers easy to predict from the information in problem 17?

EXPO (AN EXPONENT GAME)

Players: 2 or more
Materials: Two 0–5 cubes, two 5–10 cubes
Object: To come closer to a chosen goal

Rules

1. All players decide on a number that will be the goal. Try 2100, 10,000, or 0.001.

2. Roll all 4 cubes.

3. Use any signs and any operations including exponentiation, and use each number rolled once and only once. Try to make a number as close as possible to your goal. For example, if you rolled 4 3 8 10 you could make $[(10 \times 4)^3]^8$ or $[(8 \times 10)^{-4}]^3$ or $4^{10} \times 3^8$ or $4^{-10} \times 3^{-8}$ or $\frac{(-4) \times (-8)}{10^3}$.

4. The player whose number is closest to the goal is the winner.

Exponents

You know that exponents are used as a sort of shorthand to indicate repeated multiplication. When exponents were first invented, the inventor—René Descartes—did not even use the notation x^2 because xx was just as easy to write. In x^n, n is the *exponent* and x is the *base*. x^n is read "the nth *power* of x," or "x to the nth."

After using exponents for some time, people began to develop an arithmetic of exponents. From the following exercises, see if you can develop rules for an arithmetic of exponents.

Solve for the indicated unknown number.

1. $2^b = 8$
2. $2^5 = b$
3. $8 \times 32 = b$
4. $256 = 2^b$
5. $3^4 = b$
6. $b = 3^5$
7. $81 \times 243 = b$
8. $19,683 = 3^b$
9. $x^b = xxxxx$
10. $b^3 = 27$
11. $(yyyyy)(yyy) = y^b$

12. Suppose that 2 numbers are written in exponential form with the same base. Still using the same base, you can easily write the product of the numbers. What is $x^n \cdot x^m$?

13. Use your answer to problem 12 and your knowledge of inverse operations to find the quotient of the numbers. What is $x^n \div x^m$?

14. Use your answer to problem 12, and assume that fractional exponents are allowed.
    a. What exponent do you believe should replace n in the equation $x^{\frac{1}{2}} \cdot x^{\frac{1}{2}} = x^n$?
    b. What is x^1?
    c. What is a symbol for a number that when multiplied by itself produces the product x?
    d. What is another name for $x^{\frac{1}{2}}$?
    e. What do you think $x^{\frac{1}{3}}$ might mean?
    f. What do you think $x^{\frac{1}{4}}$ might mean?
    g. According to our rule for problem 12, $x^{\frac{2}{3}}$ must equal $x^{\frac{1}{3}} \cdot x^{\frac{1}{3}}$. What is $8^{\frac{2}{3}}$?

Here is a summary of the rules for the arithmetic of positive exponents that we have developed by the discussion on page 372.

---

n factors

A. $x^n = \overbrace{x \cdot x \cdot \ldots \cdot x}$

B. $x^n \cdot x^m = x^{n+m}$ (n and m are positive integers)

C. $x^n \div x^m = x^{n-m}$ (n is greater than m)

D. $x^{\frac{1}{n}} = \sqrt[n]{x}$

E. $x^{\frac{m}{n}} = (\sqrt[n]{x})^m$, which is also equal to $\sqrt[n]{x^m}$

For problems 15–29, write the answer in the simplest form, using the same base.

15. $x^3 \cdot x^5 = $ ▨

16. $x^4 \cdot x^7 = $ ▨

17. $y^{15} \cdot y^4 = $ ▨

18. $b^2 \cdot b^3 = $ ▨

19. $b^1 \cdot b^4 = $ ▨

20. $b \cdot b^4 = $ ▨

21. $b \cdot b = $ ▨

22. $x^3 \div x^2 = $ ▨

23. $x^8 \div x^5 = $ ▨

24. $x^8 \div x^4 = $ ▨

25. $x^5 \div x = $ ▨

26. $y^{20} \div y^4 = $ ▨

27. $b^{17} \div b^4 = $ ▨

28. $a^2 \cdot a^2 = $ ▨

29. $a^2 \div a^2 = $ ▨

For problems 30–59, write the answer in standard form.

30. $2^{10} = $ ▨

31. $2^{15} \div 2^5 = $ ▨

32. $2^8 \cdot 2^2 = $ ▨

33. $2^6 \cdot 2^4 = $ ▨

34. $2^{10} \div 2^6 = $ ▨

35. $2^{10} \div 2^7 = $ ▨

36. $2^{10} \div 2^8 = $ ▨

37. $2^{10} \div 2^9 = $ ▨

38. $2^{10} \div 2^{10} = $ ▨

39. $10^4 \cdot 10^3 = $ ▨

40. $10^{16} \div 10^4 = $ ▨

41. $10^5 \times 10^5 = $ ▨

42. $16^{\frac{1}{2}} = $ ▨

43. $27^{\frac{1}{3}} = $ ▨

44. $27^{\frac{2}{3}} = $ ▨

45. $16^{\frac{1}{4}} = $ ▨

46. $16^{\frac{3}{4}} = $ ▨

47. $16^{\frac{2}{4}} = $ ▨

48. $16^{\frac{1}{2}} = $ ▨

49. $8^{\frac{1}{3}} = $ ▨

50. $8^{\frac{2}{3}} = $ ▨

51. $8^{\frac{2}{3}} \cdot 8^{\frac{1}{3}} = $ ▨

52. $64^{\frac{1}{2}} \cdot 64^{\frac{1}{3}} = $ ▨

53. $64^{\frac{5}{6}} = $ ▨

54. $81^{\frac{1}{2}} \cdot 81^{\frac{1}{4}} = $ ▨

55. $64^{\frac{1}{2}} \div 64^{\frac{1}{3}} = $ ▨

56. $64^{\frac{1}{6}} = $ ▨

57. $64^{\frac{3}{6}} = $ ▨

58. $81^{\frac{3}{4}} = $ ▨

59. $81^{\frac{1}{4}} = $ ▨

Negative Exponents

Try to solve the following problems. Notice the patterns.

1. $x^4 \div x^2$ 6. $81 \div 27$ 11. $3^4 \div 3^5$

2. $3^4 \div 3^2$ 7. $x^4 \div x^4$ 12. $81 \div 243$

3. $81 \div 9$ 8. $3^4 \div 3^4$ 13. $x^4 \div x^6$

4. $x^4 \div x^3$ 9. $81 \div 81$ 14. $3^4 \div 3^6$

5. $3^4 \div 3^3$ 10. $x^4 \div x^5$ 15. $81 \div 729$

[1] How would you define x^{-n}, where both x and n are positive?

[2] How about x^0?

From the patterns that are evident in these problems, we can now define 2 more relationships for exponents.

A. x^0 is 1 (for all nonzero values of x).

B. x^{-n} is $\frac{1}{x^n}$ (for all positive values of n).

Do the following computations. Give your answers in standard form (as fractions or decimals).

16. 2^{-2} 29. 10^{10} 42. $(10^{10})^2$

17. 2^{-3} 30. 10^7 43. 4^3

18. 2^{-10} 31. 10^5 44. $(2^2)^3$

19. $2^3 \div 2^5$ 32. 10^{-10} 45. 2^5

20. $2^8 \div 2^{11}$ 33. 10^{-7} 46. 2^6

21. $2^3 \div 2^{10}$ 34. $10^{10} \times 10^5$ 47. 2^3

22. 2^0 35. $10^{10} \div 10^5$ 48. 8^3

23. 846^0 36. $10^5 \div 10^{10}$ 49. $(2^3)^3$

24. 846^1 37. $10^7 \div 10^5$ 50. 2^4

25. 3^5 38. $10^7 \div 10^{10}$ 51. 16^3

26. 3^8 39. $10^{10} \div 10^{10}$ 52. $(2^4)^3$

27. $3^8 \div 3^5$ 40. $10^7 \div 10^7$ 53. $(2^3)^4$

28. 10^5 41. $10^{10} \times 10^{10}$ 54. 1^{10}

From your work on page 374, you should see that raising a power of a number to another power can be achieved by multiplying the exponents.

$$(x^n)^m = x^{n \cdot m}, \text{ or } x^{nm}, \text{ or } x^{mn}$$

You can prove this relationship by simply counting:

$$x^n = \overbrace{xxx \ldots x}^{n \text{ factors}}$$

$$(x^n)^m = \overbrace{\overbrace{(xxx \ldots x)}^{n \text{ factors}} \cdot \overbrace{(xxx \ldots x)}^{n \text{ factors}} \cdot \overbrace{(xxx \ldots x)}^{n \text{ factors}} \cdot \ldots \cdot \overbrace{(xxx \ldots x)}^{n \text{ factors}}}^{m \text{ factors}}$$

Or, if $n = 4$ and $m = 5$,

$$(x^4)^5 = (xxxx)(xxxx)(xxxx)(xxxx)(xxxx) = x^{20}.$$

Use this rule and other rules you've learned. Rewrite each of the following expressions with just 1 positive exponent (for example, $(x^7)^5 = x^{35}$) or as a number in standard form.

55. $(x^3)^4$

56. $(x^4)^3$

57. $(x^{10})^{10}$

58. $(x^0)^3$

59. $(2^2)^5$

60. $(2^5)^2$

61. $(10^2)^3$

62. $(10^5)^7$

63. $(3^3)^3$

64. $(2^2)^2$

65. $(10^{10})^{10}$

66. $[(2^2)^2]^2$

67. $(x^2)^{-3}$

68. $(x^{-3})^2$

69. $(b^{-4})^3$

70. $(b^3)^{-4}$

71. $(b^{-3})^{-4}$

72. $(b^{-5})^{-3}$

73. $(2^{-3})^{-4}$

74. $(2^{-5})^{-3}$

More Work with Exponents

Let's look again at the problem $(b^{-3})^{-4}$.
If we use our rules, we get

$$(b^{-3})^{-4} = \left(\tfrac{1}{b^3}\right)^{-4} = \frac{1}{\left(\tfrac{1}{b^3}\right)^4} = b^{12}.$$

According to the rule on page 375, $(b^{-3})^{-4} = b^{(-3)\times(-4)} = b^{12} = (b^3)^4$. Thus our earlier rule that the product of 2 negative numbers must be positive is consistent with our rule for finding a power of a power. If these rules were not consistent, we would have to redefine something to make them consistent.

In the same way that we calculated $(b^{-3})^{-4}$ by 2 different procedures to show that $(-3) \times (-4)$ can reasonably be defined as 12, we can show that the way we defined subtraction of negative numbers is the only way consistent with our rules for exponents. We'll work a sample problem.

Consider the subtraction problem $5 - (-2)$. If 5 and -2 are exponents, then the subtraction of those exponents represents division of the powers involved. That is,

$$\frac{b^5}{b^{-2}} = b^{[5-(-2)]}.$$

You know that subtraction of negative numbers was defined so that $5 - (-2) = 5 + 2 = 7$.

Let's see if this reasoning works for exponents. You know that $b^{-2} = \frac{1}{b^2}$.

So $\frac{b^5}{b^{-2}} = \frac{1}{\left(\tfrac{1}{b^2}\right)} = b^5 \times \frac{b^2}{1} = b^7$. So $b^5 \div b^{-2} = b^5 \times b^2 = b^{5+2}$.

But, by our rule, $b^5 \div b^{-2} = b^{5-(-2)}$. For consistency, we must have $5 - (-2) = 5 + 2$.

The operations of multiplication and subtraction as defined for negative numbers also make sense for exponents that are negative numbers. We can make the same observation for addition and division.

You have learned several rules to help you do computations with exponents.

Examples: $\dfrac{x^{-3}}{x^{-5}} = x^{-3 - (-5)} = x^2$

$$\dfrac{8^{-\frac{2}{3}}}{25^{-\frac{1}{2}}} = \dfrac{\frac{1}{8^{\frac{2}{3}}}}{\frac{1}{25^{\frac{1}{2}}}} = \dfrac{1}{8^{\frac{2}{3}}} \times \dfrac{25^{\frac{1}{2}}}{1} = \dfrac{\sqrt{25}}{\sqrt[3]{8^2}} = \dfrac{5}{4}$$

$$10^4 - 10^{-3} = 10{,}000 - 0.001 = 9{,}999.999$$

Notice that, as the third example shows, there is no exponential rule to simplify addition or subtraction of powers of numbers.

Rewrite each of the following expressions as a number in standard form or as a variable with an exponent. Decimals and fractions are acceptable. Write as many steps between the problem and the answer as you like. Take shortcuts as long as they don't lead to mistakes.

1. $\dfrac{1}{x^3}$

2. $\dfrac{x^{-3}}{x^2}$

3. $\dfrac{y^{-3}}{y^{-5}}$

4. $y^{-3} \cdot y^{-5}$

5. 10^{-3}

6. $\dfrac{10^{-3}}{10^2}$

7. $\dfrac{10^{-3}}{10^{-5}}$

8. $10^{-3} \cdot 10^{-5}$

9. $10^3 \cdot 10^{-5}$

10. $10^3 \cdot 10^5$

11. $10^5 + 10^3$

12. $10^5 - 10^3$

13. $10^{-5} + 10^{-3}$

14. $\dfrac{16^{\frac{3}{4}}}{27^{\frac{2}{3}}}$

15. $\left(\dfrac{16^{\frac{3}{4}}}{27^{\frac{2}{3}}}\right)^{-1}$

16. $\dfrac{16^{-\frac{3}{4}}}{27^{-\frac{2}{3}}}$

17. $32^{\frac{3}{5}} \cdot 32^{-\frac{3}{5}}$

18. $x^{\frac{3}{5}} \cdot x^{\frac{3}{5}}$

19. $10^{100} \div 10^{99}$

20. $10^{10} - 10^9$

You have probably heard somebody say something like: "The government got 273.8 billion dollars in individual income tax last year—or was it 273.8 trillion? Maybe it was 273.8 million. Well, anyway, it was a lot of money."

Written as figures, these 3 numbers look like this:

273.8 million	273,800,000
273.8 billion	273,800,000,000
273.8 trillion	273,800,000,000,000

Clearly, the 273.8 is of far less importance in determining the size of the number than is the sound preceding "illion."

The words mean different things in different countries. In the United States and France, 1 billion is 1 thousand million (1,000,000,000), 1 trillion is 1 thousand billion, 1 quadrillion is 1 thousand trillion, and so on. In Great Britain and Germany, 1 billion is 1 million million (1,000,000,000,000), 1 trillion is 1 million billion, 1 quadrillion is 1 million trillion, and so on.

Scientific notation, which you have already studied, can help you understand and appreciate very large and very small numbers. In scientific notation, the 3 numbers above would be written as follows:

$$273{,}800{,}000 = 2.738 \times 10^8$$
$$273{,}800{,}000{,}000 = 2.738 \times 10^{11}$$
$$273{,}800{,}000{,}000{,}000 = 2.738 \times 10^{14}$$

In each case, the most important number in determining the size of the whole number is the exponent of the base ten.

Very small numbers are written with negative exponents:

$$0.000341 = 3.41410^{-4}$$

The exponent is the same as the number of places you must move the decimal point. Multiplying and dividing with numbers written in scientific notation is easy. When adding or subtracting numbers written in scientific notation, you must be very careful to add and subtract digits for corresponding values.

Examples: Multiplication: $(7.24 \times 10^7) \times (5.16 \times 10^3)$
On a calculator, $7.24 \times 5.16 = 37.3584$. You know that $10^7 \times 10^3 = 10^{10}$. Given the precision of the original numbers, the third digit of 37.3584 could be off by 1 or 2, so we usually write the answer to the same degree of precision: 37.4×10^{10}. This answer can be rewritten in scientific notation as 3.74×10^{11}.

Division: $(7.24 \times 10^{11}) \div (2.24 \times 10^8)$
$7.24 \div 2.24 \approx 3.23$, and $10^{11} \div 10^8 = 10^3$, so the answer is 3.23×10^3.

Addition: $(2.24 \times 10^8) + (8.94 \times 10^6)$
Rewrite the problem so that both numbers have the same exponent, and solve: $2.24 \times 10^8 + 0.0894 \times 10^8 = 2.3294 \times 10^8$. Round the answer to 3 figures: 2.33×10^8.

Subtraction: $(2.24 \times 10^8) - (8.94 \times 10^6)$
Rewrite the problem as above, and solve: $2.24 \times 10^8 - 0.0894 \times 10^8 = 2.1506 \times 10^8$. Round the answer to 3 figures: 2.15×10^8.

Copy and complete the following table.

Standard Form	Scientific Notation	In Words (U.S. usage)
27,600,000	2.76×10^7	twenty-seven million, six hundred thousand
	5.81×10^9	
		fifty-three billion, four hundred million
847,000,000,000		
	6.74×10^{-2}	six-hundred seventy-four ten-thousandths
	5.87×10^{-4}	
0.000035		
7		
	3.81×10^0	
		forty-two and seven tenths
0.00000000352		

Do the following computations. Write your answers in correct scientific notation. Negative answers are possible.

1. $(3.66 \times 10^6) \div (3.97 \times 10^4)$
2. $(3.66 \times 10^6) \times (3.97 \times 10^4)$
3. $(3.66 \times 10^6) + (3.97 \times 10^4)$
4. $(3.66 \times 10^6) - (3.97 \times 10^4)$
5. $(4.89 \times 10^5) \times (2.04 \times 10^7)$

6. $(4.89 \times 10^5) \div (2.04 \times 10^7)$
7. $(4.89 \times 10^5) + (2.04 \times 10^7)$
8. $(4.89 \times 10^5) - (2.04 \times 10^7)$
9. $(3.08 \times 10^8) + (1.69 \times 10^3)$
10. $(3.08 \times 10^8) - (1.69 \times 10^3)$

11. $(3.08 \times 10^8) \div (1.69 \times 10^3)$
12. $(3.08 \times 10^8) \times (1.69 \times 10^3)$
13. $(2.27 \times 10^8) \div (3.63 \times 10^6)$
14. $(4.00 \times 10^5) \div (5.66 \times 10^5)$
15. $(7.36 \times 10^6) \div (7.52 \times 10^3)$
16. $(8.74 \times 10^4) \times (7.95 \times 10^{-5})$
17. $(4.91 \times 10^8) \div (6.84 \times 10^3)$
18. $1.50 \times 10^8 \div 3.00 \times 10^5$
19. $8.7 \times (8.64 \times 10^4) \times (3.65 \times 10^2)$
20. $(7.32 \times 10^9) - (4.60 \times 10^7)$

21. The total land area of the United States (including lakes, rivers, and so on) is about 3.63×10^6 square miles. The total population, according to the 1980 census, is about 2.27×10^8. About how many people per square mile is that?

22. This table gives the total population and land area in square miles for 10 states.

State	1980 Population	Land Area (square miles)
Wyoming	4.71×10^5	9.72×10^4
Alaska	4.00×10^5	5.66×10^5
California	2.37×10^7	1.56×10^5
Texas	1.42×10^7	2.62×10^5
Rhode Island	9.47×10^5	1.05×10^3
New Jersey	7.36×10^6	7.52×10^3
New York	1.76×10^7	4.78×10^4
Connecticut	3.11×10^6	4.86×10^3
Delaware	5.95×10^5	1.98×10^3
Massachusetts	5.74×10^6	7.83×10^3

a. Which of the 10 states has the smallest number of people per square mile?
b. Which has the largest number per square mile?
c. Which of the 10 has a population per square mile closest to that of the entire country?

d. What is the difference in land area (in square miles) between the largest and smallest states listed?

e. What is the difference in population between the most populous and least populous states listed?

23. The speed of light is about 3.00×10^5 kilometers per second. The average distance of the earth from the sun is about 1.50×10^8 kilometers.

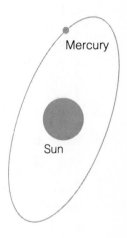

Mercury

Sun

  a. About how many seconds does it take for light to get from the sun to the earth?

  b. How many minutes is that?

24. When Mercury is closest to the sun, it is about 4.60×10^7 kilometers from the sun. How long does it take light to get from the sun to Mercury then?

25. When Mercury is farthest from the sun, it is about 6.98×10^7 kilometers from it. How long does light take to get from the sun to Mercury then?

26. What is the difference between the longest time and the shortest time it takes the sun's light to get to Mercury? Calculate your answer in 2 ways, and compare the results. Explain any differences.

27. At its greatest distance from the sun, Pluto is about 7.32×10^9 kilometers from the sun. How long does it take the sun's light to get to Pluto then?

28. Canis Major is a star that is about 8.3 light years from us. A light year is the distance it takes light 1 year to travel.

  a. About how many years does it take light to get from Canis Major to Earth?

  b. About how many seconds is that? (Assume 365 days in a year.)

29. Proxima Centauri is the closest known star to us. It is about 4.0×10^{13} kilometers from us. About how long (in years) does it take light to get from Proxima Centauri to us?

1. The associative law for addition states that for any 3 numbers x, y, and z, $(x + y) + z = x + (y + z)$.

   a. State the associative law for multiplication.
   b. Is it true?
   c. If not, give a counterexample. (A counterexample is 3 numbers for which the law is not true.)
   d. State the associative law for subtraction.
   e. Is it true?
   f. If not, give a counterexample.

2. Name a number that is between 2.3407 and 2.3408.

3. Write a fraction equal to each number.

   a. 2.3407   b. $\sqrt{\frac{1}{36}}$ c. 0.37373737373737 . . .

4. The length and width of a rectangle are correctly reported as 2.2 centimeters and 3.7 centimeters, to the nearest tenth of a centimeter.

   a. To the nearest tenth of a centimeter, what is the greatest possible perimeter of the rectangle? (Remember that perimeter means the distance around something.)
   b. To the nearest tenth of a centimeter, what is the smallest possible perimeter of the rectangle?
   c. To the nearest hundredth of a square centimeter, what is the greatest possible area of the rectangle?
   d. To the nearest hundredth of a square centimeter, what is the smallest possible area of the rectangle?

2.2 cm

3.7 cm   3.7 cm

2.2 cm

5. Evaluate each of the following expressions. Give your answer in standard form.

   a. $\frac{2^{27}}{2^{24}}$
   b. $2^5 \cdot 2^5$
   c. $2^8 \cdot 2^2$
   d. $25^{\frac{1}{2}}$
   e. $16^{\frac{1}{4}}$
   f. $16^{\frac{3}{4}}$
   g. $(2^5)^2$
   h. $(10^3)^4$
   i. 10^{-3}
   j. $(10^{-3})^2$
   k. $(2^{-5})^{-2}$
   l. $10^{-3} \cdot 10^{-2}$
   m. $\frac{10^{-3}}{10^{-2}}$
   n. $10^3 - 10^2$
   o. $10^{-3} + 10^{-2}$

6. Compute. Give your answer in scientific notation.
   a. $(2.5 \times 10^3) \times (2.5 \times 10^5)$
   b. $(2.5 \times 10^3) + (2.5 \times 10^5)$
   c. $(2.5 \times 10^3) \times (2.5 \times 10^{-5})$
   d. $(2.5 \times 10^3) \div (2.5 \times 10^5)$
   e. $(2.5 \times 10^3) \div (2.5 \times 10^{-5})$
   f. $(2.5 \times 10^{-3}) \div (2.5 \times 10^{-5})$

7. The land area of Kentucky is about 3.97×10^4 square miles, and the 1980 population was about 3.66×10^6. About how many people per square mile is that?

8. The speed of light is about 3.00×10^5 kilometers per second. When Saturn is closest to the sun, it is about 1.35×10^9 kilometers from it. At that time, how long does light take to get from the sun to Saturn?

1. The associative law for multiplication states that for any 3 numbers x, y, and z, $(xy)z = x(yz)$.
   a. State the associative law for addition.
   b. Is it true?
   c. If not, give a counterexample. (A counterexample is 3 numbers for which the law is not true.)
   d. State the associative law for division.
   e. Is it true?
   f. If not, give a counterexample.

2. Name a number that is between 2.3407 and 2.3408.

3. Write a fraction equal to each number.
   a. 3.4508   b. $\sqrt{\frac{1}{49}}$ c. 0.3763763763763 . . .

4. The length and width of a rectangle are correctly reported as 1.2 centimeters and 8.7 centimeters, to the nearest tenth of a centimeter.

   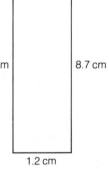

   a. To the nearest tenth of a centimeter, what is the greatest possible perimeter of the rectangle? (Remember that perimeter means the distance around something.)
   b. To the nearest tenth of a centimeter, what is the smallest possible perimeter of the rectangle?
   c. To the nearest hundredth of a square centimeter, what is the greatest possible area of the rectangle?
   d. To the nearest hundredth of a square centimeter, what is the smallest possible area of the rectangle?

5. Evaluate each of the following expressions. Give your answer in standard form.
   a. $\frac{2^{28}}{2^{24}}$ f. $81^{\frac{3}{4}}$ k. $(2^{-4})^{-2}$
   b. $2^5 \cdot 2^3$ g. $(2^4)^2$ l. $10^{-3} \cdot 10^{-2}$
   c. $2^6 \cdot 2^2$ h. $(10^2)^3$ m. $\frac{10^{-5}}{10^{-4}}$
   d. $36^{\frac{1}{2}}$ i. 10^{-2} n. $10^{-4} - 10^3$
   e. $81^{\frac{1}{4}}$ j. $(10^{-3})^{-2}$ o. $10^{-4} + 10^{-3}$

6. Compute. Give your answer in scientific notation.
   a. $(1.5 \times 10^{-3}) \times (1.5 \times 10^{-5})$
   b. $(1.5 \times 10^{3}) + (1.5 \times 10^{7})$
   c. $(1.5 \times 10^{3}) \times (1.5 \times 10^{-7})$
   d. $(1.5 \times 10^{3}) \div (1.5 \times 10^{7})$
   e. $(1.5 \times 10^{-3}) \div (1.5 \times 10^{-5})$
   f. $(1.5 \times 10^{-3}) \div (1.5 \times 10^{-7})$

7. The land area of Massachusetts is about 7.83×10^3 square miles, and the 1980 population was about 5.74×10^6. About how many people per square mile is that?

8. The speed of light is about 3.00×10^5 kilometers per second. The mean distance from the sun to Pluto is about 5.90×10^9 kilometers. About how long does light take to get from the sun to Pluto?

Sometimes when a calculator is being used to calculate, the numbers are too big to "fit" on the calculator. If you convert the numbers to scientific notation, you can still get answers that are precise enough for most practical concerns.

For example, the population of the United States, according to the 1980 census, is 226,504,825. The land area is 3,630,854 square miles. How many people per square mile is that?

If you try to punch 226504825 into an 8-digit display calculator, something will go wrong. Some calculators will simply accept 22650482 and omit the 5. Some will show some sort of error indicator. Some will convert the number to 2.2650482×10^8 (in which case you may have to push a *clear* key to proceed). Others will respond in still different ways. You should become familiar with how a calculator you're using reacts to situations like this.

In general, using scientific notation or some modification of it will allow you to work with larger numbers on a calculator. Sometimes you will find other forms of exponential notation more useful than pure scientific notation. For example, you may want to work with 226.50482×10^6 instead of 2.2650482×10^8.

Sometimes you need more digits than the calculator will show you. In 1812, at the age of 8, the calculating wizard Zerah Colburn was asked to compute 8^{16}. Suppose you were the judge for such a challenge but could use a calculator to check the answer. You might find $8^8 = 16,777,216$ quite easily. Then what would you do? Try to compute 8^{16}, using a calculator to help.

Do you remember the distributive law for multiplication over addition? Using it and the commutative and associative laws to rewrite $(a + b)^2$, we get $(a + b)(a + b) = (a + b)a + (a + b)b = a(a + b) + b(a + b) = aa + ab + ba + bb = a^2 + ab + ab + b^2 = a^2 + 2ab + b^2$.

If you want to calculate $(16777216)^2$, you can think of it as $(16770000 + 7216)^2$. Now, in the formula above, let $a = 1677 \times 10^4$ and $b = 7216$. So $(1677 \times 10^4 + 7216)^2 = (1677 \times 10^4)^2 + 2(1677 \times 10^4 \times 7216) + (7216)^2$.

On your calculator, square 1677. Multiply $2 \times 1677 \times 7216$. Square 7216.

Write in the necessary number of zeros, and add the numbers to find the answer: $8^{16} = 181,474,976,710,656$.

For practice, try these problems.

1. 9^{16} 2. 7^{18} 3. 6^{20} 4. 5^{22} 5. 4^{24}

6. Now that you've seen the answer, can you figure out a different way to solve problem 5?

7. 2^{48} 8. 2^{50}

Work problems 9, 10, and 11 twice on various calculators. The first time, push the *equals* key after each operation. The second time, wait until you have finished to push the *equals* key.

9. Square 0.001111. Multiply your answer by 1,000,000, but predict in advance what the answer will be.

10. Before completing this problem, predict what the answer will be. Divide 1 by 3. Multiply by 3. Subtract 0.5. Subtract 0.5.

11. Square 0.003166. Multiply the answer by 10. If you get different results, try to explain what the different calculators do.

Length	Weight (mass)	Liquid Volume (capacity)
millimeter (mm) 0.001 m	**milligram** (mg) 0.001 g	**milliliter** (mL) 0.001 L
centimeter (cm) 0.01 m	centigram (cg) 0.01 g	centiliter (cL) 0.01 L
decimeter (dm) 0.1 m	decigram (dg) 0.1 g	deciliter (dL) 0.1 L
meter (m)	**gram** (g)	**liter** (L)
dekameter (dam) 10 m	dekagram (dag) 10 g	dekaliter (daL) 10 L
hectometer (hm) 100 m	hectogram (hg) 100 g	hectoliter (hL) 100 L
kilometer (km) 1000 m	**kilogram** (kg) 1000 g	kiloliter (kL) 1000 L

Units of area are derived from units of length.

square centimeter (cm²)	$1 \text{ cm}^2 = 0.0001 \text{ m}^2$	The area of this square is 1 square centimeter.
square meter (m²)	$1 \text{ m}^2 = 10{,}000 \text{ cm}^2$	A square 1 meter on a side has an area of 1 square meter.
hectare (ha)	$1 \text{ ha} = 10{,}000 \text{ m}^2$	A square 100 meters on a side has an area of 1 hectare.
square kilometer (km²)	$1 \text{ km}^2 = 1{,}000{,}000 \text{ m}^2$	A square 1 kilometer on a side has an area of 1 square kilometer.

Units of volume can also be derived from units of length.

cubic centimeter (cm³)		The volume of this cube is 1 cubic centimeter.
cubic meter (m³)	$1 \text{ m}^3 = 1{,}000{,}000 \text{ cm}^3$	A cube 1 meter on a side has a volume of 1 cubic meter.

The unit of temperature is the degree Celsius (°C).

Water freezes at 0°C and boils at 100°C.

Descriptions of some common units:

kilometer	You can walk a kilometer in about 12 minutes.
meter	Most classroom doors are about 1 meter wide.
centimeter	This line segment is 1 centimeter long.
millimeter	This line segment is 1 millimeter long.
liter	4 average-size glasses hold about 1 liter of liquid.
milliliter	This cube holds about 1 milliliter:

kilogram	A pair of size-10 men's shoes weighs about 1 kilogram.
gram	A nickel (or a marble) weighs about 5 grams.

Length

inch (in) $1 \text{ in} = \begin{cases} \frac{1}{12} \text{ ft} \\ \frac{1}{36} \text{ yd} \end{cases}$

foot (ft) $1 \text{ ft} = \begin{cases} 12 \text{ in} \\ \frac{1}{3} \text{ yd} \end{cases}$

yard (yd) $1 \text{ yd} = \begin{cases} 36 \text{ in} \\ 3 \text{ ft} \end{cases}$

mile (mi) $1 \text{ mi} = \begin{cases} 5280 \text{ ft} \\ 1760 \text{ yd} \end{cases}$

Liquid Volume (capacity)

fluid ounce (fl oz) $1 \text{ fl oz} = \frac{1}{8} \text{ cup}$

cup (c) $1 \text{ c} = \begin{cases} 8 \text{ fl oz} \\ \frac{1}{2} \text{ pt} \end{cases}$

pint (pt) $1 \text{ pt} = \begin{cases} 16 \text{ fl oz} \\ 2 \text{ c} \\ \frac{1}{2} \text{ qt} \end{cases}$

quart (qt) $1 \text{ qt} = \begin{cases} 32 \text{ fl oz} \\ 4 \text{ c} \\ \frac{1}{4} \text{ gal} \end{cases}$

gallon (gal) $1 \text{ gal} = \begin{cases} 128 \text{ fl oz} \\ 16 \text{ c} \\ 8 \text{ pt} \\ 4 \text{ qt} \end{cases}$

Area

square inch (sq in or in²)
square foot (sq ft or ft²) $1 \text{ ft}^2 = 144 \text{ in}^2$
square yard (sq yd or yd²) $1 \text{ yd}^2 = 9 \text{ ft}^2$
acre (A) $1 \text{ A} = 4840 \text{ yd}^2$
square mile (sq mi or mi²) $1 \text{ mi}^2 = 640 \text{ A}$

Volume

cubic inch (cu in or in³)
cubic foot (cu ft or ft³) $1 \text{ ft}^3 = 1728 \text{ in}^3$
cubic yard (cu yd or yd³) $1 \text{ yd}^3 = 27 \text{ ft}^3$

Dry Measure (capacity)

pint (pt)
quart (qt) $1 \text{ qt} = 2 \text{ pt}$
peck (pk) $1 \text{ pk} = 8 \text{ qt}$
bushel (bu) $1 \text{ bu} = 4 \text{ pk}$

Weight

ounce (oz) $1 \text{ oz} = \frac{1}{16} \text{ lb}$
pound (lb) $1 \text{ lb} = 16 \text{ oz}$
ton (T) $1 \text{ T} = 2000 \text{ lb}$

The unit of temperature is the degree Fahrenheit (°F).

Water freezes at 32°F and boils at 212°F.

GLOSSARY

absolute value The numerical value of a real number without consideration of its sign. It is the (positive) distance of the number from zero on a number line. $|-7| = 7, |+7| = 7$.

acute angle An angle that measures less than 90°.

These are right angles: These are acute angles:

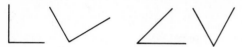

addend A number that is added to another number to make a sum. For example:

$$35—\text{addend} \qquad 7 + 8 = 15—\text{sum}$$
$$+ \ 48—\text{addend}$$
$$\overline{\quad 83—\text{sum}} \qquad \text{addend} \quad \text{addend}$$

algorithm A step-by-step procedure for solving a certain type of problem.

approximation An answer to a mathematical problem that is not precise but is close enough for the purpose. Sometimes an approximate answer is more appropriate than a precise answer. (See *estimate*.)

area The number of square units enclosed by a figure. The area of this rectangle is 6 square centimeters:

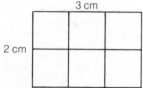

arrow operation A notation for showing an action of a function machine. In 7 —(×8)→ 56, 7 goes in and is multiplied by 8 to give 56. The *function rule* in this case is ×8. In the operation 6 ←(−5)— 11, 11 goes in and 5 is subtracted from it to give 6. The function rule in this case is −5.

associative law In both addition and multiplication, the law that states for any numbers x, y, and z, it doesn't matter whether y is first combined with x or with z. $x + (y + z) = (x + y) + z$; $x \times (y \times z) = (x \times y) \times z$.

average A number that can sometimes be used to describe a group of numbers. To find the average

of a set of numbers, add the numbers and divide the sum by how many numbers were added. The average of 5, 6, 6, 8, and 10 is 7 ($5 + 6 + 6 + 8 + 10 = 35$ and $35 \div 5 = 7$). (Also called *mean*.)

axes (of a graph) The 2 zero lines of a graph that give the coordinates of points. The horizontal axis is the x-axis. The vertical axis is the y-axis.

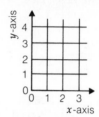

balance 1. The amount of money remaining in an account. 2. A double-pan balance is an instrument used to measure weight.

bar graph A graph in which quantities are shown by bars. Also called *histogram*. Each bar in this bar graph shows the average number of rainy days per year in a selected U.S. city:

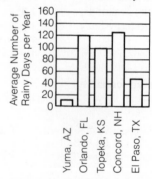

base 1. The side or face of a geometric figure used with the altitude or height to calculate area or volume. 2. The number on which a number system is built. 3. In exponential notation, the number that is used as the factor. In 6^3, 6 is the base and 3 is the exponent: $6^3 = 6 \times 6 \times 6$.

bisect To divide into 2 equal parts.

bound A number that an answer must be greater than or less than. For example, 36×21 must be less than 40×30, or 1200. So 1200 is an *upper bound*. The answer to 36×21 must be greater than 30×20, or 600. So 600 is a *lower bound*.

Celsius (C) A temperature scale, named after a Swedish astronomer, in which 0° is the temperature at which water freezes and 100° is the temperature at which water boils under standard conditions.

circle A figure (in a plane) in which all the points are the same distance from a point called the center. In this figure, for example, points *A*, *B*, and *C* are the same distance from point *O*, the center of the circle:

commutative law In both addition and multiplication, the law stating that for any numbers *x* and *y*, the sum or product will be the same regardless of the order in which they are added or multiplied: $x + y = y + x; x \cdot y = y \cdot x$.

composite function A function with 2 or more operations. For example:

composite number A whole number with factors other than 1 and itself.

congruent Figures that are the same size and same shape; that is, they fit perfectly when placed on top of each other.

These triangles are congruent: These are not:

coordinates Numbers that give the position of a point on a graph. In the figure shown, for example, the coordinates of point *A* are (2, 3). 2 is the *x*-coordinate. 3 is the *y* coordinate.

cube A solid figure with 6 equal square faces. For example:

decimal point A dot used to separate the ones digit from the tenths digit.

degree 1. A unit of measure of temperature. See *Fahrenheit* and *Celsius*. 2. A unit of measure of angles. There are 360° in a circle. There are 90° in a right angle.

denominator The part of a fraction written below the line. The part written above the line is called the *numerator*. The denominator tells how many equal parts something is divided into; the numerator tells how many of those parts are being referred to. In the fraction $\frac{3}{4}$ the denominator (4) indicates that something is divided into 4 equal parts. The numerator (3) says to consider 3 of those parts.

deposit To add money to an account. (Also, the amount of money added.)

diagonal Any line connecting 2 vertices of a polygon that is not a side of a polygon. *AD* is a diagonal of *ABCD*:

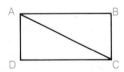

diameter A line segment, going through the center of a circle, that starts at one point on the circle and ends at the opposite point on the circle. (Also, the length of that line segment.) *AB* is a diameter of this circle:

difference The amount that one number is greater or less than another. For example:

43—minuend
− 16—subtrahend
27—difference

$10 - 7 = 3$—difference
subtrahend
minuend

digit Any of the numbers 0, 1, 2, 3, 4, 5, 6, 7, 8, and 9. The two digits in 15 are 1 and 5.

distributive law For both multiplication and division, the law stating that for any numbers x, y, and z, the product or quotient will be the same whether the operation is carried out on the whole or on its parts: $x(y + z) = xy + xz$; $x(y - z) = xy - xz$; $x \div (y + z) = (x \div y) + (x \div z)$; $x \div (y - z) = (x \div y) - (x \div z)$.

dividend A number that is divided by the divisor. For example:

$6 \div 3 = 2$—quotient
divisor
dividend

43—quotient
divisor—8)347—dividend
32
27
24
3

divisor A number that the dividend is divided by. (See *dividend*.)

equation A mathematical statement with an equal sign stating that 2 quantities are equal. For example, $4 + 2 = 6$ and $6 + n = 10$ are equations.

equilateral triangle A triangle with all 3 sides the same length. For example:

equivalent fractions Fractions that have the same value. $\frac{2}{6}$, $\frac{4}{12}$, and $\frac{1}{3}$ are equivalent fractions.

estimate A judgment about the size or quantity of something. (Also, to make such a judgment.) Sometimes it is more appropriate to make an estimate than to measure or count precisely. (See *approximation*.)

even number Any multiple of 2. 0, 2, 4, 6, 8, and so on are even numbers.

exponent In exponential notation, the superscript number that tells how many times the base is used as a factor. In 6^3, 3 is the exponent and 6 is the base: $6^3 = 6 \times 6 \times 6$.

Fahrenheit (F) A temperature scale, named for a German physicist, in which 32° is the temperature at which water freezes and 212° is the temperature at which water boils under standard conditions.

fraction $\frac{1}{2}$, $\frac{3}{4}$, and $\frac{7}{8}$ are examples of fractions. The fraction $\frac{3}{4}$ means that something is divided into 4 equal parts and that we are considering 3 of those parts. (See *denominator* and *numerator*.)

function machine A device (sometimes imaginary) that does the same thing to every number that is put into it. (See *arrow operation*.)

function rule See *arrow operation*.

hexagon A polygon with 6 sides.

histogram See *bar graph*.

hundredth If a whole is divided into 100 equal parts, each part is one-hundredth of the whole.

improper fraction A fraction in which the numerator is greater than the denominator.

inequality A statement that tells which of 2 numbers is greater. For example: $4 > 3$ is read "4 is greater than 3." $3 + 6 < 10$ is read "3 plus 6 is less than 10."

intersecting lines Lines that meet. In this figure lines AB and CD intersect at point E.

inverse operation An operation that "undoes" the results of another operation. Multiplication and division are inverse operations; addition and subtraction are inverse operations.

isosceles triangle A triangle with two equal sides. These are isosceles triangles:

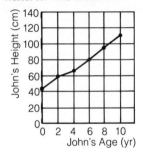

line graph A graph made up of lines. This line graph shows John's height at different times in his life. The marked points show his height at the times when he was measured.

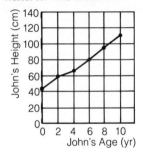

line segment A part of a line with 2 endpoints. For example, *AB* is a line segment; points *A* and *B* are its endpoints.

mean See *average*.

median The middle value in a group of numbers arranged in increasing order. The median of 5, 6, 6, 8, and 10 is 6.

minuend A number from which another number is subtracted. (See *difference*.)

mixed number A number made up of a whole number and a fraction. $1\frac{1}{2}$, $2\frac{3}{4}$, and $7\frac{7}{8}$ are mixed numbers.

mode The most common value in a group of numbers. The mode of 5, 6, 6, 8, and 10 is 6.

multiple A number that is some whole number of times another number. 12 is a multiple of 3 because $3 \times 4 = 12$.

multiplicand A number that is multiplied by another number, the multiplier. For example:

5—multiplicand
× 3—multiplier
15—product

$3 \times 5 = 15$—product
multiplicand
multiplier

The multiplier and multiplicand are also called the factors of the product.

multiplier See *multiplicand*.

negative number A number less than zero. For example, −2 is 2 less than zero.

numerator The part of a fraction written above the line. (See *denominator*.)

obtuse angle An angle that measures between 90° and 180°.

These angles are obtuse: These are not:

octagon A polygon with 8 sides.

odd number A whole number that is not a multiple of 2. All whole numbers that are not even are odd. 1, 3, 5, 7, 9, 11, and so on are odd numbers.

odds The ratio of the number of favorable cases to the number of unfavorable cases.

ordered pair Two numbers written so that one is considered before the other. Coordinates of points are written as ordered pairs, with the *x*-coordinate written first. For example: (3, 4). (See *coordinates*.)

parallel lines Lines in a plane that do not intersect. Lines *AB* and *CD* are parallel:

Lines *EF* and *GH* are not parallel:

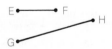

parentheses A symbol ( ) used in mathematics to show in which order operations should be done. For example: (3 × 5) + 7 says to multiply 5 by 3 and then add 7; 3 × (5 + 7) says to add 5 and 7 and then multiply by 3.

partial product The product that comes from multiplying the multiplicand by one of the digits of the multiplier. For example:

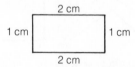

pentagon A polygon with 5 sides.

perimeter The distance around a figure. The perimeter of this rectangle is 6 centimeters:

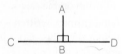

percent Parts per hundred, shown by the symbol %. For example, 95 out of 100 is 95%.

perpendicular bisector A line that bisects another line and is perpendicular to it.

AB is a perpendicular bisector of *CD*.

perpendicular lines Lines that intersect at right angles.

These lines are perpendicular:

So are these: But these are not:

place value The value of a digit in a number. The value of 7 in 27 is 7 ones; in 74 its value is 70, or 7 tens; in 726 its value is 700, or 7 hundreds.

polygon One of a certain type of figure. These figures are polygons:

These are not:

Here are the names of some common polygons and the number of sides:

Number of Sides	Name
3	triangle
4	quadrilateral
5	pentagon—a regular pentagon has 5 equal sides:

6	hexagon—a regular hexagon has 6 equal sides:

8	octagon—a regular octagon has 8 equal sides:

polyhedron A 3-dimensional figure with faces formed by planes. The tetrahedron, cube, octahedron, dodecahedron, and icosahedron are the 5 regular polyhedra.

positive number A number that is greater than zero. For example, +2 is 2 more than zero.

prime number A whole number divisible only by 1 and itself.

probability How likely something is to happen. The probability that some particular thing will happen is a fraction in which the denominator is the total number of possible things that can happen and the numerator is the number of ways this particular thing can happen. The probability that an ordinary coin will show heads when flipped is about $\frac{1}{2}$.

product The result of multiplying 2 numbers together. (See *multiplicand*.)

profit In a business, the money that is left after all expenses have been paid.

proper fraction A fraction in which the denominator is greater than the numerator.

quadrilateral A polygon with 4 sides.

quotient The result (other than the remainder) of dividing one number by another. (See *dividend*.)

radius A line segment that goes from the center of a circle to a point on the circle. (Also, the length of such a segment.) *OA* is a radius of the circle shown here. The radius of the circle is 1 centimeter.

range The 2 numbers that show the highest and the lowest values of a group of numbers. The range of 5, 6, 6, 8, and 10 is 5 to 10.

rational number A number that can be expressed as the ratio of 2 integers.

rectangle A quadrilateral in which all 4 angles are right angles.

regroup To rename a number to make adding and subtracting easier.

Example of regrouping in subtraction:

$$\begin{array}{r} \overset{\scriptstyle 1\,15}{\cancel{2}\cancel{5}} \\ -17 \\ \hline 8 \end{array}$$ (To subtract in the ones column, 2 tens and 5 is regrouped to 1 ten and 15.)

Example of regrouping in addition:

$$\begin{array}{r} \overset{\scriptstyle 1}{\cancel{2}9\,6} \\ +44\,2 \\ \hline 73\,8 \end{array}$$ (After adding the tens column, 13 tens is regrouped to 1 hundred and 3 tens.)

relation signs The 3 basic relation signs are $>$ (greater than), $<$ (less than), and $=$ (equal to). (See *inequality*.)

remainder A number less than the divisor that remains after the dividend has been divided by the divisor as many times as possible. For example, when you divide 25 by 4, the quotient is 6 with a remainder of 1:

$$\begin{array}{r} 6 \text{ R1} \\ 4\overline{)25} \\ \underline{24} \\ 1 \end{array}$$

right angle An angle that forms a square corner.

These are right angles: These are not:

rounding Changing a number to another number that is easier to work with and that is close enough for the purpose. (See *approximation*.)

similar Figures that are the same shape but not the same size.

These triangles are similar: These are not:

square A quadrilateral with 4 equal sides and 4 equal angles.

straight angle An angle that forms a straight line.

This is a straight angle: These are not:

subtrahend A number that is subtracted from another number. (See *difference*.)

sum The result of adding 2 or more numbers. (See *addend*.)

tenth If a whole is divided into 10 equal parts, each part is one-tenth of the whole.

transversal A line that intersects 2 or more lines. *AB* is a transversal.

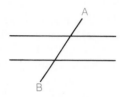

triangle A polygon that has 3 sides.

unit 1. An amount used as a standard for measuring. For example, meters, liters, seconds, and kilograms are units in the metric system of measure, and feet, quarts, and pounds are units in the traditional system of measure. Sometimes nonstandard units are used for measuring. See pages 424–425 for tables of metric and traditional measure. 2. One of anything.

unit cost The cost of 1 item or 1 specified amount of an item. If 20 pencils cost 40¢, then the unit cost is 2¢ for each pencil. If dog food cost $9 for 3 kilograms, then the unit cost is $3 per kilogram.

vertex The point where the 2 sides of an angle meet. *B* is the vertex of $< ABC$.

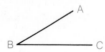

vertical angles The equal angles formed by 2 intersecting lines.

< 1 and < 2 are vertical angles.

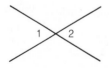

whole number The numbers that we use to show how many (0, 1, 2, 3, and so on). 3 is a whole number, but $3\frac{1}{2}$ and 4.5 are not whole numbers.

zero The number that tells how many things there are when there aren't any. Zero times any number is zero; zero plus any number is that number: $0 \times 3 = 0$ and $0 + 3 = 3$.